CW00765901

SUNBEAM AERO-ENGINES

SUNBEAM AERO-ENGINES

Alec Brew

Airlife
England

Acknowledgements

Though IMI Marston, the spiritual descendant of The Sunbeam, gave me what help it could in researching this book, the company is the successor to the radiator side of John Marston's businesses, and the records for the Sunbeam Motor Car Co., which made the aero-engines, largely perished with the company, over sixty years ago. I relied heavily therefore on official archives at the Public Record Office, the RAF Museum, and the West Midland Aviation Archive, administered by the Boulton Paul Association.

An invaluable source of information on the histories of Sunbeam-built aircraft, and which RNAS aircraft had Sunbeam engines, was Ray Sturtivant's book *Royal Navy Aircraft Serials and Units 1911–1919*, published by Air Britain. This almost unbelievable reference work should be an essential starting point for any research on RNAS aircraft, and it was at my elbow throughout the writing of this book. I am particularly grateful to Jack Bruce for lending me numerous photographs from his extensive collection.

Many other people helped me to a greater or lesser degree, but I am particularly grateful to Jim Boulton for lending me various books and brochures from his vast library, to John Ryder for lending me the original Sunbeam photographs which his father rescued after the company's crash, and to Basil Wilding for lending me photographs from his large collection, many coming from his father, who worked in Sunbeam's Experimental Department.

Others to whom I am grateful are Clive Bunyan of the Science Museum, Ron Cooper, Trevor Davies and Ray Jones of IMI Marston, Doug Hill of the National Motor Museum, Bill Gunston, R.M. Iliff, George Jones, Peter Lisle, Alec Lumsden, Wallace McNair of Straight 8 Restorations in New Zealand, Graham Mottram of the Fleet Air Arm Museum, Barry Peerless, Sandy Skinner, Ian Walker of the STD Register, Michael Ware of the National Motor Museum, and Wendy Matthiason.

In the five years during which I have undertaken research there may be others to whom I also owe thanks, so if I have forgotten anyone I am truly sorry.

First published in the UK in 1998
by Airlife Publishing Ltd

British Library Cataloguing-in-Publication Data
A catalogue record for this book
is available from the British Library

ISBN 1 84037 023 8

Typeset by Servis Filmsetting Limited
Printed in England

Airlife Publishing Ltd
101 Longden Road, Shrewsbury, SY3 9EB, England

CONTENTS

The Dyak-engined Avro 504 at Dunstall Park Racecourse, Wolverhampton, 1919.

Introduction

Sunbeam is one of the most famous names in British manufacturing, and yet the company has not existed for over sixty years. Sunbeam cars and motor-cycles, and to a lesser extent bicycles and aero-engines, are nationally and even internationally famous, and in the home of the Sunbeam, Wolverhampton, there is still a great deal of pride in Sunbeam products, and people who are proud to say that they worked at The Sunbeam.

The name Sunbeam belonged to two Wolverhampton companies however, both branches of the same industrial empire founded by John Marston. It was first used on the bicycles produced by John Marston Ltd, a japanware (black enamelware often richly decorated in the oriental style) and tinplate manufacturer, and was then applied to the cars the company began to produce in 1899, but the motor-car side of the business was floated as a separate company in 1905. John Marston Ltd continued to make Sunbeam bicycles and later motor-bikes, but Sunbeam cars and the aero-engines were the products of the Sunbeam Motor Car Co. Ltd.

Sunbeam aero-engines should more properly be known as Sunbeam–Coatalen aero-engines, coupling the company name with that of the designer, the Frenchman Louis Coatalen, but for the purposes of brevity they will be referred to as just Sunbeam engines in this book. They were only produced for a few more than the years of the First World War, the original running for the first time very late in 1912, and the last production engine being built in 1919. Apart from a late fling in 1928–30, Sunbeam therefore only produced aero-engines for six years, and yet during the First World War they were one of the two great suppliers of water-cooled engines, along with Rolls-Royce, their major rivals.

At the start of the war Sunbeam aero-engines were in fact the only modern British aero-engine available, and remained the only powerful engines of more than 120 hp in production for over a year. They were principally used by the Royal Naval Air Service, and were the main powerplant used in a whole range of seaplanes, in particular the ubiquitous Short Type 184, the most famous seaplane of the war.

There has been a great deal of confusion concerning Sunbeam engines over the years, springing from the fact that there have been no company records for over sixty years, and that there were so many different engines, reflecting the mercurial personality of Louis Coatalen. He was a skilled and inventive engineer, but seems to have preferred continually to move on to the next project, rather than doggedly work on the slow but steady development of his engines, as Henry Royce so ably did. Sunbeam aero-engines were largely referred to by their horse power for the first three years of the war, and as by 1917 there were several with the same horse power and even with similar configurations, there was often great doubt as to which engine was being referred to in official records. For instance, a '150 hp Sunbeam' could be either the original V8 side-valve engine, or the new V8 overhead camshaft engine. A system of naming the engines, after various 'tribes', was therefore adopted in 1917, earlier engines being retrospectively named, and these two 150 hp engines became the Crusader and Nubian respectively.

The confusion has continued over the years however, as all official references to Sunbeam engines before 1917 still of course refer to them only by their horse power, so that historians have been deceived into assigning the wrong engine to particular aircraft. To avoid this confusion continuing I shall refer to all Sunbeam engines by their name from the outset, even though chronologically speaking this is incorrect.

The sheer number of Sunbeam engines produced in such a short time – twenty-two in the four years of the war alone – seems very confusing at first, but many of them were only developments of earlier engines. The increase in the bore of an engine was enough for Sunbeam to give it a new name, but production records make it clear that there were usually only two engines in full-scale production at any one time, with the occasional low-level production of one or two more. The main Sunbeam production engines for the first two years of the war were the side-valve V8 Crusader/Zulu and V12 Mohawk/Gurkha, supplanted in mid-1916 by two V12 OHC engines, the Afridi/Maori and the Cossack. The Cossack was then replaced by the V8 Arab at the end of 1917, making just five main production engines in all. There were also very small production runs of the W18 Viking, the straight six Amazon and the V8 Nubian; all the other engines were only built as prototypes.

The company also built aircraft during the war: Short Type 827 and Type 310 seaplanes, Short Bombers and Avro 504s, as well as just one aircraft of their own design, the Sunbeam Bomber. A total of 647 aircraft was built in all, and though the exact number of aero-engines is not known it was in excess of 3,000 by Sunbeam itself, with more than 720 Sunbeam engines produced by other manufacturers.

Sunbeam engines never had a great reputation for reliability, despite the fact that the most typical Sunbeam-powered operation was a long seaplane or airship patrol over the inhospitable waters of the North Sea. Perhaps the aviators involved had a heightened sense of the importance of reliability, but certainly the early side-valve engines had a poor reputation, though there was nothing else available. The most successful engines were the Cossack and the Maori, and these never seem to have been developed into engines as reliable as the marvellous Rolls-Royce Eagle.

The most famous Sunbeam engine was the Arab, which was also the company's biggest disaster. Ordered in huge numbers when only a handful had been bench-run, it only became apparent that it suffered tremendous insoluble vibra-

tion problems when it was tested in the air. It was the only Sunbeam engine used in any numbers by the Royal Flying Corps – or rather the former Royal Flying Corps units, as the Royal Air Force had been born before the Arab reached squadrons in any numbers. It is hard to avoid the conclusion that the awful Arab terminally sullied the reputation of Sunbeam as an aero-engine producer, and led to the collapse of all sales after the war.

Faced with competition from cheap war-surplus engines, including their own, and the marvellous new Napier Lion, as well as the Rolls-Royce engines, Sunbeam hardly won a single post-war order. The only exception was the 100 hp Dyak, a handful of which was produced, even against the competition of dirt-cheap war-surplus engines. The Dyak may well have been the best engine Sunbeam ever produced, but it came just too late to restore their reputation, and too early for the peacetime aero-engine market.

Throughout their development Sunbeam aero-engines were always linked with the company's car engines. Not only was the technology switched from one to the other, but aero-engines found their way into cars, sometimes even before they were flown. The side-valve technology and cylinder size of Sunbeam's 1912 racing cars was used in the V8 Crusader and V12 Mohawk aero-engines, and both were raced in Sunbeam cars before they were ever fitted to an aircraft. The overhead camshaft technology of the 1914 Sunbeam Grand Prix cars was the basis for subsequent aero-engines, and two of Sunbeam's land speed record-breaking cars were powered by their own aero-engines, remarkably at speeds never achieved by Sunbeam-powered aircraft!

The Five Families of Sunbeam Aero-engines

The Side-Valve Family

110 hp V8 80 mm × 150 mm		
150 hp V8 Crusader 90 × 150	— 225 hp V12 Mohawk 80 × 150 90 × 150	
160 hp V8 Zulu 100 × 150	240 hp V12 Gurkha 100 × 150	

The Cossack Family

310 hp V12 Cossack I 110 × 160	— 160 hp INL6 Amazon 110 × 160	— 450 hp W18 Viking 110 × 160
320 hp V12 Cossack II dual ignition	— 160 hp INL6 Amazon II dual ignition	
400 hp V12 Matabele alu. blocks 122 × 160	— 200 hp INL6 Saracen alu. blocks 122 × 160	

The Maori Family

150 hp V8 Nubian 95 × 135	— 200 hp V12 Afridi 92 × 135	
	250 hp–275 hp V12 Maori I–IV Dual ignition 100 × 135	
	325 hp V12 Manitou Alu. blocks 110 × 135	— 300 hp V12 Tartar 110 × 135

The Arab Family

200 hp V8 Arab 120 × 130	— 100 hp INL6 Dyak 120 × 130	— 300 hp W12 Kaffir 120 × 135 500 hp X20 Malay 120 × 130
↓ 200 hp A8 Bedouin 120 × 130	↓ 100 hp INL6 Pathan (diesel) 120 × 130	

The Sikh Family

850 hp V12 Sikh 180 × 210	— 425 hp INL6 Semi-Sikh 180 × 210	
1000 hp V12 Sikh III 180 × 210		

PART ONE
THE SUNBEAM HISTORY

PRE-1914

The name John Marston is an integral part of the industrial history of the Staffordshire town of Wolverhampton, but John Marston was not a Wulfrunian by birth. He was born in Ludlow, Shropshire, in 1836, the son of Richard Marston, a local landowner, alderman, Justice of the Peace, and Mayor of Ludlow. He was educated at Ludlow Grammar School and Christ's Hospital School, London, but in 1851, at the age of fifteen, he was apprenticed first to Darby's Ironworks and then to Edward Perry, who had a japanware business in the Jeddo Works, Paul Street, which was just off the Penn Road on the west side of Wolverhampton. Edward Perry was a self-made man who had entered the business at Old Hall, Wolverhampton, before building up an important business in Paul Street. He became a prominent man in the town and was elected mayor in 1855 and 1856.

By the time he was twenty-three years old John Marston had already left the Jeddo Works and had obtained his own business as a manufacturer of tinplate and japanware by buying Daniel Smith Lester & Co. of Bilston, a well-known enterprise which had been amalgamated with Walton & Co. and Thurston & Co., two other well-known japanners. In 1865 Marston married his wife, Ellen, with whom he was to have ten children, eight of which survived beyond infancy.

In 1871 Edward Perry died and Marston purchased his company from his nephews who had inherited it, and moved the centre of his operations to the Jeddo Works, then taking up further premises in Paul Street. Marston was a hard-working, fastidious man who looked and acted like the typical Victorian industrialist. He became large in stature with a close-clipped grey beard and long matching moustache. He worked long hours at his factories, and expected nothing less from his employees; he was a rigid disciplinarian, known in the local fashion as 'Mr John'. It was and still is a Black Country custom to work on Good Friday, and he was in the habit of going to the factory in the morning on Good Fridays to make sure that everyone was at work, before going off to church with his fellow directors.

He was elected to the council in 1885, and was then elected mayor in 1889 and 1890. He took his sons into partnership, and was anxious to expand his business.

John Marston was a keen cyclist, usually cycling to the factory each morning from Tettenhall, and he recognised the possibility of expanding his business in an appropriate manner soon after the bicycle became popular. Bicycle races held in the Molineux grounds, which were then the town park, attracted crowds of up to 15,000 people, and by 1879 there were a handful of cycle-makers in Leicester, five or six in Nottingham, and thirty in Wolverhampton, which had become the centre of the trade.

John Marston, the founder of The Sunbeam, and his wife Ellen shortly before the First World War.

In 1887 Marston founded the Sunbeamland Cycle Factory in the Paul Street Works, Wolverhampton. The Sunbeam cycles were black with gold lines in the style of much of his japanware products, and the line began to sell well after some models were exhibited at the Stanley Show of 1889, and at the opening of a London showroom in May of that year. The Sunbeam cycles were not particularly novel until the adoption of Harrison Cater's chaincase in 1892, which was to be marketed as 'the little oil bath', a fundamental feature of Sunbeam cycles – and, later, motor-cycles – for the next seventy years. Marston's philosophy was to market a restricted range of very high-quality cycles, which was reflected in the price and symbolised by the 'Golden Range' introduced after 1900, finished with gold-leaf pinstripes and gearcase.

During the years 1896–7 there was a huge demand for bicycles far outstripping supply, and the company prospered, as did many other bicycle manufacturers in the town, such as the Star Cycle Co. just round the corner from Sunbeamland. By the turn of the century there were about 3,000 people making cycles in Wolverhampton. With the huge injection of capital this boom entailed a number of cycle companies began to look at motorised transport.

In 1895 the company name was changed to John Marston Ltd, and Marston's right-hand man was Thomas Cureton, who had joined the company as an apprentice straight from Rugby School. Marston came to trust him implicitly, so when Cureton made a study of the possibility of Sunbeam producing a motor-car, Marston supported him against the opinion of the other directors.

The first Sunbeam car was hand-built by a toolmaker named Henry Dinsdale and a boy apprentice named Harry Wood. They worked in a disused coach-house in Upper Villiers Street, and the first task for this new enterprise, which was to become the Sunbeam Motor Car Co., was for Dinsdale to knock a nail in the wall on which to hang his coat! Nevertheless, every part of the car was made in the Paul Street Works, including the radiator. Radiators were to become a significant part of the Marston business from then on. Dinsdale assembled the car in the Upper Villiers Street building working from little more than rough sketches, and with much use of the hand file made every part fit by hand. The first Sunbeam car, completed in 1899, had a single vertical cylinder and gave a nominal 5 hp. The car was fitted with twenty-eight-inch solid-tyred wheels at the front and thirty inches at the back, and tiller steering, though a steering wheel could be fitted.

The first engine could not have been entirely satisfactory because during the following year a new engine was fitted to the first chassis. This was a single-cylinder horizontal engine giving 6 hp at 700 rpm. This car was exhibited at the Crystal Palace Show in November 1901, but was not to go on sale. Marston and Cureton had come to realise that the development of a satisfactory motor-car from scratch was likely to be an expensive business. They adopted the strategy of putting into production someone else's design to bring in an income while the motor-car side of the business was built up and further development work took place.

The first Sunbeam car to go on sale was the Sunbeam-Mabley voiturette, designed by an ornamental ironwork manufacturer named Mabberley Smith, and powered by a 2.75 hp de Dion engine. It was rather like a Victorian S-shaped sofa on four wheels. It had two driving wheels on either side, amidships, a centrally placed steering wheel at the back which the driver operated with a tiller from his seat at the back, knees facing to starboard, and another centrally placed wheel at the front, alongside which was the engine, and behind which sat two passengers facing to port.

Sunbeam's first production car, the Sunbeam-Mabley, with the driver at the rear. This car was built in 1901, but is shown after restoration between the wars.

This device went on sale in 1901 for £130 and sold very well, 130 being produced in only eighteen months. The garden of a private house adjacent to the coach-house had been purchased and a shed erected to produce the Mabley cars, with power for a few machine tools being taken by shafting from the Villiers Company next door. Villiers had been formed in 1898, with John Marston's eldest son Charles in charge, to supply cycle components such as pedals. After a while sales of the Sunbeam-Mabley began to decline and a backlog of unsold cars began to build up. During 1902 the company built a car with a steel tube frame powered by a two-cylinder Formen engine giving 6 hp; it also had a gearbox power transmission, but only five were sold, and so the powerplant was increased to an 8 hp two-cylinder.

Thomas Charles Pullinger, who joined the company in 1902 as works manager after working for some years in various motoring concerns in France, made a formal proposal to the directors that they obtain the rights to manufacture a four-cylinder car produced by the little-known M. Berliet of Lyons. Though some directors were still against taking further risks in this new motor-car venture, the rights to the Berliet car were obtained, and it was marketed as the Sunbeam 12/14, soon with the innovation of a Sunbeam oil-bath chaincase. This car was shown on the Sunbeam stand at the December 1903 Paris Show, and in the same month authority was given for the development of a six-cylinder car, and the construction of two prototypes. Pullinger drove one of them, in May 1904 in the Scottish Reliability Trials, but failed because of a slipping clutch, and the cars were not proceeded with.

Factory extensions were made to produce the Berliet cars, with several houses and gardens between Moore Street and Cross Street being added to the factory and new sheds erected. Portable engines were purchased to drive the machinery. At the beginning of 1905 a separate Sunbeam Motor Car Co. Ltd was formed with an authorised capital of £40,000. The chairman was John Marston and the directors were Samuel Bayliss, Thomas Cureton, Dr Edward Deansley (a Wolverhampton surgeon who had married one of John Marston's daughters), Henry Bath, and Herbert Dignasse (who had a London motor business and acted as Sunbeam's export agent). Pullinger left the company to work for Humber's in Coventry, and Angus Shaw, who had started in the drawing office, emerged as chief engineer. Thus there were three Marston family companies grouped together in the same area of Wolverhampton: Marston, Sunbeam, and Villiers.

From 1904 Berliet cars were imported directly into this country, in competition with Sunbeam's licence-built examples, so Angus Shaw designed a most successful 16/20 hp car. It was of 3.5 litres with a bore of 95 mm and stroke of 120 mm, and had a four-speed gearbox. In 1906 Shaw, with Frederick Eastmead, drove one of these cars from John O'Groats to Land's End and back without stopping the engine. Several acres of fields on the other side of Upper Villiers Street were purchased to extend the factory so that ten of these cars per week could be produced. Five hundred cars a year was a large number for those days, but the car sold well, even during 1907 when there was something of a slump in the motor-car industry. In that year Shaw also designed a six-cylinder car based on the same cylinder size as the 16/20, but this car did not sell well.

The 12/16 hp Sunbeam of 1904, which was built mainly of French parts, outside the Moorfield Works.

A new four-cylinder 14/18 hp model was designed by Shaw in 1908, being offered for sale from November. It featured 95 × 135 cylinders cast in pairs, unlike his first cars where the cylinders were cast individually. The car was well received, but Shaw was nevertheless about to give way to a new, French, designer.

Louis Hervé Coatalen was born in 1879 in the Breton town of Concarneau. After school in Brest he went to the Ecole des Arts et Métiers for three years, and then after his military service worked for Panhard, Clement, and De Dion Bouton, three of the great French motor manufacturers of the day. He came to realise that to really make his name in the motor industry he would have to leave France, where the ground had already been covered, and come to England, where companies were lagging far behind.

Still only twenty-one, he joined the Crowden Motor Co. of Leamington Spa, but left after only a few months and became the chief engineer at Humber just down the road in Coventry. Humber's attempts at designing cars had met with little success, but Coatalen soon designed the first mid-sized four-cylinder cars to be produced in this country, the Humber 8/10 hp and 10/12 hp selling for about £300, and these sold so well that for a time they had to be assembled outside in the street because Humber's premises could not be expanded quickly enough. Coatalen spent nine years with Humber, and at the end of this period formed a partnership with William Humber to manufacture the Hillman–Coatalen car which was to record the fastest lap at the 1908 TT Race.

In 1909 Coatalen joined the Sunbeam Motor Car Co. as chief engineer, a position he was to occupy for twenty years. Within a year he had designed two cars, firstly the 16/20 hp with four 95 × 135 mm cylinders, the first three of which had chain drive but all further versions having a live axle. Coatalen followed this up with a smaller 12/16 hp car with four 80 × 120 mm cylinders. So well did these cars sell that in 1910 there were further extensions to the factory to cope, with expansion into what were then open fields.

Coatalen was keen on experimentation, and he also recognised the advantage of publicity, and that the combination of these two themes would enhance Sunbeam's knowledge and standing – 'racing improves the breed'. Sunbeam cars had competed in reliability trials and hill-climbs, but now Coatalen turned his attention to the world of closed-circuit racing and Brooklands. He designed a purpose-built single-seat racing car, which he named Nautilus. The engine was a four-cylinder 92 × 160 mm giving 21 hp, and fitted with sixteen

Louis Coatalen, aged thirty-three, just after his appointment as Sunbeam's chief engineer in 1912.

overhead valves operated by push-rods and rather lengthy rockers from two camshafts on either side of the crankcase. Most remarkably the entire car was encased in a streamlined body from which only the driver's head protruded. Its Achilles' heel was insufficient cooling, which resulted in it having to race with the rear half of this bodywork removed, but the engine still proved rather unreliable.

On the production front a new 25/30 hp model was introduced in 1911, alongside the 12/16 hp and 14/20 hp cars, and the Shaw-designed cars were finally dropped from the catalogue. From October 1910 a six-cylinder 18/22 model had been produced. All this expansion was overseen with great energy by Coatalen who placed large orders for plant and machinery. The gas main was brought across fields from Wolverhampton to drive two big gas engines, which in turn drove the machine tools from overhead shafting.

To oversee the expansion Sidney Guy was brought in as works manager. Guy had been born in Wolverhampton, but his family had moved away. He had served an apprenticeship with the General Electric Co. and then went to Humber in Coventry as repairs manager and assistant to the works manager. He was thus well-known to Coatalen, and was offered the post of works manager despite his age – twenty-three years and six months. He continued to work for Sunbeam until 1914, when he started his own company, Guy Motors, on the other side of the town. C.B. Kay then became general works manager, a post he was still holding in 1928 when he became a director. Kay had joined Sunbeam in 1906 and became Coatalen's assistant in 1912, so he was to watch the fortunes of the company rise and fall.

At the beginning of 1910 Sunbeam Motor's biggest rival in the town, the Star Motor Car Co., whose factory in Frederick Street was only a few hundred yards away, had entered the field of aviation, employing a young Lancashire lad named Granville Bradshaw to design not only a four-cylinder aero-engine, but also a monoplane in which to try it. The very first all-British Flying Meeting was held at Dunstall Park racecourse, Wolverhampton, in June of that year, and though the Star monoplane was entered it was a conspicuous failure. Coatalen and many of the other Sunbeam notables attended the meeting, which may well have had an effect on their future thinking.

The Star monoplane was redesigned the following year and flew successfully at Dunstall Park and Brooklands, but Edward Lisle, the chairman of Star Motors, was so alarmed when he saw his son flying it he stopped all further aviation work. There is no doubt that the Star company derived much prestige and pride from its brief foray into aviation, and its workers were able to cock a snook at their Sunbeam counterparts.

In 1911 Coatalen designed another single-seat racing car, which he named *Toodles II* after his wife. This had four 80 × 160 mm cylinders and eight valves operated by a chain-driven overhead camshaft. During the year *Toodles II*, driven by Coatalen himself, won twenty-two prizes and set a class record at Brooklands at 86.16 mph. Although a new engine with a gear-driven overhead camshaft was developed for this car, its success was to be followed up by a team of 12/16 hp side-valve cars for the Coupe de l'Auto.

In the autumn of 1911 Sunbeam produced a new 25/30 hp six-cylinder car with side-valve cylinders cast in two blocks of three. A standard chassis was fitted with a single-seat body for an attack on the twelve-hour record. Not only was this record broken with a distance of 907 miles and 1,535 yards at an average speed of 75.66 mph, but the car set eight other world records in the process. The same car, now named *Toodles IV*, was also successfully raced at Brooklands, driven by Coatalen, and with some modifications broke the world fifty-mile record at 93.73 mph.

The name of Sunbeam was really brought to the attention of the world in the 1912 Coupe de l'Auto at Dieppe with the entry of three of its new side-valve cars. One such car had been raced the previous year at Boulogne, but the driver hit a kerb while lying seventh and was forced to retire with a broken steering connection. For 1912 the cars were powered by four-cylinder 80 × 149 mm engines totalling 2,996 cc, and giving 73.7 bhp. The three-litre race was held at the same time and over the same forty-seven-mile road course as the Grand Prix. The three Sunbeams came first, second, and third in the three-litre class and even came third, fourth, and fifth in the big race itself, beaten only by a 7.6-litre Peugeot and a fourteen-litre Fiat, an amazing achievement which shocked the French motoring world. At a banquet organised by the RAC to celebrate the victory Louis Coatalen praised the help given by the Brooklands circuit which had enabled him to increase the speed of the cars from 65 mph to 87 mph, and said that the production of a team of racing cars was good for a factory because 'it crushes out the conservatism which is always apt to prevail in a works, bucking up the designers and the constructors, and putting everyone on his mettle'.

The win put the name of Sunbeam foremost among British motor manufacturers, but Coatalen was already thinking ahead to the Grand Prix of 1913, in which the formula had been changed to put an emphasis on fuel consumption, ruling out the giant engines which many manufacturers had produced until then. He designed for installation in a team of cars to enter this race a straight six side-valve engine of 80 mm bore and 150 mm stroke (4,524 cc), with the cylinders cast in two blocks of three, which gave 110 hp at 3,000 rpm. At the same time he designed a V8 side-valve engine based on the same cylinders as the Grand Prix engine, 80 mm bore and 150 mm stroke, but cast in four blocks of two, the two banks of cylinders being set at a ninety-degree angle. This was to become Sunbeam's first aero-engine.

The new V8 engine, which was later named Crusader after it had been given a larger bore, gave 120 hp at 2,500 rpm, and was being bench-tested before Christmas 1912. Mention of it was made in *The Aeroplane* in the 19 December 1912 edition, when it was stated that Coatalen had kept in close touch with the developments in aviation, which was certainly true as he had flown as a passenger at Brooklands in a two-seater Deperdussin monoplane as early as October 1911. He stated that it was his intention to test-fly the new engine in a Martin-Handasyde monoplane, which was currently flying at Brooklands fitted with a 90 hp Antoinette engine, but this was not to be.

Though the V8 was envisaged as an aero-engine, with its weight of only 425 lb, giving only 2.83 lb/hp, its first actual application was in a powerboat. In February M. Tollier of France obtained two of the engines and installed them in a powerboat he was to race at Monaco. Another one of these new V8 engines was installed in the chassis of a 24 hp Sunbeam car and raced at the Shelsley Walsh hill-climb by C.A. Bird in June 1913. He put up the second fastest time of 58.4 seconds, and Louis Coatalen also drove it himself, achieving 60.2 seconds. The engine was then apparently taken out of the car, and was never raced on the road again.

The engine was more widely announced to the British aviation press in March 1913 and was warmly greeted by British aircraft manufacturers, who were producing airframes as good as any in the world but were forced to fit European engines because there were no suitable British ones. The only exceptions to this were when there were races or prizes offered for which only all-British aircraft could compete; the usual expedient was to remove the foreign engine and fit the reasonably reliable but far too heavy 100 hp water-cooled straight six Green, an engine rarely chosen on its own merits.

Sunbeam's first aero-engine, the V12 side-valve, after the change to a 90 mm bore, which made it the 150 hp Crusader.

The first aircraft to which the V8 engine was fitted was the Radley-England Waterplane No. 2, which was entered for the 1913 Circuit of Britain Race, which required an all-British aircraft. The waterplane was a twin-hulled flying boat capable of carrying aloft a pilot and five passengers, and originally powered by three 50 hp Gnôme engines on a common propshaft. The aircraft crashed on 26 May, and was rebuilt for the race, with the V8 Sunbeam installed. It is not certain whether the engine fitted was still with the 80 mm bore of the original prototype or as later modified with a 90 mm bore, but it was almost certainly the former. Taxiing trials began on 6 August, but in the event the aircraft never apparently managed to fly. This was as much to do with the design of the twin hulls, which buried their sterns in the water under acceleration, as with the teething problems of the new engine.

The Sunbeam Motor Car Co. decided to purchase an aircraft in which to test-fly the new engine, and chose a standard Maurice Farman biplane, which arrived at Brooklands from Paris late in September. Why a French aircraft was chosen is not known, but it may have had something to do with Coatalen's nationality. To fly this aircraft a full-time pilot was

engaged, a young man who had been building quite a reputation at Brooklands during the preceding months, Jack Alcock.

History has always linked Jack Alcock with Arthur Whitten Brown, the first men to fly the Atlantic non-stop, in their Vickers Vimy in 1919. Alcock was born in Old Trafford, Manchester, on 5 November 1892, and went to Manchester Central High School. He was determined to become an engineer and his first job was as a technical apprentice at the Empress Engineering Works where cars and motor-bikes were built and repaired. In 1909–10 the works manager, Charles Fletcher, designed and built both a monoplane and a biplane, assisted by young Jack Alcock. His interest in aviation was further stirred when he was one of the thousands who crowded into a field in Didsbury to watch the end of the 1910 London to Manchester Air Race, won by Louis Paulhan in his Farman biplane.

Jack Alcock, Sunbeam's company pilot, in front of the Farman biplane purchased to test the new engine.

In 1911 Alcock went to work for the Crossland Motor Co. as mechanic in charge. The owner of the company, Norman Crossland, was the founder of the Manchester Aero Club and a good friend of Arthur Whitten Brown, and he encouraged Jack's interest further. When a rotary aero-engine arrived for repair Alcock was the only one who knew much about it and he finished the job. He then accompanied the engine to Brooklands to be fitted to the owner's aircraft, the owner being Maurice Ducrocq, a well-known French aviator. Ducrocq took on the nineteen-year-old Alcock as his mechanic, and also began to teach him to fly. Alcock went solo after only two hours' instruction, and on 26 November 1912 was awarded Aviator's Certificate No. 368, flying Ducrocq's Henri Farman biplane. He quickly built a reputation as a skilled pilot and found plenty of work at Brooklands, test-flying aircraft for Ducrocq, teaching in the Ducrocq–Lawford Flying School, and erecting and test-flying Avros. In August 1913 he was busy testing the Parsons biplane fitted with a new automatic stabiliser, and the following month he tested Ducrocq's new racing Farman.

As both a skilled pilot and mechanic Alcock was an ideal choice for Sunbeam to test-fly its new engine. The Farman was probably to be based at Brooklands, rather than at Wolverhampton's airfield at Dunstall Park racecourse, because as one of the two main centres of aviation in the country (Hendon was the other) it would be a shop-window for the new Sunbeam engine, and the company also had a considerable presence at Brooklands because of their racing cars.

The Farman was erected and made its first flights during the second week of October, with the first Sunbeam aero-engine to fly. There may have been trouble with the aircraft initially because flying ceased after a short while and the engine was brought back to Wolverhampton, accompanied by Alcock. It was reinstalled and flying again during the third week in December. It is probable that an engine with the bore increased from 80 mm to 90 mm was the one refitted to the Farman, as all subsequent mentions of the engine quote this figure, and 90 mm × 150 mm was to be the standard production specification of the Crusader. The Sunbeam–Farman then began a period of intensive test-flying which ranged right across southern England and was to last right up to the beginning of the First World War, and it is possible that during this period Jack Alcock put in more flying hours than any other pilot.

Before the end of 1913 a second Sunbeam aero-engine appeared at Brooklands for testing, but this time in a racing car. The engine was a V12 and, like the initial version of the V8, had cylinders of 80 mm bore and 150 mm stroke totalling 9,048 cc, giving 200 hp at 2,400 rpm. Unlike the V8 the banks of cylinders were set at sixty degrees and were cast in four blocks of three. This engine was to become the 225 hp Mohawk and Coatalen installed it initially in a car because he saw it as a way of challenging some of the closed-circuit world records, and endurance-testing in a car was both easier and cheaper than using an aircraft. There is no doubt, though, that the engine was designed specifically for aircraft as non-adjustable tappets were fitted.

The car was named *Toodles V*, and first appeared at the Brooklands August Bank Holiday Meeting, but trouble with its cone clutch made it a non-starter. At the autumn meeting on 4 October, driven by Jean Chassagne, the car took third place from scratch in the Short Handicap, averaging 105.75 mph; later in the meeting in the Long Handicap the Sunbeam won at an average of 110 mph, the fastest race-winning speed recorded up to then.

On 11 October Chasagne made an attempt on the world one-hour record in the car. Lapping the track at a speed limited by the tyres he achieved a world record of 107.57 mph, and then after changing tyres in fifty-four seconds he continued to set a new world record for 150 miles, at 105.57 mph. When all the intermediate records were checked as well, it was

The V12 side-valve Mohawk, with either the original 80 mm bore or the more usual 90 mm bore.

The specially built car Toodles V *fitted with the prototype Mohawk with an 80 mm bore, shown at Brooklands where it broke eight world endurance records in an hour and a half.*

discovered that the car had broken eight world records in an hour and a half! It had also, by the way, demonstrated the reliability of the new V12 engine.

In June 1913 the Air Ministry had announced a competition, to take place in 1914, to find a new all-British aero-engine. There was a first prize of £5,000 with a promise of orders of up to £40,000. The horse power of entered engines was to be between 90 and 200, and they were to have more than four cylinders. The tests were to include two runs of six hours during which power, fuel, and oil consumption would be measured. The tests would take place at the Royal Aircraft Factory, Farnborough. There was a £50 deposit per entry, returnable on delivery of the engine. Sunbeam entered only their V8 engine; possibly the V12 Mohawk exceeded the upper power limit. The winner of the competition was the 120 hp six-cylinder inline Green. The Green was, as always, very reliable, but rather heavy, and the Sunbeam Crusader had a much better power:weight ratio, and was awarded a £50 consolation prize. The big reward, of course, was large orders from the Air Ministry to power a new generation of seaplanes. Like the 1912 Military Aircraft Competition, which had been won by the Cody biplane, which was then quietly forgotten, the Green had best suited the criteria for winning the prize, but was not a suitable basis for future engine orders.

Despite the fact that Coatalen's two new aero-engines were fitted with side valves, he was already in the process of abandoning the system for his new racing-car engines. The Sunbeam side-valve racing cars had acquitted themselves well in the 1913 Grand Prix at Amiens, Chassagne coming third, but they had not done as well as the previous year in the Coupe de l'Auto at Boulogne, when they also came third. The winning cars in both cases were Peugeots with twin overhead camshafts and four valves per cylinder, and they were clearly superior to the Sunbeams, something noted by Coatalen and every manufacturer with racetrack aspirations.

By some devious means, with the help of two of the Sunbeam racing drivers, Jean Chassagne and Dario Resta, Coatalen managed to acquire one of the Coupe de l'Auto-winning three-litre Peugeots. It seems that the car which won the race, driven by Georges Boillot, was to be taken around all the Peugeot agents by Dario Resta for publicity purposes. Resta arranged for Chassagne to drive it to Wolverhampton. It was brought to Coatalen's own home – Waverley House,

Goldthorn Hill, Wolverhampton – and there, in the drawing-room, secretly stripped down by a small team from the factory which included Hugh Rose, Ted Hatlands, two draughtsmen who made drawings of all the parts, and A.P. Mitchell, a fitter from the experimental shop and Chassagne's usual mechanic. After the drawings were completed the engine was reassembled and the car driven down the road to the Moorfield Works, where the engine was bench-tested.

There can be no doubt that the Sunbeam racing-car engines produced for the 1914 season were copies of the Peugeot, though the capacity was changed to 3.3 litres, with 81.5 mm × 156 mm cylinders to take advantage of the larger capacity allowed in the 1914 TT Race, and 4.441 litres with 94 mm × 160 mm for the Grand Prix. In Coatalen's defence it must also be said that two other British manufacturers, Vauxhall and Humber, entered cars with twin overhead camshafts and sixteen valves for the TT Race, also obviously inspired by the Peugeots, but perhaps without the detailed inside knowledge Sunbeam had garnered. This is perhaps why the Sunbeam of Kenelm Lee Guinness won the TT in the absence of the Peugeots. In the Grand Prix it was to be a different story, with Dario Resta's Sunbeam coming in only fifth behind three Mercedes and a Peugeot.

The Sunbeam Isle of Man TT racers for 1914, fitted with the new overhead camshaft engines which were to be the basis for subsequent Sunbeam engines. They are shown outside Sunbeam's canteen.

Sunbeam's Experimental and Racing Department was severely stretched, for in addition to producing the two teams of racing cars with about a dozen overhead camshaft engines being built by hand, they were also producing powerboat engines for the racing at Monaco, and developing both aero-engines. A.P. Mitchell, for instance, was sent to France to work on V8 Crusaders fitted to powerboats with Brookes hulls built for the Smiths Financial Group.

The V8 Crusader and V12 Mohawk were displayed at the Olympia Aero Show of 1914, and by now both featured a bore of 90 mm with the stroke of 150 mm. The only one flying was the V8 Crusader in Alcock's Farman, which was racking up the hours all over the south of England, but an example had been bought by the Royal Aircraft Factory and was under long-term test. It was described as 'the first modern British aero-engine to be purchased by the Royal Aircraft Factory'. A Crusader was tried out in one of the Royal Flying Corps' RE.5 biplanes during 1914, but details of the test have eluded all research.

New applications for the engines were in the offing. Two entries for the Circuit of Britain Race which was to take place in August ordered Sunbeam engines, a V8 Crusader for a new large seaplane, the Avro 510, and a V12 Mohawk for the Sopwith Bat Boat, a handsome flying boat. The *Daily Mail*'s prize for the first non-stop flight across the Atlantic also resulted in an order for a V12 Mohawk to be fitted to a large monoplane being built by Martin-Handasyde at Brooklands.

Events in Sarajevo were to put paid to all such races, aerial or road, and the aero-engine side of the Sunbeam Motor Car Co.'s business was suddenly to become the most important feature, instead of just a sideline. In fact, in 1917 Louis Coatalen stated that having tried repeatedly and failing to get a production order for its aero-engines from the government, Sunbeam were thinking of giving up aviation:

> French engines were held up before us as ideals we should try to attain, and, as it were, on the principle of 'if you could only do as well we should think a lot of you': the fact that we had something up our sleeve, and available, which could do even better being apparently never suspected; and, of course, until someone gives you an order you cannot improve. In fact we had thought of giving up the manufacture of aero-motors altogether, and were just about to drop it when the war broke out.

The Sunbeam engines were the only high-power British engines available at the start of the war, and French engines were hard to come by, so the Admiralty sent for Coatalen and placed an immediate order for thirty to forty engines, and even larger orders for them were soon forthcoming.

An aerial view of the Sunbeam factory at the end of the war. The 1914 factory was largely to the left of the road running through the site from St Luke's church. The experimental shop is the three-storey building to the rear, and the coach-house where the first Sunbeam car was built is by the chimney to the extreme left.

A head-on view of a production Sunbeam Crusader, the main engine with which the company went to war. 1914–18

Aero-engine production at the Moorfield Works in 1916 showing both V8 and V12 side-valve engines being built.

1914-18

At the outbreak of the war the Sunbeam V8 and V12 were immediately ordered in substantial numbers for a number of Royal Naval Air Service projects. The 110 hp engine, the earlier version of the Crusader with a 80 mm bore, was specified for the Sopwith Type 806 Gunbus and the forthcoming Short Type 827 seaplane, and the Crusader also for the Type 827 and the Avro 510 seaplane. The Mohawk was essential for the three torpedo-carrying seaplanes the Navy had ordered: the Short Type 184, the Sopwith Type 860, and the Wight Type 840.

For the remainder of 1914 these three side-valve engines were produced in small numbers, virtually hand-built, a total of seven 110 hp Sunbeams, ten Crusaders, and sixteen Mohawks being delivered to the end of the year, by which time the Moorfield Works had been reorganised for wartime production. The 110 hp was dropped from production to allow the two larger engines to be built in greater numbers. It may even be that the seven 110 hp engines delivered were those already existing development engines with the smaller 80 mm bore, and parts made up into engines, at a time when powerful aero-engines were in very short supply. The 110 hp Sunbeam was only installed in a couple of the Sopwith Type 806s, the Crusader going into the rest, and was the engine finally installed in all the Short Type 827s.

At the outbreak of war Mervyn O'Gorman at the Admiralty had long foreseen the inescapable search for more power, a belief equally held by Cdr Murray Seuter and the Head of the Admiralty Air Engine Section, Wilfred Briggs, and his assistant W.O. Bentley. The Air Department of the Navy, foreseeing shortages of the Mohawk, the engine they had commissioned Coatalen to design, were anxious to bring other companies into the production of large water-cooled engines, and to see the development of more powerful engines. Rolls-Royce was encouraged to produce an engine of 200–250 hp, and it was suggested they copy the widely admired Mercedes engine; the company was even given a Mercedes Grand Prix car which had been acquired by the Admiralty during the first week of the war. Rolls-Royce was also given an example of the RAF.3 V8 water-cooled engine newly developed at the Royal Aircraft Factory, as were Napier and Armstrong-Whitworth, both of whom chose to put that engine into production. Henry Royce began the design of a new V12 water-cooled engine which was to be named the Eagle, and it was first bench-run at Derby in February 1915, giving 25 hp more than the planned 200 hp, and it was soon cleared to 250 hp at 1,800 rpm. Sunbeam now had a powerful competitor in the production of water-cooled aero-engines.

Coatalen had already responded to the quest for more power by the simple expedient of increasing the bore of his two side-valve engines by a further 10 mm to give them 100 mm × 150 mm cylinders. The larger V12 engine, which would be named Gurkha, was first bench-run in October 1914 and gave 240 hp. The V8 was to give 160 hp and would be named Zulu. The reduction gear ratio for both these engines was also reduced from 2:1 to 1.86:1.

At the same time Coatalen was transferring the principles of his 1914 Grand Prix car engines to the production of a series of new overhead camshaft, four valves per cylinder engines. The first of these was to be a V8 engine with the banks initially set at sixty degrees, giving 150 hp, to be named the Nubian. This engine suffered tremendous teething troubles, and was not to go into small-scale production until much later in the war by which time it had been totally redesigned with a ninety-degree Vee. The V12 cousin of the Nubian, the 200 hp Afridi, continued under development throughout 1915, together with a totally different and much larger V12 engine, the 310 hp Cossack.

The sole production engines throughout 1915 remained the Crusader and the Mohawk however, averaging 10.25 and 12.5 engines delivered per month respectively. Apart from a

A side view of the V12 Mohawk, the most powerful British aero-engine available at the outbreak of War.

small number of Sopwith Type 806s and Avro 510 seaplanes, neither of which was a very successful aircraft, the majority of Crusaders went into the new and very successful Short Type 827 seaplane. A total of 108 were ordered from Short Bros and five other contractors, including the Sunbeam Motor Car Co. itself.

A number of small changes was also introduced to the two engines to improve them. Firstly there was a different design of valve cap coupled with different plug positions, a change which gave an extra 1% in power and decreased the liability of the valves to overheat. An end bearing was added to the crankshaft, there was improved mounting of the reduction gear wheel, the nose piece was cast solid with the crankcase, there were alterations to the lubrication system, and aluminium alloy pistons were substituted for the original steel ones. On the Mohawk only, there was a new method of taking the end thrust on the oil pump.

The first order for aircraft to be built by Sunbeam was placed on 13 May 1915 (contracts CP 49441/15 and CP70484/15) for a batch of twenty Short Type 827s. On 29 May another batch of twenty was ordered under contrat No. CP78661/15. To aid their introduction into the new field of aircraft production Short Bros provided tuition for Sunbeam staff down at Rochester, and around 1,000 blueprints were provided at cost. The first Sunbeam-built Short 827 was delivered to RNAS Grain by lorry on 8 November 1915. From that time on, production continued at about four aircraft per month.

The Crusader was also fitted to most of the Coastal Class of non-rigid airships, two to each airship operating in tractor and pusher mode. Sunbeam engines were to be associated with a large number of airships, and the Coastals were the first. The Mohawk was fitted to the three torpedo-carrying types, the first into production being the Sopwith Type 860, though this was to prove the least capable. This was followed by the first Wight Type 840 in March 1915, and the best and most famous of the three, the Short Type 184 from the following month.

The torpedo-carrying seaplane was a brand-new weapon of war, but the power available, even from the Mohawk, was at best only marginally enough. By 27 May 1916 it was announced that the improved running achieved on the Mohawk meant the Short Type 184 was now capable of lifting a fourteen-inch torpedo with a radius of action of 100 miles, though only when the aircraft was new and good sea states prevailed. Nevertheless, when the German Navy's battle cruisers shelled Yarmouth the eleven aircraft available – three at Yarmouth itself, two at Felixstowe, and six in the Nore Command – did not venture out. It was decided that it would be suicide, as the Short 184 had to fly at a height of only twenty feet to within 1,000 yards of the target. Against battle cruisers it was felt the Short 184 should only attack at night, or when the ships were distracted in a surface action.

Aircraft production at the Moorfield Works. The top three pictures show Short Type 827 seaplanes, with Crusader engines in production. At the bottom there is a line of Avro 504K fuselages outside the works, much later in the war. The wings were made by Star Engineering just down the road. At the bottom is the novel way the company transported 504 fuselages two at a time.

A close-up of a Mohawk installed in a Short Type 184 seaplane that had been captured by the Germans.

On 2 January 1915 Coatalen patented a novel engine layout which illustrated the imaginative way his mind often worked. It was for two Vee engines, each driving its own crankshaft, geared to a central crankshaft, to be mounted side by side with the inner cylinder banks bolted together with a common water jacket. This idea was further developed with a patent on 6 February for an engine with eight banks of cylinders created from two engines from the earlier patent, one above the other to create an engine of a 'Star' layout, with each pair of cylinders driving its own crankshaft, geared to a central crankshaft. There was also provision in the patent for further cylinder blocks to be bolted on in different places. There is no evidence that Sunbeam ever tried to make this unnecessarily complicated layout work.

On 29 March 1915 the Society of British Aircraft Constructors was formed, and Louis Coatalen was Sunbeam's representative on the board. Among the others, with whom Sunbeam were to have substantial dealings, were Herbert Austin, Frederick Handley Page, H.T. Vane of D. Napier & Sons, H.V. Roe, S.E. Saunders, E.C. Gordon England of Frederick Sage & Co, and E.B. Parker of Short Bros.

On 6 May 1916 John Marston was to relinquish the day-to-day control of his two neighbouring companies, Sunbeam and John Marston Ltd. Thomas Cureton assumed control of the Sunbeam Motor Car Co., but John Marston still came to the factories frequently, cycling to the tram terminus from his home in Tettenhall, and continuing by public transport.

Amazingly, while the Moorfield Works was struggling to meet the Navy's requirements of aero-engines, Coatalen found time and resources to build six-cylinder racing cars to take to America. These were based on his pre-war racing cars but showed the influence of the new aero-engines and fea-

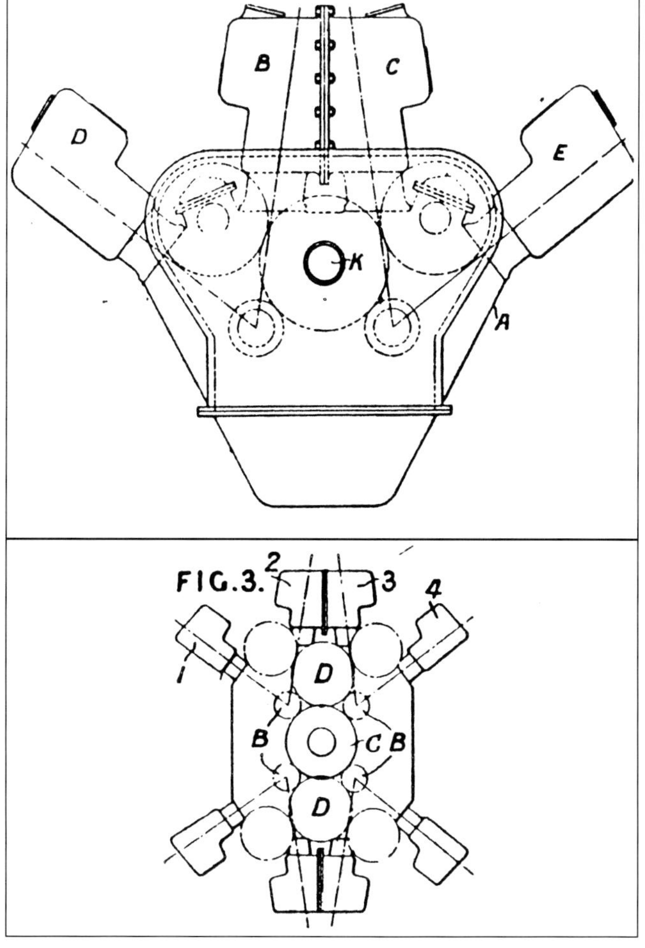

Sunbeam patent drawings showing a four-bank aero-engine (Fig. 1) with the central banks bolted together, and each Vee driving its own crankshaft. Fig. 3 shows a second patented design for two of the first engines bolted together, a very complicated eight-bank design.

tured a great deal of aluminium, especially for the crankcase, though the bore and stroke of 80 mm × 156 mm was entirely new. The man chosen to go over and race these cars was Jean Christiaens, a Belgium pilot who had escaped when the Germans occupied his home in 1915 and had been working for Sunbeam flying experimental aircraft. He had been a racing driver for Excelsior before the war, and was an ideal choice. Christiaens was second in his first race on 13 May 1916 at Sheepshead Bay on Long Island, but could only manage fourth in the Indianapolis Race (averaging only 79.66 mph), which that year was reduced to 300 miles. On 11 June at the Chicago 300-Mile Race he came third at a much improved 95.78 mph. Christiaens came back to England and became manager of the Experimental Department, but was tragically killed in March 1919 when driving a car up the road from the Moorfield Works.

In 1916 Sunbeam's representative in Paris, supervising the testing of Sunbeam aero-engines by the French armed forces, was Sidney Reed. He was immensely proud of the fact that he managed to get a Sunbeam engine through the French tests before the rival Rolls-Royce Eagle. He was later to become engine testing supervisor back at the Moorfield Works.

The Sunbeam side-valve engines fitted to the RNAS seaplanes and airships operated on long patrols over cold waters, but never had a great reputation for reliability, though that was not entirely the fault of the engines themselves. It was normal policy to carry a spare magneto on every flight of the Coastal airships because they had so much trouble with them. One which operated from Pulham had double-engine failure because of leaking radiators. The drifting airship was pursued across country by Warrant Officer Archie Binding and a hastily gathered team of engineers with quickly arranged ladders, scaffolding, and cylinders of hydrogen. The Coastal eventually came to a halt in a tree and could be repaired. The radiators were removed and taken to the nearest plumber to be fixed! The side-valve engines were also difficult to start, often needing their spark plugs to be heated beforehand, and though they ran quite well once started, the valves tended to become too hot. When the engines cooled down after a flight the valves would warp. If at all possible the engines would be replaced after each flight, which was obviously a time-consuming and wasteful process.

Nevertheless the side-valve Sunbeam engines performed sterling work when no other large-capacity engines were available, and took part in some of the most remarkable exploits of the early years of the war. Four Crusaders – serial nos. 297, 345, 371, and 372 – were fitted to four Short Type 827 seaplanes, 3093–5 and 8219, transferred to the Belgians in Africa. The first three of these seaplanes were actually the first three built by Sunbeam, though which engine was fitted to which aircraft has not been recorded. The Belgians were facing the Germans across Lake Tanganyika, and had nothing to counter two powerful German warships on the lake, the *Graf von Goetzen* and the *Hedwig von Wisman*, which could shell the Belgian positions on the eastern shore with impunity. The Belgians cobbled together a naval force and managed to sink the *Hedwig von Wisman*, but asked for help to deal with the powerful 1,200-ton *Graf von Goetzen*.

The four Short seaplanes had been assigned to No. 8 Squadron in Zanzibar; they were sent overland to the Belgian Congo and were erected on a small side lake to Tanganyika, Lake Tongwe. The first Short was ready to be test-flown on 14 May 1916 and the first bombing raid on the German ship at Kigoma on the other side of the lake was scheduled for 10 June. Only one Short 827 was available for the raid and Lieutenant Orta took off at about six p.m. carrying two 65 lb

OILING DIAGRAM OF SUNBEAM-COATALEN AIRCRAFT MOTORS

The oiling system common to all of the Sunbeam side-valve aero-engines.

Sunbeam-built Short Type 827 being launched on Lake Tongwe by the Belgians, for use against the Germans in Tanganyika.

bombs. Ten miles from the German port of Kigoma he went down to about 500 feet, and when he was about two miles out the German warship began shooting at him. Orta swooped over the warship and dropped his bombs, one of which struck the *Graf von Goetzen* on the stern. Orta turned for home, but twenty miles from Kigoma the Crusader began coughing and Orta had to land on the lake; the seaplane's floats had been holed by the German fire and the Short began sinking. Once Orta was overdue the armed trawler *Vigeur* sailed along his course and came across the stricken aircraft. Both the Short and its gallant crew were rescued. Further raids and reconnaissance sorties were carried out by the Short seaplanes and the Germans were eventually driven from the shores of Lake Tanganyika, the *Graf von Goetzen* taking no further part in this obscure little war.

Other Short Type 827s powered by Crusaders took part in another side-show campaign in Mesopotamia, where for a time General Townsend and 13,000 men from early December 1915 were trapped by the Turkish forces at a bend of the Tigris River at Kut. Three Short 827s – serials 822, 825, and 827 – had joined Force D of the Royal Flying Corps in September, coming from East Africa. Force D had been cobbled together as the air component for operations in what would now be called Iraq.

The Short 827s were among the aircraft used to attempt the world's first operation to supply a large military force by air. The Short seaplanes carried 300 lb bags of flour slung between their floats, and dropped them to the besieged garrison. Operations in the hot and humid conditions of the region placed a huge strain on men and machines and the Crusader engines had a tendency to over-rev in the hot, thin air. The RNAS mechanics fashioned new four-blade propellers from palm tree wood to replace the two-blade British propellers, though all propellers had to be covered with moist sacking when not in use to prevent distortion. The rivers of Mesopotamia were not really suitable for seaplane operation, being too narrow, and in the hot and humid air the pilots found it difficult to get airborne, so all three Type 827s were converted to landplanes for a while, but not before 825 had hit a native boat while attempting to take off. Serial 822 crashed ten miles south of Kut and was written off, but the other two were later converted back to seaplanes.

Serving alongside them were four Mohawk-powered Short Type 184s, 8044–7, and these too were pressed into service attempting to supply General Townsend's army at Kut, and 8044 was shot down while in the process of dropping food to the beleaguered garrison. From the start of supply-dropping operations in January 1915, 16,000 lb of supplies were dropped by air to the garrison, but this fell far short of the 5,000 lb per day which were deemed the minimum necessary.

The two most famous RNAS seaplane actions of the war, however, were by Short Type 184s powered by Sunbeam Mohawk engines. The Short Type 184/Sunbeam Mohawk combination had been designed to produce an aircraft capable

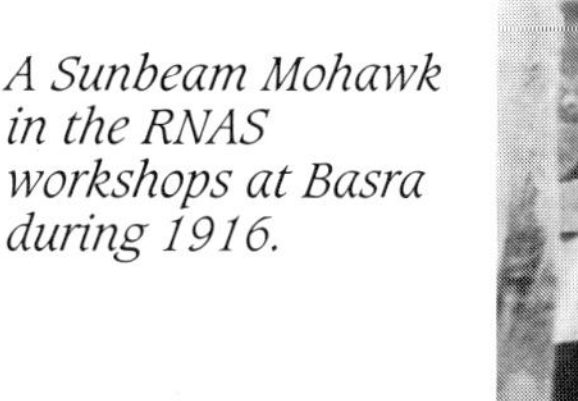

A Sunbeam Mohawk in the RNAS workshops at Basra during 1916.

of attacking enemy ships with a fourteen-inch torpedo, and on 12 August 1915 this was achieved for the first time. F/Cdr C.H.K. Edmonds took off from alongside the seaplane carrier *Ben-my-Chree* in the original Short Type 184, serial 184, in the Aegean with enough petrol for forty-five minutes' flying. He found a Turkish transport ship in the straits and attacked, flying at fifteen feet and launching his torpedo at 300 yards. He scored a direct hit, though the ship had already been crippled by a British submarine. On the 17th Edmonds repeated the feat and torpedoed one of three transports in the straits, leaving it on fire. On the same day F/Cdr G.B. Dacre was flying *Ben-my-Chree*'s other Type 184, serial 185, when the hot conditions prevented him remaining in the air with the weight of the torpedo. He landed on the sea, and then saw a Turkish tug, which he torpedoed and sank while taxying. Without the torpedo he was then able to take off again and return to his ship. This was the first time a ship had ever been torpedoed and sunk by an aircraft, though these were the only such successes in the war.

A short while later Dacre was flying from HMS *Raven* off Palestine. On 2 July he flew an armed patrol in a Short 184 over Haifa accompanying a Sopwith Schneider. He bombed a road bridge and a railway shed, just missing both, and then returned to the ship. The Schneider had not returned and so Dacre had the Short refuelled and refloated, with his observer, Brown, taking a Lewis gun this time. They found the Schneider in the water only a few yards from the shore, with the pilot on the top wing. They landed alongside and the pilot clambered on board and took the observer's seat. To balance the aircraft as they flew back, Brown had to sit on the fuel tank right behind the huge radiator on top of the forward fuselage, and take the full blast of the hot air coming through it.

The only aircraft to take part in the Battle of Jutland was the Short 184 serial 8359 flown by F/Lt F.J. Rutland with Assistant Paymaster G.S. Trewen as observer. Ordered by Admiral Beatty to search for German forces, Rutland and Trewen took off from alongside the seaplane carrier HMS *Engadine* and located the German light cruiser force. This was the first time an aircraft had ever taken part in a major naval battle. The remains of this aircraft, just the foward fuselage, are now on display in the Fleet Air Arm Museum, but the engine fitted is a 240 hp Gurkha, which had replaced the Mohawk after Jutland.

The majority of the service performed by the side-valve-engined seaplanes was of a far more mundane nature: long sea patrols, often in appalling conditions. In December 1916 the company received a report of a Short Type 184 which had flown a seven-and-a-half-hour patrol almost to the Dutch coast in rainstorms and patchy fog. The engine used was Mohawk No. 608, built in 1915 but overhauled by Sunbeam in September 1916. It was reported fitted with New York Bosch Magnetos Type DU, six Claudel-Hobson carburettors, KLG spark plugs, and 'new type' valve springs, as well as water-cooled valve caps, the latter seemingly a modification to overcome the problem of overheating valves.

Though envisaged as a torpedo-carrier, many of the Type 184s were pressed into service as bombers, making raids on naval priority targets such as the Submarine Repair Works at Ostend and the seaplane stations at Ostend and Zeebrugge. To increase their effectiveness as bombers some of them were converted to Type D single-seaters able to carry nine 65 lb bombs. One of the biggest raids attempted in the war was on 20 March 1916 when nine Mohawk-powered Type 184s, each carrying three 65 lb bombs, planned to bomb Zeebrugge. One, serial 8053, failed to take off, but the others – 8035, 8037–8, 8040, 8086, 8093, 8346, and 8383 – dropped their bombs successfully. On another raid on the Hoyer Airship Base five days later, 8040 dropped its bombs but was then forced to land off the Belgian coast, and the aircraft and its crew were captured by the Germans.

The remains of the Short Type 184 which was the only aircraft to fly at the Battle of Jutland.

The second Short Bomber, built by Sunbeam and fitted with their 240 hp Gurkha engine, at Dunstall Park racecourse, which had doubled as Wolverhampton's airfield since 1910.

One particular Mohawk-powered Type 184, serial 8015, built by S.E. Saunders & Co., had a particularly adventurous career as a bomber. It was delivered and tested at Calshot on 1 August 1916, and was delivered to Dunkirk on 15 October. Its first raid was against the Zeebrugge Mole on 4 April 1917 followed by others on the nights of the 5th/6th and 7th/8th. The night after that it bombed the Submarine Repair Works at Ostend, and then the Zeebrugge Seaplane Station on the 30th. All these raids had been piloted by F/Lt R. Graham DSC, but the following night F/Lt G.W. Price flew 8015 on a raid against Ostend Seaplane Station. Graham was back in the pilot's seat on a raid against the same target on 10 May, and Price bombed Zeebrugge Mole on the night of 31 May. The aircraft's ninth and last bombing raid was again to Zeebrugge Mole with Graham in charge on 3 June. The aircraft was then returned to Dover and converted to a reconnaissance type, and was still in service on 31 January 1919.

The other category of aircraft for which the large water-cooled engines were required was the strategic bomber. Handley Page was developing the twin-engined Type O, and this was originally ordered, in December 1914, to be powered by two Crusaders, and serials were allocated for two prototypes (1372 and 1373). This order was changed to take advantage of the new engine at Rolls-Royce, and the first O/100, re-serialled 1455, made its inaugural flight on 18 December 1915, the first time a Rolls-Royce aero-engine had flown. Meanwhile, an interim type had been designed, the single-engined Short Bomber. The prototype was fitted with a Mohawk, but production aircraft were to be fitted with the Rolls-Royce Eagle, except for a batch produced by Sunbeam itself.

Production of the forty Short Type 827s finished in July 1916, apart from a late one which did not go until October. An order was placed for twenty Short Bombers, to which Sunbeam was allowed to fit its own engines. By this time the two engines in production at the Moorfield Works were the 100 mm × 150 mm V12 Gurkha and V8 Zulu, and so the Sunbeam-built Short Bombers were fitted with the 240 hp Gurkha. The first, serial 9356, was finished in July 1916 and was tested at Dunstall Park racecourse, for part of the time with a fin having a straighter leading edge than the usual pronounced curve of Short designs. Production of the Short Bombers continued at about two per month until the turn of the year, at which point the last five were cancelled, only fifteen being delivered in all. The availability of the far more capable Handley Page Type O/100 had superseded the need for the Short. It is not clear if all the Short Bombers were test-flown at Dunstall Park, but they were delivered by road and rail to Chingford and Eastchurch.

Three views of the Sikorsky four-engined Il'ya Mouromets bomber powered by 150 hp Crusader engines. How many of these aircraft were powered by Sunbeams is not known.

A Sunbeam-built Avro 504B, N6134, which had been delivered in January 1917.

The Short Bombers were replaced on Sunbeam's aircraft production lines by orders for Avro 504B trainers, the first being delivered in November 1915. Some of these Avro 504Bs were dual-control aircraft but many were used as gunnery trainers, and a number were converted, possibly by Sunbeam, into the Avro 504H version, with a strengthened airframe, catapult pick-up points, and a padded seat for the pilot. Production of the Avro 504B/H ceased in May 1917 after sixty had been delivered.

By September 1916 the large 310 hp V12 Cossack engine was into large-scale production initially alongside the older side-valve engines, and Sunbeam's productive capacity was being stretched to the limit. An American company – the Sterling Engine Company of Buffalo, New York, a large manufacturer of motor-boat engines – took out a licence to build the Cossack, as well as the Crusader and Mohawk, to be known as Sterling-Sunbeams, and though it is known that at least one prototype Cossack was built and tested, there is no evidence of any deliveries being made, certainly not to this country, and it is probable that none of the side-valve engines was actually manufactured.

There had been a continual demand for Sunbeam ambulances and the three-litre, 16 hp, side-valve staff car, and the War Office desired that production of these should continue. At the end of 1916 the production of these Sunbeam vehicles, including all jigs, tools, patterns, and drawings, was transferred to the Rover Car Company in Coventry so that the whole of Moorfield Works could be devoted to aero-engine and aircraft production.

By mid-1916 Sunbeam, for a short while, had four aero-engines in production side by side. The last few Zulu and Gurkha side-valve engines were being built; the very last of 389 side-valve engines built during the war, a Zulu, was delivered during November 1916. The two new overhead camshaft V12 engines, the Afridi and the Cossack, were also in production and about to supplant the older engines. The 310 hp Cossack was destined to be fitted mainly to a new large Short seaplane, the Type 310-A4, far more capable and able to carry a standard eighteen-inch torpedo, but destined, as things turned out, never to do so in earnest. The Cossack was also installed in a small number of the Handley Page O/400 heavy bombers.

Sunbeam received orders for fifty of the Short Type 310 seaplane, replacing the Avro 504 in the airframe production shops, but the first was not delivered until September 1917, so there was a gap in airframe production of three months

A Sunbeam 16 hp staff car in France. Production of these was eventually transferred to Rover so that Sunbeam could concentrate on aero-engines.

(ABOVE):
The rear of the new V12 Cossack engine, showing the twin overhead camshafts which derived from the Sunbeam 1914 TT cars. This view shows the four magnetos of the dual-ignition Cossack II.

(BELOW):
The first Sunbeam-built Short Type 310-A4 seaplane with the Cossack engine, serial N1360.

when no aircraft were delivered. This was the only such gap since airframe production began until well into 1919, the change-over from one type to the next usually overlapping by four months or more. This may not be unconnected with Sunbeam's decision to initiate its own aircraft design.

One of the requirements formulated by the Committee for Imperial Defence in November 1916 was the Type 7 single-seat bomber, to be powered by a 200 hp engine. Sunbeam submitted a design proposal in January 1917, and an order was placed for two prototypes.

The smaller overhead camshaft V12 engine designed by Coatalen, the Afridi of 200 hp, had started to be delivered in July 1916 and by the end of the year, when the Zulu and Gurkha had been phased out, Sunbeam was producing just the two V12 engines, the 200 hp Afridi and the 310 hp Cossack, twenty-six and twenty-eight respectively being delivered during December, a far higher combined production than had been achieved up to then, caused mainly by the hand-over of road vehicle production to Rover.

The Afridi was being produced against an order for 300, but Coatalen was already developing the engine, increasing its bore by 8 mm to 100 mm to produce a 250 hp engine, which was also fitted with dual ignition instead of the earlier engine's single ignition; it was renamed the Maori. The change to dual ignition was a requirement of the Admiralty, and was due to the continued unreliability of British-built magnetos. All pre-war magnetos had been German, and the art of building them had not been perfected in this country. The Afridi had gone into production as a single-ignition engine just as the change in requirement came into effect, and was therefore something of a casualty of it. The increase in the bore of the engine to produce the Maori may not have been unconnected to the need to make room to install two spark plugs instead of one. At the same time the larger Cossack was also converted to dual ignition, to become the Cossack II, but did not receive an increased bore.

The Maori was undoubtedly Sunbeam's most successful engine of the war, and it supplanted the Afridi on the production line in April 1917. In fact the two engines were built side by side for three months, but the last 100 Afridis were converted to Maoris before delivery by fitting the larger blocks and dual ignition, and the last Afridi was cancelled, making 299 delivered altogether. Most of the Afridis seem to have been installed in Curtiss R.2 two-seat biplanes, replacing unsatisfactory Curtiss engines, though a few Afridis went into one-off designs. The converted Afridis were redesignated Maori Is, and the first new-build Maoris were designated Mk IIs.

(LEFT):
Louis Coatalen's most successful aero-engine, the Maori; in this version the Maori III with outside exhausts

(BELOW):
A Short Type 184 fitted with a Maori I/II engine, with inside exhausts. The Type 184 was the most common application of the Maori, many replacing Sunbeam side-valve engines.

The Maori was ordered in substantial numbers, and production quickly built up to a high of seventy-two delivered in August 1917. As with the side-valve engines the majority of them went into RNAS seaplanes, most commonly the Short Type 184, being fitted to new examples and replacing the older side-valve engines. At least one Type 184, serial 8048, was built with a Mohawk, being delivered by Short Bros in January 1916, had that replaced by the more powerful Gurkha in February 1917, and was then re-equipped for a second time with the Maori in June 1917. A total of 532 Type 184s have been identified as being powered by Sunbeam Maori engines, most of them fitted new, and there may well have been others that had their older engines replaced by Maoris without records having survived. The rival Wight seaplane was also equipped with Maoris in small numbers, a total of twenty-seven Wight 'converted' seaplanes having been identified as Maori-powered. The other major recipients of the engine were the Fairey Campania and Type IIIA seaplanes, a total of 132 being so powered.

A view of the Moorfield Works showing an abundance of Maoris and women workers.

Like the Mohawk- and Gurkha-powered Type 184s before them, the basic role of the Maori-powered version remained the same: long, uneventful sea patrols, with the North Sea being the most typical theatre of operations. It was a theatre contested by German seaplanes, and combat over its

(LEFT):
A Maori I/II installation in a Fairey F.22 Campania

(BELOW LEFT):
A close-up of the Maori I/II installation in a Short Type 184, serial 8076, which apparently had broken engine bearers at the time.

(BELOW RIGHT):
A head-on view taken at the same time as the last photograph, which shows that the pilot could actually see through the radiator blocks which were usually placed on the forward fuselage of Sunbeam-powered seaplanes.

cold, stormy waters was not uncommon. For example, on 18 July 1918 two Maori-powered Type 184s operated by No. 406 Flight at Westgate in Kent, N2927 and N2937, both built by Robey & Co. and powered by 260 hp Maori IIs, were attacked by seven Brandenberg seaplanes four miles south-east of Kentish Knock. Despite being escorted by two Sopwith Camels, in the ensuing battle both Shorts were shot down and their crews killed.

The Maori also found its way into a substantial number of prototypes, and was one of the specified engines for the Handley Page O/400 bomber. Orders for 250 of these from different manufacturers had Eagle, Liberty or Maori engines specified, as available, though apparently the Eagle was the engine preferred, with the Liberty the second choice, both being more powerful than the Maori.

The Maori was the one Sunbeam engine which Coatalen developed in several versions. The original Maori I, the converted Afridi, developed 250 hp at 2,000 rpm, and was fitted with a geared propeller; this developed into the Maori II with less weight, which gave 260 hp. Both these marks had inside exhaust valves, which must have made their fitment in certain aircraft quite difficult. The Maori III was designed with outside exhaust valves to overcome this, and it developed more power at 275 hp at 2,000 rpm. Finally, the Maori IV was developed for airship use, five of them being specified for the forthcoming R.33 and R.34 airships. These had direct drive, with a governor to control engine speed, and special water-cooled exhausts, for safety reasons.

Both the V12 Cossack and the V12 Maori, which were in production alongside each other, were part of a large family of engines. The Cossack was to spawn the straight six 160 hp Amazon based on one bank of the Cossack, and then the W18 450 hp Viking based on three Cossack banks in a broad-arrow arrangement, and as already mentioned the Maori had been developed from the Afridi which was related to the V8 Nubian, which was still under development.

At Rolls-Royce Henry Royce had a different philosophy of engine development. Having designed the V12 Eagle which was quickly cleared to run at 1,800 rpm, producing 250 hp, a development programme was instituted to refine the engine to make it even more powerful, while retaining its proven reliability. By the end of the war the Eagle was giving an impressive 375 hp, although it was still basically the same engine drawn up in 1914. Rolls-Royce did produce two other engines during the war, the small 75 hp Hawk intended for training aircraft and another V12, the 190 hp Falcon, an engine for fighters designed to fit in beneath the ever-increasing power of the Eagle. Late in the war the company also initiated the design of a much larger V12, the 600 hp Condor, when ever larger aircraft were requiring ever more power.

Louis Coatalen seems to have had an entirely different design philosophy from Henry Royce. Although Sunbeam engines were increased in power during the war, this was usually done by the simple expedient of increasing the bore, something Royce never did. The resulting engine was then given a new name, and spoken of as if it was a completely new engine, as with the Mohawk/Gurkha and the Crusader/Zulu. Whereas Henry Royce was tremendously meticulous in all he did, Louis Coatalen gives the impression of being very mercurial, easily bored with whatever project he was working on, and anxious to move on to the next.

During 1916 he had a new overhead camshaft V8 engine running on the bench, an engine different from all his other engines in every way, the most famous engine ever produced by Sunbeam, and probably Coatalen's nemesis: the Sunbeam Arab. The Arab was of radically different construction from the other OHC engines. The blocks were of aluminium monobloc construction – that is, cast whole – and there was a single overhead camshaft driving only three valves per cylinder. The Arab is usually regarded as being a copy of the Hispano-Suiza 200 hp V8, and certainly it was very similar, especially in appearance, but there were fundamental differences: the Hispano-Suiza had screwed in steel liners, whereas the Arab had pressed-in liners; the Hispano-Suiza had forked connecting rods, but the Arab had Coatalen's normal articulated connecting rods; and the two engines had very different crankcases.

Of course, if Coatalen had set out to copy the French engine, as he had with the Peugeot Grand Prix car engines before the war, he would have designed sufficient changes to be able to claim his engine was not a copy. It will probably never be known to what extent the Arab was a copy of or just inspired by the Hispano-Suiza, which had first run in low-compression 150 hp form as early as February 1915. When Henry Royce designed the Eagle he certainly looked at the construction of Mercedes engines, and chose the same single-cylinder construction, but he has never been accused of copying the German engine. It is probably true to say that Coatalen drew a larger measure of inspiration from the Hispano-Suiza than Royce from the Mercedes.

In January 1917 the National Advisory Committee for Aeronautics had its Internal Combustion Engine Committee look at four new 200 hp engines which were under test at the time. Apart from the Hispano-Suiza 8B and the Arab, there were also two straight six engines, the BHP and Sunbeam's own Saracen. Coatalen had increased the bore of his straight six Amazon from 110 mm to 122 mm, retaining the same stroke of 160 mm, to produce a 200 hp straight six, the Saracen. In the same way the Amazon's progenitor, the V12

A Short Type 184 with the later Maori III with outside exhausts, the twin exhaust stacks replacing the single central stack of the earlier version.

The monobloc 200 hp Sunbeam Arab, built in larger numbers than any other Sunbeam engine, but the company's biggest disappointment.

Cossack, had its bore increased to 122 mm, as well as having its cast-iron blocks replaced with cast aluminium, becoming the 400 hp Matabele. The Saracen was rejected as being already an obsolete design, though the BHP did received large orders, but the Arab and the Hispano-Suiza received the bulk of the orders, the latter both from French companies and under licence from Wolseley Motors. Sunbeam received an initial order for 1,000 Arabs, later increased to 2,110, and 4,050 more were eventually ordered from four other contractors: Austin Motors, Lanchester Motor Co., D. Napier & Sons, and Willys-Overland in Toledo, Ohio.

In May 1917 the question of naming Sunbeam engines was raised by the Director of Inspection of the AID. The system of referring to the engines solely by their horse power had worked up to a point, but now there were engines of indentical power outputs and configuration, most confusingly the 150 hp V8 side-valve engine (Crusader) and the 150 hp V8 OHC engine (Nubian). With Sunbeam engines proliferating all the time, something had to be done. The director suggested a system of universal nomenclature for all aero-engines, but especially with regard to Sunbeam engines. The company suggested a series of tribal names for the engines and provided the following list, though a number of them, for instance Crusader and Saracen, could hardly be described as tribal names:

H.P.	Cylinders (mm)	Suggested Name	Valve Type
150	8 × 90 × 150	Crusader	Side valve
155	8 × 95 × 135	Nubean (*sic*)	OHC 4 valves
160	8 × 100 × 150	Zulu	OHC 4 valves (*sic*)
170	6 × 110 × 160	Amazen (*sic*)	OHC 4 valves
200	8 x	Arab	3 valves
200	6 x	Saracen (BHP Type – obsolete)	
210	12 × 92 × 135	Afridi	OHC 4 valves
225	12 × 90 × 150	Mohawk	Side valves
260	12 × 100 × 150	Gurkha	Side valves
275	12 × 100 × 135	Maori	OHC 4 valves
320	12 × 110 × 160	Cossack	OHC 4 valves
450	18 × 110 × 160	Viking	OHC 4 valves

It is clear from this list that Coatalen developed the straight six Saracen by increasing the bore of his Amazon engine before he built up the power on the related V12 Cossack by increasing its bore by the same amount to produce the Matabele, because the latter does not appear on the list.

On 13 June the Director of Air Services commented that the names suggested torpedo-boat destroyers, or conveyed nothing. He suggested using planets, English county towns, or plants. Of course there were not enough planets in the solar system for the number of Sunbeam–Coatalen engines, and the county towns would quickly have been used up. The Sunbeam suggestion was taken up, and continued to be used from then on.

Sunbeam produced water-cooled engines throughout their history, but there was apparently one attempt at pro-

Two lines of Arabs awaiting delivery. In the background there are also some Maoris, the other engine in production at the end of the war.

ducing an air-cooled engine. This was the Spartan, produced at about the same time as the Arab, and amazingly a V12 engine with single overhead camshaft and four valves per cylinder. There were large numbers of V8 air-cooled engines produced during the war, all derivatives of the 70 hp Renault, but a V12 air-cooled was very unusual. It had cylinders of 105 mm bore and 135 mm stroke, and may therefore have been related to the Afridi/Maori, but it only produced 200 hp from fourteen litres, so any weight saving was at a penalty. Certainly the engine never progressed beyond the project stage.

The Arab may well have been the first Sunbeam aero-engine to be referred to by its name at the outset. Despite the promising bench tests which had taken place late in 1916 the Arab did not progress into production without considerable difficulty. It relied heavily on aluminium in its construction, with Coatalen's first monobloc cylinder blocks cast in groups of four, with die-cast aluminium cylinders. There was continual trouble with the casting of the blocks and the prevention of porosity in their construction. The Arab's biggest problem, however, was vibration, which became most apparent when it was finally tested in the air. Whereas the Hispano-Suiza 8B had forked connecting rods of equal length on each side, Coatalen used a master and articulated connecting rod layout, which meant the piston on one side travelled fractionally further than its counterpart, making balancing them very difficult. The vibration set up was transmitted to the crankshaft bearings, and by chance they were arranged in such a way that it was then transmitted to the engine mountings.

The first Sunbeam-built Arab was delivered in May 1917 and there were three more delivered the following month, and then no more until September. It would seem likely that at least one of these first four engines would have been air-tested, but no trace of the aircraft concerned has been found. The first aircraft known to have been fitted with an Arab was the Martinsyde F.2 two-seat fighter, which had already flown with an Hispano-Suiza engine. In the first week in July the Martinsyde was at Wolverhampton having the Arab fitted, and having to have alterations to the oil tank and exhaust pipe, presumably to make it fit the airframe. Two weeks later it was badly damaged during testing by Sunbeam, and following repairs it was not despatched to Martlesham Heath, by road, until 11 August. By 15 September this engine had been removed from the Martinsyde, a design which was not to be ordered into production, and was sent to Farnborough to be fitted to an SE.5a, the aircraft which was supposed to be the recipient of a substantial part of Arab production.

Another Arab had been fitted to Sunbeam's own Type 7 single-seat bomber, the first prototype of which, N515, was delivered to Castle Bromwich for erection by October 1917. There was obviously a great number of problems with the aircraft as it was not delivered to Martlesham Heath for testing until July the following year, and most of the problems probably lay with its engine.

In September 1917 Sunbeam was still making the Cossack, with thirteen being delivered, but Cossack production would shortly be ended prematurely, with the last thirty-two of 382 on order being suspended so as to help build up Arab production. The straight six Amazon was also in low-volume production at about six per month, but the main production engine was the Maori, with forty-seven delivered that month. Eight Arabs were delivered in September, but production began in earnest the following month with seventeen delivered, followed by twenty-three in November and twenty-nine in December, but this was lagging far behind the anticipated requirements, and none of the other contractors had delivered any at all. The monthly requirement for Arabs for December delivery had been set at sixty back in August, rising in steady increments to 213 for June 1918.

The effects of Arab production problems were made worse because the rival Hispano-Suiza engine was also experiencing difficulties, though not nearly as bad as the Arab's. At the turn of the year 400 SE.5a aircraft were in store, waiting for their engines. The SE.5a had gone into service in April 1917 powered by the 150 hp Hispano-Suiza, with the high-compression 200 hp Hispano-Suiza supplanting it during the year, though there were continual reliability problems with the engine. Nevertheless, by the end of the year Wolseley Motors had delivered 445 Hispano-Suiza 200 hp engines and there were 467 more from French manufacturers.

A direct-drive version of the French engine was produced by Wolseley Motors, and Sunbeam also produced a direct-drive Arab, which was called the Arab II. An inverted Arab was also built and renamed the Bedouin, one of the first examples of an aero-engine being inverted to aid forward visibility for the pilot in single-seaters, but the engine remained a prototype only.

Both geared and ungeared Arabs were tested on the SE.5a, but it was decided that the bulk of production Arabs would now go to Corps Reconnaissance Bristol F.2b Fighters, production of which was suffering from a shortage of Rolls-Royce Falcons. Two were hastily fitted with Arabs and flown to France for evaluation, but the vibration was so great parts of the engines fell off on the way. This was followed by a programme of testing Arab-powered Bristol Fighters at Martlesham Heath which was to go on well into 1919, its prime aim to cure the vibration problems. A whole host of combinations of different engine mountings and modified engines was tried, but the problem was never entirely cured.

Luckily for the aircrew concerned very few Arab-engined aircraft actually reached operational squadrons, as large-scale deliveries of Arab-powered Bristol Fighters were only just being made in the last weeks of the war. Nevertheless, these were almost the only Sunbeam engines with which the former Royal Flying Corps units, by then Royal Air Force units, had any experience, the bulk of Sunbeam engines going to the Royal Naval Air Service. It is just a pity that the Arab was such a disaster. While not, of course, the worst engine of the war, the Arab, with the single exception of the ABC Dragonfly, represented the greatest débâcle in aero-engine procurement by any nation. It's hard not to develop the suspicion that the Arab's reputation tainted the industry's view of all Sunbeam aero-engines.

(RIGHT): *The majority of Arabs fitted to aircraft went into Bristol F.2bs like this one, D7860, shown serving with No.59 Squadron at Duren, Germany, after the war.*

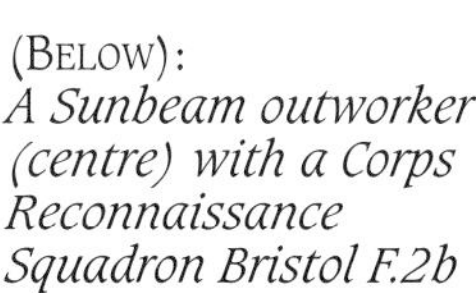

(BELOW): *A Sunbeam outworker (centre) with a Corps Reconnaissance Squadron Bristol F.2b*

On 8 March 1918 John Marston, the founder of the company, died, aged eighty-one. His employees erected a commemorative plaque in St Peter's Church, Wolverhampton, which testified that he had been a just and honourable employer, and his integrity, public spirit, and Christian faith was an example to all. The new chairman of the Sunbeam Motor Car Co., Thomas Cureton, was in ill health, and would not survive long himself. The premier figure in the factory was undoubtedly Louis Coatalen, as indicated by the fact that all 'Sunbeam' aero-engines were officially Sunbeam–Coatalen engines, and this fact was cast in their crankcases.

In the last months of the war a number of new engines were under development. The main two production engines were the Arab and the relatively successful Maori, but at the start of the year two other engines had been in low-volume

production: the 160 hp straight six Amazon and the redesigned 150 hp Nubian. The latter had been changed from a sixty-degree V8 to a ninety-degree V8, and production of the order for fifty finally started in October 1917, continuing to July 1918, when the last of thirty-six were delivered. The final fourteen Nubians were cancelled, the design having already been overtaken by the new 200 hp V8 engines. The order for 100 Amazons was also curtailed, and only seventy-seven had been delivered when production ceased in April 1918. To try to aid the build-up of Arab production even deliveries of the Maori had been cut back in the spring, but built up again towards the end of the year, until during October, the last full month of the war, fifty-two Arabs and sixty Maoris were delivered.

The last of the fifty Short Type 310-A4 seaplanes was delivered to Westgate during the week ending 20 June 1918, but production of the Avro 504 had already started up again, with the first of several orders for 504J and 504K models being delivered in February 1918. Production of the 504 reached its zenith in August when fifty-nine were delivered, and was to continue at a high level until March 1919. The company devised a novel way to deliver the aircraft fuselages – two of them side by side on a lorry, facing backwards, with the rear fuselages over the driver's open seats and projecting in front to a considerable degree. Orders for the 504J/K totalled 550, but only 481 were delivered, the last sixty-nine being cancelled. The very last aircraft built by Sunbeam, Avro 504K H2077, was delivered in the week ending 28 June 1919.

The total number of aircraft built by the Sunbeam Motor Car Co. was 647, including the single Sunbeam Bomber, the only one of their own design. This had finally reached Martlesham Heath for testing on 18 July 1918, where it was

(LEFT): *A Norman-Thompson NT.2B flying boat trainer, N2400, one of the other Arab-powered aircraft to be built in numbers.*

(BELOW): *A Sunbeam float showing Avro 504 parts, and highlighting the increasing part played by women workers as the war progressed.*

A Sunbeam-built Avro 504K, F2579, in service. This aircraft was delivered in October 1918.

found to be slightly inferior to the rival Sopwith B.1 single-seat bomber. The requirement had largely been superseded by the success of the DH.4/DH.9 and no single-seat bombers were ordered. The second Sunbeam Bomber, N516, was cancelled, with no evidence that it was ever built.

In the last months of the war Coatalen built a number of new aero-engines, most of them aimed at producing more power than had hitherto been available. He had made one earlier attempt to produce a more powerful engine than the Cossack by putting three Cossack blocks in a 'W' or broad-arrow layout to produce the 450 hp Viking, but at 1,450 lb this was just too heavy for aircraft use. Fifty Vikings were ordered but only thirteen were delivered before the contract was concelled, and these all went into high-speed naval launches with the exception of three which briefly powered the huge AD.1000 seaplane. It is interesting to note, however, that a sub-contractor of Sunbeam, Napier, was able to adopt the broad-arrow layout and to make it work well with their superlative Lion.

As already related, Coatalen switched his most successful engines from cast-iron to aluminium blocks, with as few further changes as possible. He increased the bore of the Cossack to produce the 400 hp Matabele, and he did the same to his other V12 production engine, the Maori. This had already been increased in bore from the 92 mm of the Afridi to 100 mm, and it was now increased again to 110 mm to produce the essentially similar 300 hp Manitou. Maori orders were changed to substitute the delivery of forty Manitous for forty Maoris, and the first three of these were delivered in November, with ten more the following month, alongside forty-four and forty-six Maoris respectively.

A new W12 engine, the 300 hp Kaffir, was also developed with 120 mm × 135 mm cylinders and three valves per cylinder, indicating a relationship with the Arab. A much more complicated relative of the Arab was also produced, the 500 hp Malay, with an incredible layout consisting of five Arab cylinder blocks arranged in a star layout around a central crankcase. Neither of these engines was developed beyond the prototype stage, which is not surprising in the case of the Malay, but another large engine had a more substantive existence, though it was never destined to be fitted to an aircraft or an airship, the application for which it was really designed.

Both Sunbeam Cossack and Maori engines were planned to be fitted to some of the rigid airships under construction at the end of the war, and this may well have inspired Coatalen to the development of a really large airship engine. The first stage in its development may have been the V12 Tartar, an engine stemming from work done in 1917 and fundamentally different from other Sunbeam engines in that it had single cylinders bolted to its crankcase in the manner of all the Rolls-Royce, Mercedes, and Liberty engines. It had four valves per cylinder and a single overhead camshaft, and was expressly designed for airship use.

The Tartar probably led to the new, very much larger engine, the 850 hp Sikh. This too was a V12 engine with single cylinders bolted to the crankcase which contained the single camshaft. It was designed to be a slow-revving engine, giving maximum horse power at 1,450 hp, with a geared propeller. Probably alongside the Sikh, rather than after it, Coatalen performed his usual trick of producing a straight six engine from half of a V12. The six-cylinder 425 hp Semi-Sikh, sometimes called the Sikh II, was ordered before the end of the war, but none had been delivered before the Armistice. The first bench tests of the Sikh were not to be made until May 1919.

The testing process for Sunbeam aero-engines is one operation which was recorded at the time in a magazine article which reveals something of the workings of the Moorfield Works. After assembly an engine was bench-tested for four hours, running on coal gas taken directly from the mains, with only the occasional burst of power provided by the mechanic in charge. The engine was then dismantled and examined in detail before being reassembled and run again for four hours, this time on petrol with carburettor and magneto fitted so that fuel consumption could be monitored. It was also connected to the brake so that power output could be determined. The engine was then dismantled again and examined once more, this time with a widespread use of the gauge to ascertain any wear on the parts. There was then another run of four hours, and another disassembly and examination, before the engine was taken outside for its most rigorous test.

Outside Moorfield Works was the engine-testing shed, little more than two end walls supporting a roof. It was divided into compartments by partitions, and each one contained a wheeled chassis not unlike an aircraft undercarriage, heavily chocked and anchored. The engine, with a two-blade propeller fitted, was installed in this chassis and operated by a mechanic on a raised platform behind, like the footplate of a locomotive. Each 'footplate' contained a panel of instruments and a bottle of compressed air for starting the engine, and sideboards enabled the mechanic and his assistant to work alongside the engine.

With the engine connected up compressed air was fed into the starting gear and the engine turned over, began picking up petrol, and fired. It was throttled back to tick over until warmed up, and then was wound up to its maximum permissible rpm of 2,500. The noise was deafening, and the entire district knew when Sunbeam was testing an aero-engine. In the confined space the propeller virtually created a wind tunnel, and there was a barrier to prevent anyone walk-

ing into it. The mechanic throttled the engine forward and back to try to recreate the evolutions it would go through on a normal flight, all the time noticing its condition on the instruments. The test chassis bucked and vibrated alarmingly to anyone not used to it. The test went on for four hours, and the engine was then switched off, returning the area around Upper Villiers Street to blessed silence. The engine was then lifted by crane back onto its trolley and returned to the works where it was stripped down and examined for the fourth time. Only then, if all was well, was it reassembled and passed for service.

During the war the Sunbeam's companion company, John Marston Ltd, had continued to produce motor-cycles in large numbers, having started building them in 1911 in spite of Marston's own antipathy to them. Though he was a keen cyclist he had banned all work on motor-cycles before the turn of the century after one of his men had been killed testing one he had built. Even though Sunbeam motor-cycles were to become among the most well-built and famous in the land, his own children and grandchildren were banned from owning them.

During the war Sunbeam 3.5 hp and 8 hp machines served with the armies of Great Britain, France, Russia, and Italy, both in War Department green and their standard black and gold finish. Some motor-cycles had ambulance side-cars fitted to carry one casualty. Even Sunbeam bicycles were used in large numbers; the 'Military Sunbeam', complete with Joseph Lucas rifle clips, was sold in large numbers to the French Army, and was even sold to civilians. Charles Marston's company, the Villiers Engineering Co., had also entered the motor-cycle trade in 1913, but only as manufacturers of two-stroke engines, producing one of the first successful designs and supplying a number of motor-cycle manufacturers. During the war, however, Villiers had been turned over to the manufacture of munitions.

Even before the war John Marston Ltd had become one of the country's premier radiator manufacturers, a business founded when car production started. The Marston Honeycomb radiator became one of the most famous in the country, and production was hugely expanded for both military vehicles and aircraft. At the Armistice it had current orders for 4,100 aero-engine radiators of which 1,490 had been delivered:

Marston Radiators	Ordered	Delivered to 18.11.18
DH.4	150	30
DH.9a	1,200	660
Bristol F.2b	1,250	210
FK.8	200	80
SE.5a	700	480
O/400	300	30
FE.2b	250	–
Short 184	50	–

After the Armistice the Ministry of Munitions began immediately to apply the brake on the tremendous output of armaments, and all contracts for aircraft and aero-engines were reviewed on 18 November 1918. The following list represented the orders at the time with the Sunbeam Motor Car Co.: (See list below)

As can be seen decisions on some of the contracts had still to be taken, though it was clear that the immediate opportunity was taken to start cancelling the Arab. For a while production at the Moorfield Works went on as before, though Arab deliveries showed an immediate cutback. In December Sunbeam delivered seventeen Arabs, forty-six Maoris, ten Manitous, and forty-two Avro 504J/Ks, but this situation was not to last for much longer.

The amount of business lost to the company with the advent of peace can be illustrated by the value of the products they were delivering. The Arab and Maori engines were £1,017 10s and £1,391 10s respectively, while the Avro 504K was priced at only £898 19s. Sunbeam, like companies all over the country, had to find peacetime products to replace their wartime ones, but unlike many of the other aircraft and aero-engine manufacturers who had grown big since the start of the war, Sunbeam at least had its pre-war products to fall back on, and awaiting them a far more car-minded population than had been the case four years before.

Engine	Contract	Ordered	Delivered	Decision
Dyak	34a/1477/C1390	160	nil	4 mths notice
Amazon	CP.138965	100	80	contract under suspension
Arab	AS.1659	360	360	completed
Arab	AS2740/18	200	200	completed
Arab	34a/807/C727	100	6	4 mths notice
Arab	34a/1406/C1319	100	nil	(1000, of which 900 cancelled)
Maori	AS.11776	100	98	no action
Maori	AS.29772	300	234	(incl. 40 Manitou) 4 mths notice
Manitou	AS.29772	40	1	see above
Manitou	34a/247/C209	800	nil	
Cossack	34a/1478/C1392	32	nil	
Viking	CP.116175	25	13	suspended
Direct-Drive Arab II	34a/10751/C1001	1	nil	to be completed
Semi-Sikh	34a/1630/C1457			to be completed (Awaiting Admiralty reply)
Avro 504J/K	35a/2031/C2313	250	2	no action
Sunbeam Arabs from other contractors				
Austin	AS.397/17	1000	344	(2000 of which 594 settled, and 1000 cancelled)
Napier	AS.486/17	300	67	(settled 550)
Napier	34a/663/C589	150	nil	(settled 550)
Lanchester	AS1660	300	49	(settled 810)
Lanchester	34a/913/C838	300	nil	(settled 810)

1919–37

One of the last Avro 504Ks built by Sunbeam, H2063, shown behind the Moorfield Works. It was delivered in March 1919.

Although contracts for both engines and aircraft were cancelled en masse at the end of the war, all production did not cease instantly. Sunbeam continued to build the Avro 504 well into 1919, and aero-engines remained in production, though most orders were cancelled. The Maori continued to be fitted to new Short Type 184 seaplanes which were still being turned out by a number of manufacturers, and many of these were to go to another war. Britain's ill-fated and ill-advised operations against the Bolsheviks in Russia in 1919–20 were supported by large numbers of both Short Type 184 and Fairey seaplanes powered by Sunbeam Maoris. At least eight Type 184s and one Fairey IIIB operated in north Russia round Archangel, eleven Type 184s operated in the Baltic, another eleven on the Dvina River, and eleven more, with eight Fairey IIIBs, in south Russia. Many of these aircraft were lost on these operations and others were handed over to the White Russian forces.

More of these post-war-built Short Type 184s were also exported, including some that were given free to wartime allies. Four went to Chile and others to Greece and Japan. Eight went to Estonia, and two of these were to become the longest surviving of all Sunbeam-powered Short seaplanes. The former N9132 and N9134, coded '40' and '41' by Estonia, were not retired from service until November 1933 after one of them crashed. A number of Arab-powered Norman-Thompson NT.2B flying boats were also exported after the war. Three went to Norway, two to Estonia, and one each to Japan, Canada, Peru, and Chile. The latter, N2284, was exhibited at the Atlantic City Air Exposition of 1919, while on its way to Chile.

The most successful export of Sunbeam aero-engines post-war was to Australia. The Australian Aircraft and Engineering Co., begun by Harry Broadsmith, the former manager of Avro's Manchester factory, began erecting 504Ks from imported parts, and many of them were fitted with Dyak engines which proved far more reliable in bush conditions than rotary engines. At least nine of these 504s were to be powered by Dyaks, including the first aircraft operated by the Queensland and Northern Territories Air Service (Qantas) and Butler Air Transport. Arthur Butler later said his first aircraft, a Dyak-powered Avro 504K, was the safest aircraft he ever flew.

One of these Dyaks was the last Sunbeam engine ever to power an aircraft, when Qantas fitted one to a preserved Avro 504 in the 1970s and painted it to represent their first aircraft. It took part in many air displays before the engine was removed and installed in an Avro 504 replica in the Stockman's Hall of Fame Museum. The last aircraft built by Sunbeam that ever flew was also an Avro 504, F2588, a 504K built in October 1918. It went on the civil register as G-ACOK, and was converted to an Avro 504N with the fitment of a 150 hp Armstrong-Siddeley Mongoose IIIA engine. It served as a joy-riding machine with Alan Cobham's Aviation Day Displays and their successors, and finally crashed at Rhyl on 14 August 1938.

Many of the Avro 504Ks built post-war by the company, particularly those from the last, partially completed order in

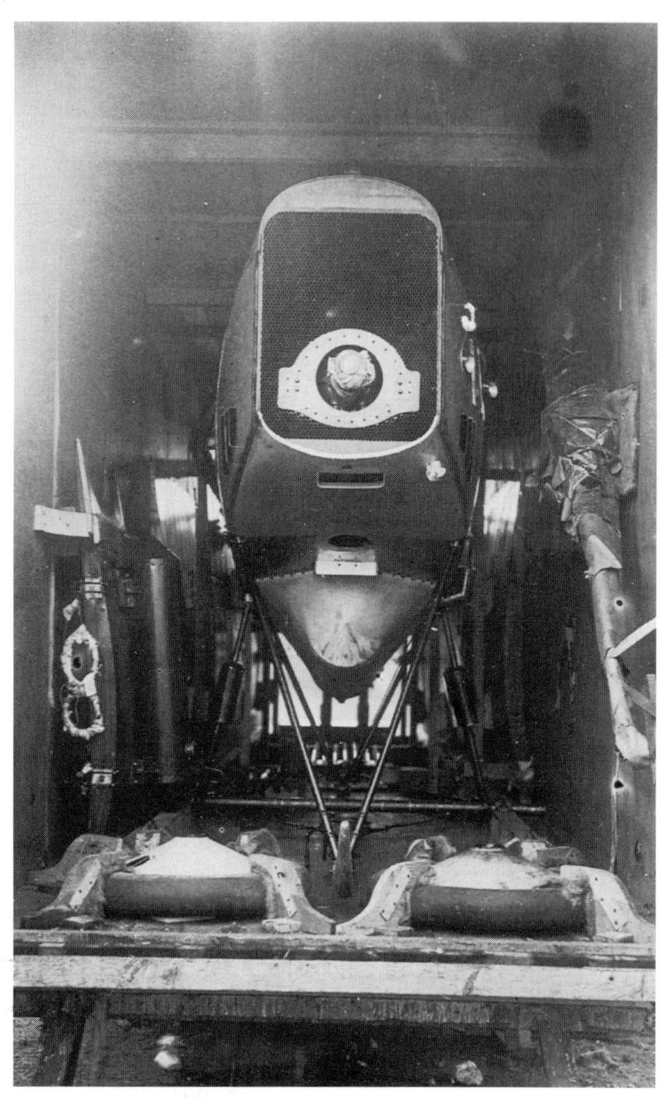

(ABOVE LEFT):
The rear end of the six-cylinder inline Dyak engine, showing the feature which endeared it to bush pilots in Australia, the cockpit starting handle.

(ABOVE RIGHT):
A Dyak-powered Avro 504K being packed at the Moorfield Works.

(LEFT):
The Avro 504K Dyak installation first completed by Sunbeam, showing the frontal radiator.

(Above):
A Dyak-powered Avro 504K, serial unknown, at Dunstall Park, Wolverhampton. This was probably the only British 504 powered by the Dyak.

(Below):
Sunbeam-built Avro 504K, H1966, pictured at Christchurch, New Zealand, where it became G-NZAL.

(Above):
Another Sunbeam-built Avro 504K, H2043, in Canada as G-CYCX, after an accident from which it was repaired.

(Below):
One of the last Sunbeam-built Avro 504Ks, H2045, part of the imperial gift to Canada, and registered G-CYDA.

the serial range H1896 to H2077, also found their way onto the civil register both in this country and elsewhere. A substantial number of them was in the imperial gifts of aircraft donated to Canada, New Zealand, and Australia, a number of those going to Canada being converted to 504L floatplanes for use on fire and forestry patrols. Two more of them, H1911–2, were also converted to 504L floatplanes and went to Sweden, becoming S-IAB and S-IAG, the former becoming, in 1923, the first aircraft on the new Swedish register, S-AAAA.

As was found in Australia, if the rotary engine of the 504 could be replaced with an inline engine like the Sunbeam Dyak, there were savings to be made in reliability and economy. A number of 504s were converted to take the venerable 80 hp Renault V8, which was readily available for very low prices, and thus became Avro Type 548s. Most of these conversions were made by private contractors rather than Avro, including four Sunbeam-built 504s – H2025, H2053, H2067, and H2070 – all for the de Havilland Company's Reserve Flying Training operation at Stag Lane. Other Sunbeam-built 504s were converted to 504Ns for the Royal Air Force, with the fitment of Armstrong-Siddeley Lynx engines, including D4430, D4432, D4452, and F2588. Another, F2575, was converted by Avro as a special lightweight 504N and was exhibited at the Czechoslovakian Aeronautical Exhibition in Prague in June 1924. Other Sunbeam-built 504s were exported, both by the government and the Aircraft Disposal Company, to Denmark, Argentina, Spain, Eire, and Belgium (where six of them were given the first six Belgian Air Force serials A-1 to A-6).

After the death of John Marston in March 1918, his successor as chairman, Thomas Cureton, died the following year, and Louis Coatalen was left in *de facto* charge of the company, able to dictate policy along with the company secretary, C.M. Iliff, and the company's Wolverhampton solicitor, Charles Wright, who joined the board in 1918. It seemed to them that Sunbeam needed a strong figurehead. Financially the company was in a strong position with £600,000 owed by the government for aero-engines. Its production side was a little chaotic, though. As aero-engine orders were cancelled *en masse*, car production was being restarted. The 16 hp four-cylinder sidevalve which had been built by Rover during the war was brought back to Wolverhampton. Nevertheless, there were still aviation orders to fulfil, for airships.

Louis Coatalen, pictured in 1918 when he was in de facto charge of Sunbeam.

A number of new rigid airships had been under construction at the end of the war, and the most famous of these were to be the R.33 and R.34. Both had been ordered in April 1916, and their design was based on the Zeppelin L.33 which had come down in this country. R.33 was built by

A post-war Sunbeam advertisement showing the range of eight engines they promoted, without a great deal of success.

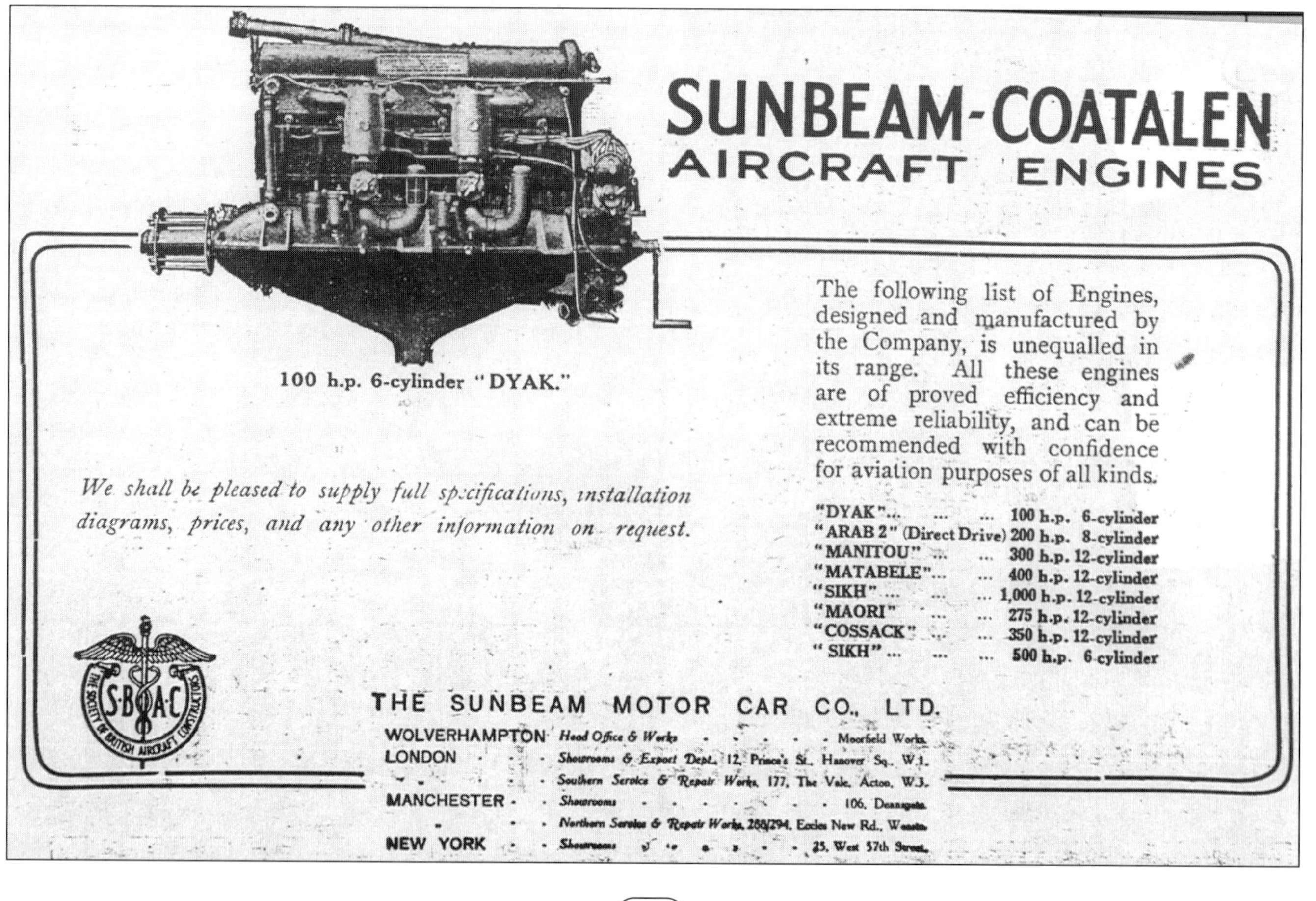

R34
THE FIRST
AIRSHIP TO CROSS
THE ATLANTIC
is fitted with five
"MAORI" TYPE 12 CYL. 275 H.P.
SUNBEAM-COATALEN
AIRCRAFT ENGINES
— abundant testimony to Sunbeam
RELIABILITY & EFFICIENCY

SUNBEAM 1919 CAR MODELS:
16 h.p. 4-cyl. with touring body - £790
24 h.p. 6-cyl. ,, ,, - £1,100
Equipped with electric starting & lighting set, spare wheel & tyre.

A WORD OF WARNING.—The above are the retail list prices for the new Sunbeam models, and intending purchasers are warned against anyone offering to sell at higher prices. It is tantamount to profiteering, which the manufacturers neither authorise nor desire to encourage. You will be rendering a service if you will notify the Sunbeam Motor Car Co. of any case which may come to your notice.

THE SUNBEAM MOTOR CAR CO., LTD., WOLVERHAMPTON.
CONTRACTORS TO THE WAR OFFICE, ADMIRALTY AND AIR MINISTRY.
Manchester Showrooms: 106, Deansgate.
London and District Agents for Cars: - - - J. Keele, Ltd., 72 New Bond Street, W.1.

(ABOVE):
The two Maori-equipped wing-cars of the R.34 airship

(TOP LEFT):
The airship R.34 returning to Pulham after its historic double crossing of the Atlantic.

(BOTTOM LEFT):
A Sunbeam advertisement emphasising the use of Sunbeam Maori engines in R.34's transatlantic flight.

Armstrong-Whitworth at Barrow and her sister ship was built by Beardmore at Inchinnan. Each was powered by five Sunbeam Maori IV engines, a mark specially designed for use in airships, giving 275 hp at 2,100 rpm and directly driving the propellers, fitted with a governor. They also had water-cooled exhausts as a safety measure. R.33 was first launched on 6 March 1919, with R.34 following on 14 March. R.34 made the first east–west air crossing of the Atlantic on 2–6 July 1919, and followed that by returning on 9–13 July to complete the first double crossing.

Sunbeam also attempted to secure a certain amount of prestige from the first non-stop crossing of the Atlantic by an aircraft, which was of course by Alcock and Brown in a Rolls-Royce Eagle-powered Vickers Vimy. Being Sunbeam's pre-war test pilot, Jack Alcock was photographed sitting in a Sunbeam car in front of a Sunbeam Maori-powered Vimy, though I am not certain how many people this fooled!

R.33's record, though not so spectacular, was also remarkable as it became the longest-surviving British airship, and achieved the record of 735 hours' flying before she was finally dismantled in 1928. In September 1919 she had made the first commercial airship flight to the Continent. Captain J.S. Irving of Sunbeam was invited to join the flight by the Air Ministry, and among his fellow passengers were Major-General Sir Sefton Brancker, Benjamin Guinness, and J. Dunn of Dunn, Fisher & Co. of Threadneedle Street. He travelled from Wolverhampton to Pulham to join the flight in a

(ABOVE):
Jack Alcock, pre-war Sunbeam company pilot, sitting in a Sunbeam car in front of a Sunbeam Maori-powered Vickers Vimy, a cheeky attempt by Sunbeam's publicity department to gain some kudos from Alcock and Brown's transatlantic flight in a Rolls-Royce-powered Vimy. Alcock was killed two days after this photograph was taken.

The airship R.33 after suffering extensive damage to its nose, which was repaired; she went on to become the most successful British airship.

company car, covering the 177 miles in a commendable five and a half hours. On the 12th the sister airship, R.32, took off first, and accompanied R.33 for some of the journey, which went over Ostend, Zeebrugge, and Amsterdam. Captain Irving had to sleep on the floor as there was no bunk available for him, and during the night he was awoken by the ship ascending at a steep angle. All the other passengers woke up when two water bottles crashed to the floor, and shortly afterwards R.33 regained level flight. It was suspected that one of the passengers had been lying on the elevator cables which ran by the bunks!

Later in the night Captain Irving was called to look at one of the Maoris in the starboard wing-car, which had seized. It had been shut down for a period and had failed to restart. They removed one of the cylinder heads and found the connecting rod nearest to the centre bearing was seized hard on the crank pin. There was nothing they could do in the air, so the engine remained shut down for the rest of the flight.

The unscheduled ascent had caused a great deal of gas to

be vented off, and then it was discovered that a ton of ballast water had been lost because the last person to use the hand basin in the keel had left the tap running. It seems extraordinary, considering the value of ballast on an airship, that this was able to happen, and it resulted in a planned landing at Paris being cancelled. The flight continued over many of the wartime battlefields, and Captain Irving was able to pick out some of the destruction caused by the bombing of his former squadron, No. 21. The R.33 returned to Pulham, and Captain Irving was able to investigate the failure of the starboard Maori.

Larger airships – the R.36, R.37, and R.38, the first two based on the Zeppelin L.48 – were under construction at the end of the war to be powered by six Sunbeam Cossack engines, but they had far less auspicious careers. The R.36 was built by Beardmore at Inchinnan, and was actually designed to have three Cossacks and two Maori Mk IVs, but the availability of two Maybach M6 engines meant they were used instead of the Maoris. The R.36 was not finished until April 1920 and had flown only eighty hours when it suffered a mooring accident at Pulham and was broken up. Sister ship R.37 was started by Vickers but they did not have a big enough shed to erect her at Barrow, and so she was continued by Short Bros at Cardington, fitted with six Cossacks, four in single gondolas and two in a paired arrangement amidships. Sunbeam not only built the engines but also the entire gondola and associated equipment, delivering them complete to Bedfordshire. When R.37 was 95% complete she was cancelled and broken up.

The other large ship, the R.38, was allowed to continue because the United States Navy was interested in buying her. She was built by Short Bros at Cardington, actually alongside R.37, and was also powered by six Cossacks, but in three paired gondolas. Before completion the Short Bros operation at Cardington was nationalised to become the Royal Airship Works. The R.38's first flight was on 23 June 1921, and by the third flight the US emblems and her new number ZR-2 had been applied. Unfortunately she had been built too lightly, as a high climbing ship, and was not able to stand up to abrupt manoeuvres in thicker air at low altitude. On her fourth flight on 23 August she broke up over the Humber estuary and most on board lost their lives.

Although the company was continuing to try to sell its

(LEFT): *Gondolas for the R.38 and R.37 airships under construction at Moorfield Works. Sunbeam built the complete gondola, with their Cossack engines.*

(BELOW): *The massive Sunbeam Sikh, a 64-litre, 800 hp engine under development for airship use at the end of the war.*

aero-engines, it was competing with its own products being sold by the government. On 12 November 1919 the Aircraft Disposal Department had a sale of war-surplus aero-engines priced at 30% to 80% of cost. Among them were Sunbeam Maoris, Amazons, Cossacks, Arabs, and Dyaks. At the Paris Salon de l'Aéronautique in December Sunbeam displayed its newer engines – the Dyak, Matabele, Manitou, and Sikh – which represented a broad range of engines from 100 hp to 800 hp. It was noted that they were not 'faked up' with special plated pipes and polished parts which was the usual custom of the Sunbeam Motor Car Company. The only orders received at the show were for six engines for three Japanese Navy airships – four Dyaks and two Maoris.

Sunbeam also took Stand 56 at the Olympia Aero Show of April 1920, displaying these four engines plus four others: the Maori, Arab, Cossack, and Semi-Sikh. The Sikh was the largest engine on display and therefore drew a great deal of comment, but it was Napier who stole the thunder with the Lion, which developed 450 hp, weighed only 840 lb, and had a fuel consumption of only thirty gallons per hour. Napier was also secretly developing an engine even bigger than the Sikh, the 1,000 hp Cub. The new high-power radial engines – the Armstrong-Siddeley Jaguar and the Bristol Jupiter – were also creating a great deal of interest and it was these, the Lion, and the Eagle which were to power the majority of post-war British aircraft, together with war-surplus engines sold at knockdown prices by the Aircraft Disposal Company.

There is little doubt that the engines Sunbeam had to offer at the end of the war were inferior to these engines, and so, apart from the Dyak, it was always going to struggle to sell any more. The Lion, Jaguar, and Jupiter were 'state of the art' engines, under development as the war ended, and the Eagle, and the smaller Falcon, though older in design had been refined until they were among the most reliable engines in the world. Sunbeam's main offerings post-war were the 300 hp Manitou and 400 hp Matabele, but, though they had cast aluminium blocks, these were developments of 1915 designs, the Afridi and Cossack, and were no match for the Lion and the new air-cooled radials in particular. In the immediate post-war climate, even Rolls-Royce could see no future in investment in aero-engines, though it continued to build Eagles and Falcons to small orders, resisting the call of some of its directors to pull out of aviation altogether. Beardmore and Gwynne were other aero-engine companies that baulked at further development.

In September 1919 Coatalen took the first of the post-war production six-cylinder cars to France on an extended tour, the first of an increasing number of stays in his native country. He resigned the post of joint managing director and became instead the company's chief engineer, announcing his intention of establishing a drawing office and experimental department in Paris, which he did in the early part of 1920. Not only did he divide his time between the two countries, but he returned to his interest in motor racing, and his quest to build a car capable of winning the French Grand Prix. With the main figure in the Sunbeam Motor Car Company preoccupied with other things, the aviation side of the business was bound to suffer.

In 1920 the French firm of Darracq had taken over the business of Clement-Talbot Ltd, with James Todd as its chairman. He and other Talbot–Darracq directors became friendly with members of the Sunbeam board, who were very impressed with him and felt he might be the strong figurehead they thought they needed. There was also a feeling that in the post-war age, car companies needed to be large to survive the fierce wave of competition. In June 1920 it was announced that the two companies were to amalgamate, holders of 500,000 Sunbeam ordinary shares receiving Darracq ordinary shares on a one for one basis. On 5 August it was revealed that the combined group would be known as STD Motors Ltd, English observers and shareholders taking comfort in the order of the initials, which was part of a deliberate attempt to anglicise the whole company; in fact the name Darracq was soon to be dropped altogether.

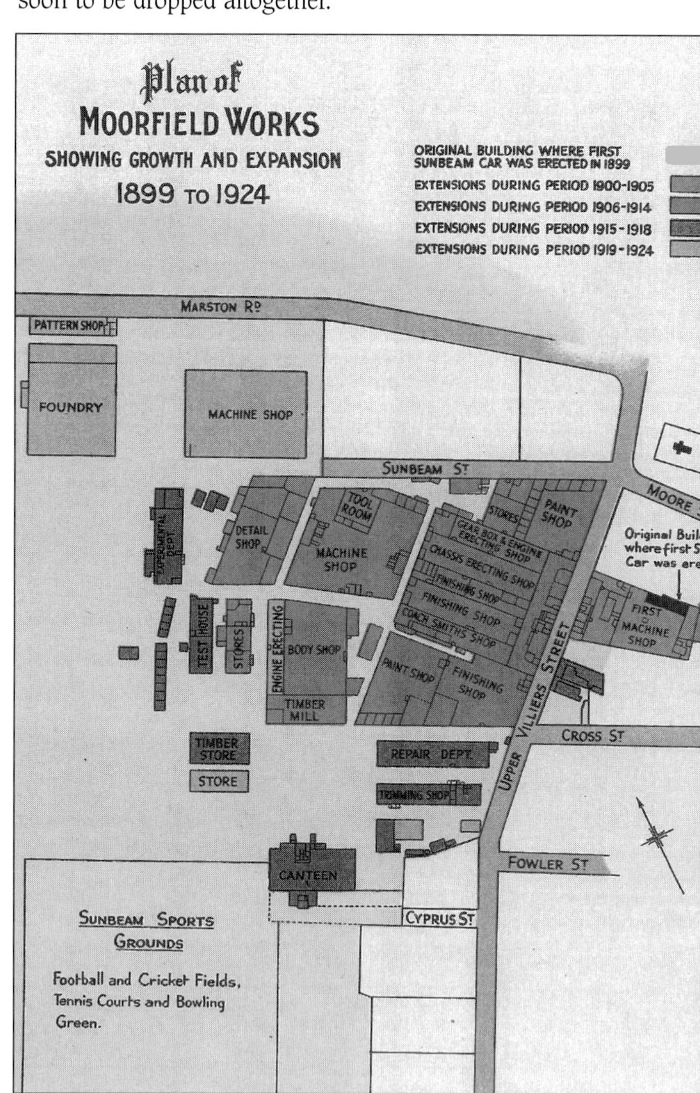

A plan of the Moorfield Works showing further expansion taking place, with the Foundry and Machine Shop being built along Marston Road.

Coatalen's marriage to Olive Bath, who was the daughter of Henry Bath, the pre-war director, ended in 1922, and the following year he married Mrs Enid van Raalte, who had been born Enid Florence Graham. The year 1923 was also a happy one for him in another respect. His greatest interest continued to be in car racing, and this is where his greatest energies were expended. He had his greatest of all triumphs in 1923 when Henry Segrave won the French Grand Prix in a

The 350 hp Sunbeam car, with a specially built version of the Manitou aero-engine, on Pendine Sands. In this form it became the first car in the world to exceed 150 mph.

Sunbeam, and Sunbeam should have won the following year too, with a technically superior car which was dogged by mechanical problems. One of the first racing cars he produced after the war was fitted with a Manitou aero-engine, albeit a specially built one which had one block slightly larger than the other, and only three valves per cylinder, the valve gear possibly being taken from the Arab. This car was known as the 350 hp Sunbeam for most of its existence, until Malcolm Campbell named it *Bluebird* for its last exploits.

The famous pilot, Harry Hawker, had a great deal to do with the early testing of this car. Hawker had an affinity for speed, not only in the air but also on the water, where he had already raced a Napier-Lion-engined hydroplane, and on the road, where he had re-engined a large Mercedes 35 hp car with one of two Sunbeam 225 hp Mohawk engines he had bought. In the winter of 1919–20 Hawker had found himself with little to do on the flying front and visited Sunbeam at Wolverhampton to see the new six-cylinder racing car the company had built for the Indianapolis 500 Race. It had been arranged that he would race it at the Whit Monday Meeting at Brooklands.

He was very impressed with Sunbeam's Racing Department: 'The Sunbeam people do the whole thing properly,' he said. The car was taken to Brooklands a few days before the meeting; Hawker tested it, and then had some very successful races. The success inspired him to modify his own Mercedes–Sunbeam for racing, removing unwanted extra weight, like the headlamps, mudguards, and windscreen. He entered it for a race, but when he was doing 107 mph one of the front tyres shed its tread, and he only recovered control after a series of violent skids. He had plans to fit a new streamlined body to the car, but shelved these after driving the new 350 hp Manitou-engined Sunbeam. He decided that in comparison his own car was only fit for touring, as it could only do about 110 mph, so he returned it to street condition.

The 350 hp Sunbeam arrived at Brooklands a few days before the midsummer race meeting which was to take place on 26 June 1920, and Hawker took it on the track to try it out. The white-painted car with its black nose was hurtling comfortably round the banking at 125 mph when the front offside tyre burst. The car pulled to the outside and crashed through the corrugated fencing, before hurtling down a four-foot bank and coming to rest, luckily, right side up with Hawker unhurt. The car was repaired and Hawker was to drive it in the 2 August meeting, but he stalled it on the line and did not race, so his next experience of Sunbeam-powered racing was eight days later on the Solent. He drove a Saunders-built powerboat, *Maple Leaf V*, in the British International Trophy. It was thirty-nine feet long and was powered by four 400 hp Sunbeam Matabele aero-engines. The rival American boats seemed to displace far less water, and they won the trophy despite on the whole having less power available. *Maple Leaf V*, even with 1,600 hp available, seemed to plough through the water between two walls of spray, and rarely managed more than thirty knots.

In December Hawker again returned to the 350 hp Sunbeam at Brooklands where he attempted to beat many of the short-circuit land-speed records, but the track was wet and the car suffered a great deal of wheel spin, and the attempts failed. It had a successful subsequent racing career and was then bought and modified by Captain Malcolm Campbell (later Sir Malcolm Campbell), and was used to break the world land-speed record, thus bringing a great prestige to Sunbeam at no cost.

There were a number of Sunbeam aero-engine-powered cars produced after the war, but none was as successful as the 350 hp Sunbeam, which is now preserved in the National Motor Museum at Beaulieu. Its engine is one of two surviving Manitous, the other being in the visitors centre of IMI Marston Ltd in Wolverhampton, the current incarnation of John Marston Ltd, which feels itself the spiritual successor of all the Marston companies, including Sunbeam. Their Manitou is a genuine airworthy example, unlike the special one in the car.

In 1924 the members of the Board of STD Motors were James Todd (chairman), Owen Clegg of Darracq, Coatalen and Iliff of Sunbeam, Charles Wright, John Marston's

Wolverhampton solicitor. Harold Newcombe, Lord Queensborough, and A. Huntley Walker. Financial difficulties were already beginning to show. The money owed for Sunbeam's aero-engines had not been paid, it had just been set against the purchase by Talbot of war-surplus vehicles which were reconditioned. The benefits of combining the companies had not been realised, and cars which competed with one another were still being turned out; although Sunbeam was selling all the cars it could make, it was not doing so at a price which reflected quality.

More and more pressure was put on Coatalen to cut back his car-racing activities, and he was spending more and more time in France. C.B. Kay was running the Moorfield Works, and during 1928 was given a seat on the board.

During 1926 it was announced that Sunbeam's road-racing activities were to be severely curtailed as 'all experience required for the next year or two has been obtained'. As chief engineer, Coatalen was able to initiate a new attack on the world land-speed record using two Matabele engines in a specially designed car, a project led by Captain J.S. Irving (who had joined Sunbeam in January 1917 from the Royal Aircraft Factory's engine section). The 1,000 hp Sunbeam duly became the first car to exceed 200 mph, thus keeping the company's name firmly in the public eye at a minimal cost.

In 1928 Sunbeam began to investigate the diesel engine principally for aircraft use, though it was also under development in their commercial vehicle department. A Dyak engine was converted to a diesel and renamed the Pathan, and under test was found to give 100 hp with a fuel consumption of only five gallons per hour. A redesign of the Sikh was also undertaken, as the basis of a massive engine for airship use, the Sikh III. This differed from the original Sikh in the camshaft/valve layout, and was claimed to give 1,000 hp at 1,400 rpm. Sunbeam exhibited at the 1929 Olympia Aero Show, and the Sikh dominated the stand, as it would being over seven feet long, but it shared the interest of the industry with the Pathan, British diesel aero-engines being very few in number at the time. Despite the interest there were no orders for these two new engines. The British Airship Programme, the only possible application for the Sikh, was cancelled the following year, and there was no demand for a small diesel.

In November 1929 Sunbeam made a new attack on the world land-speed record in a huge car named *Silver Bullet*. In charge of the project was Huge Rose, though he was overseen

The Mayor of Wolverhampton congratulating Henry Segrave after he broke the land-speed record in the 1,000 hp Sunbeam, with the first speed recorded over 200 mph. On the right is Louis Coatalen, but the other gentleman is unknown.

The 1,000 hp Sunbeam under test in Moorfield Works in 1927. The sound of the two Matabele aero-engines was said to have been deafening.

(ABOVE): *A gathering of Sunbeam employees in the Victoria Hotel, Wolverhampton, during a celebration of the 200 mph record. Henry Segrave is one of those holding the model of the 1,000 hp Sunbeam.*

(LEFT): *The redeveloped version of the Sikh, the 1,000 hp Sikh III, under test at Moorfield Works in 1925.*

by Coatalen. Rose had joined Sunbeam at the same time as Coatalen, but after the war had left to join Guy Motors on the other side of Wolverhampton. After six years he returned to design commercial vehicles for Sunbeam, thus founding the company's successful trolley-bus business. The *Silver Bullet*'s two tandem V12 engines were specially designed for the car, but Coatalen stated that they were to be the first stage of the development of a new aero-engine for large aircraft. The *Silver Bullet*'s attempt on the record ended in failure because of technical reasons and adverse weather conditions, and with it went Sunbeam's last chance of re-entering the aero-engine business.

When Norman Cliff joined the Royal Air Force at the start of W.W.II he was shown a Merlin engine for the first time, and was asked if he thought he could dismantle it. He replied that he could because he had helped build them, meaning that the Merlin looked so like the *Silver Bullet* engines he had worked on ten years before. Of course, there were significant differences in that the Merlin was a sixty-degree Vee, not fifty-degree, and the *Silver Bullet*'s cylinders were cast in groups of

(LEFT): *The Sikh III aero-engine was primarily intended for airships, but the British Airship Programme folded as it was being developed.*

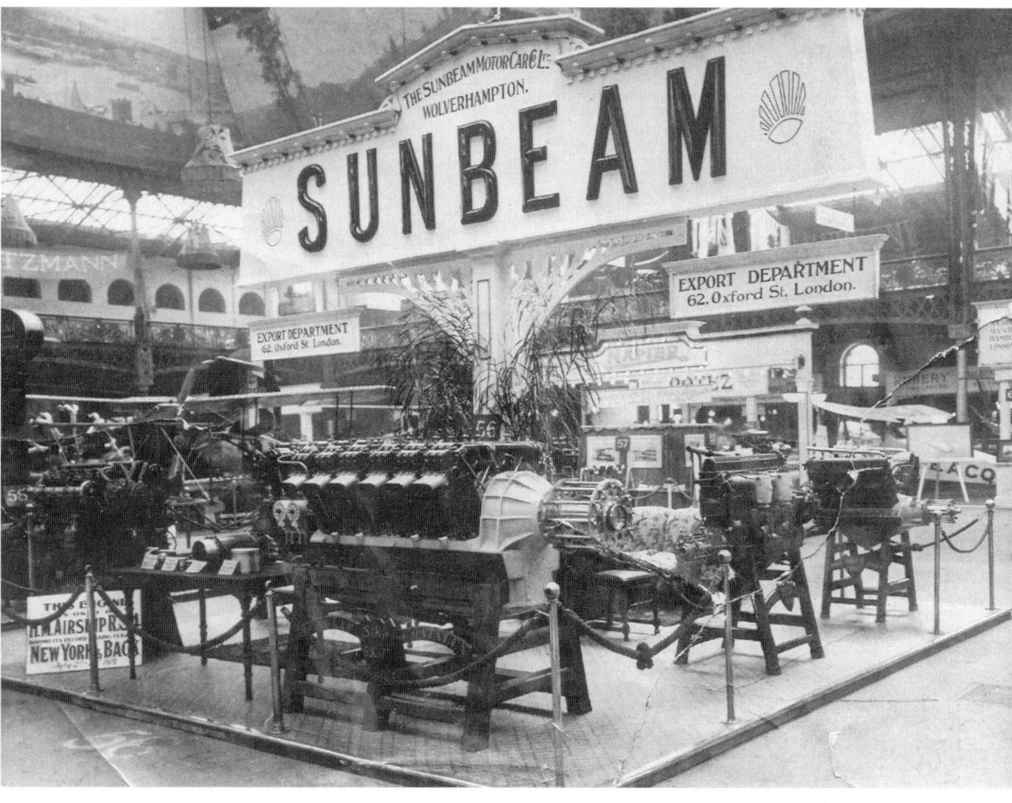

(BELOW): *The seven-foot-long Sikh III dominates Sunbeam's stand at the 1929 Olympia Aero Show. To the right are a Dyak and Arab, to the left is a Maori IV, 'as used on the R.34'.*

three, not monobloc. The *Silver Bullet* engines were also slightly smaller, at only twenty-four litres, (whereas the Merlin was twenty-seven litres) and gave less power, only 490 bhp unsupercharged, but this was several years before the Merlin was bench-run. It is interesting to speculate how good an aero-engine the basic *Silver Bullet* engine might have become if fully developed by Sunbeam, assuming the company had had the capital and the will to do so.

In fact, S.T.D. Motors was still in dire financial trouble, and after a report by Price Waterhouse severely criticised the lack of co-ordination between the various companies, the Board resigned *en masse*. Three outside directors were brought in – Lt-Gen. Sir Travers Clarke, Sir Daniel Neylan, and J.F. Marrian – who then co-opted Newcombe and Lord Queensborough from the old Board. It was recommended that Louis Coatalen become consulting technical director, but he never seems to have taken up this post, now spending almost all his time in France. It was at this time that the first rumours of a take-over by Humber–Hillman were circulated. It was also announced in the local press that SS Cars, the forerunner of Jaguar, was also intending to take over Sunbeam, precluded from doing so because the Rootes brothers had already loaned money to the company and claimed precedence.

The new Board made attempts to restructure the company and to adapt the recommendations of the Price Waterhouse report, centralising buying, sales, accounting, and other departments. They were doing too little too late and further decline followed. In February 1935 Clement-Talbot Ltd came under the control of Rootes Securities Ltd, and then in July 1935 they also took over the entire undertaking, assets, premises, and goodwill of the Sunbeam Motor Car Co. The Moorfield Works were closed down, though Sunbeam cars were still made in other factories of the Rootes Group, and

(LEFT):
The two V12 Silver Bullet *engines being tested in the chassis in Moorfield Works, with a gathering of the Experimental Department workforce behind.*

(ABOVE):
The Sunbeam Silver Bullet *on Daytona Beach. The umbrella helps to show the poor weather conditions which were a contributing factor in Sunbeam's last throw of the dice in the world of land-speed records, and by association aero-engines.*

(BELOW):
Various Sunbeam notables beside the Silver Bullet *before despatch to America. Left to right: Harry Wilding, Louis Coatalen, Hugh Rose, Kaye Don (driver), Martinuzzi, C. M. Iliff (company secretary), Tommy Harrison, C. B. Kay, unknown, F. Howarth, Huggins, Dabbs, unknown.*

badge-engineering began in earnest. Just up the road at Marston, the production of Sunbeam motor-cycles continued, but not for long. In September 1937 the Sunbeam motor-cycle business was taken over by AMC in Woolwich, and from the following year Sunbeam motor-cycles were London-built and badge-engineered from other models in the AMC catalogue.

The other Marston company, Charles Marston's Villiers Engineering, prospered for much longer. After the war it had gone back to making engines, and had expanded into new premises in the newly named Marston Road, running at right angles to Upper Villiers Street. The factory eventually covered 17.5 acres, and was to continue in production until overtaken by the tide of Japanese motor-cycles in the 1960s.

STD Motors was to have one last association with aero-engines, however. During the Second World War Talbot Motors in London, whence 'Sunbeam' models had been produced since the closure of the Moorfield Works, was to take on the overhaul of Rolls-Royce Merlin engines. If there were any survivors of the Sunbeam aero-engine production lines who had moved to Talbot, it must have been a bitter pill to swallow, having to overhaul engines from their great rival in Derby.

Like so many companies, particular those from Victorian times, Sunbeam was the creation of the enterprise and hard work of one man, John Marston. He was a man who built a successful business in japanware and tinplate manufacture, but was astute and bold enough to see a new business opportunity when he saw one, turning to the manufacture of bicycles, and then motor-cars, motor-bikes and aero-engines. Yet he was no bold buccaneer rushing blindly into new ventures; he was careful to split his new companies so that risks might be lessened, and to develop new businesses one step at a time.

In a way the personality of the chief engineer he employed in 1909, Louis Coatalen, was very different from his own. Coatalen was undoubtedly a brilliant and innovative engineer, and yet he seems to have had a mercurial mind, always anxious to move on to the next project, and so different from his great rival in the production of water-cooled aero-engines, Henry Royce. The two engineers worked on aero-engines for about the same length of time, and in that time Louis Coatalen developed twenty-six different engines, whereas Henry Royce worked on only seven: the Eagle, Falcon, Hawk, Condor, Kestrel, Buzzard, and 'R' Type. Of course, many Sunbeam engines were only developments of earlier engines, with usually only the bore changed, but even discounting these there is no doubt that the output from Coatalen's drawing-board was large, and clearly too large.

Once John Marston had died in 1918, followed very shortly afterwards by his right-hand man Thomas Cureton, the impetus for the company had gone. There was no one to guide it through the ups and downs of the post-war business environment. Like so many companies created and built into great businesses by one man, Sunbeam was on a downhill path once John Marston had died. Linking up with Talbot and Darraq to make STD Motors, whatever the order of the initials, only made Sunbeam a provincial outpost of a multi-national organisation based in London.

Back in France Louis Coatalen introduced the KLG spark plug company and bought the Lockheed Brake Co., but he did not relinquish his interest in aero-engines. He developed a diesel engine from the Hispano-Suiza V12 engine, though it had not attracted any applications when the Germans invaded. The Lockheed Brake Co. was evacuated to Bordeaux, but Coatalen returned to Paris during the occupation. During the war his elder son served with the Royal Navy, and his younger son was a pilot in the Royal Air Force. When he was shot down over France he sought refuge at his father's house near Paris. His father hid him and arranged his escape from France, and he was able to rejoin the RAF.

After the war Coatalen continued to manage the Lockheed Brake Co. He had been made a Chevalier de la Légion d'Honneur after the First World War, and in 1953 he was elected President of the Société des Ingénieurs de l'Automobile. Great Britain, the country in which his greatest achievements were made, the country which derived great prestige from the performance of Sunbeam racing cars, Sunbeam land-speed-record cars, and Sunbeam-powered airships and aircraft, never honoured him. The Wolverhampton Civic Society partially redressed the omission in 1997 when Coatalen's daughter unveiled a blue plaque on the site of one of his former houses on the Penn Road.

PART TWO
THE AERO-ENGINES

150 HP CRUSADER

The first aero-engine designed by Louis Coatalen was never referred to by its name while in production, and probably never while in service. It was possibly the only Sunbeam–Coatalen engine which had finished its period of service by the time Sunbeam's engine naming system came into use in 1917, earlier engines being retrospectively named. It was always referred to as the Sunbeam 150 hp, though on occasions before the war it was referred to as the 100 hp, 110 hp, or 135 hp Sunbeam.

It was produced in two versions, the first with an 80 mm bore, and then for the bulk of its life with a 90 mm bore. The earlier version fell outside the naming system and was only referred to as the 110 hp Sunbeam in official records. As the 110 hp Sunbeam and the 150 hp Crusader were regarded as different engines by Sunbeam, a separate section will deal with the 110 hp engine, but only in reference to its wartime use. As it is important to examine the whole history of the development of Sunbeam's first production engine, the side-valve V8, both its forms up to the outbreak of war will be examined in this section.

Head-on view of the Crusader from a company brochure, showing the ninety-degree Vee of the cylinder banks and the inside exhaust valves.

Coatalen began work on the new aero-engine in 1912, and it was ready to begin bench tests by Christmas. Coatalen used the side-valve system of his successful 1912 racing-car engines, with the valves inclined to the cylinders. The Crusader was an eight-cylinder engine with two rows of cylinders set in a ninety-degree Vee with the cylinders cast in iron, *en bloc* in groups of two. Basically it was two blocks from his three-litre racing-car engine bolted to a common crankcase in a Vee arrangement. To begin with the bore was 80 mm and the stroke 150 mm, as with the car engines, giving an overall displacement of six litres. The water-cooling jackets were copper electrolytically deposited. The pistons were those used in his three-litre racing-car engines and were machined from the solid, and the gudgeon pins were supplied with a central support from the centre of the piston to make it possible to use a smaller and therefore lighter gudgeon pin and connecting rod.

Access to the side valves was via a screw plug on top of the cylinder head over each one. Each valve could be removed through the resulting hole, and a new one lapped in by hand using carborundum paste to make a tight gas seal between the valve head and seat. The blocks were cast with the outer side open, and after machining this was then sealed with a rectangular plate bolted to the block. Each block was held down by ten studs sited at the ends and between each cylinder.

Lubrication was by castor oil pressure-fed at 40/45 lb/sq.in. by a gear pump placed in the sump via the interior of the crankshaft to all the shaft bearings. An oil lead was taken from the main lubricating circuit to the camshaft for oil to float over the valve mechanism and then the timing wheels into the crank chamber. The cylinders were staggered to allow the connection of two connecting rods to one crank, with a bearing between each crank, the starboard block being slightly in front of the port side.

The single Bosch magneto, driven by spur gears, was placed within the Vee, and there was single ignition with one spark plug per cylinder. Each cylinder head also housed a compressed-air non-return valve to start the engine from two cylinders housed in the aircraft fuselage, with air held at 1,800–2,000 lb/sq.in. Compressed-air starting was necessary on seaplanes, as the propeller could not be swung as it could on landplanes. A single Claudel-Hobson carburettor was initially used, and with this the weight of the engine was 425 lb. Bench tests ran on well into 1913 and the engine was found

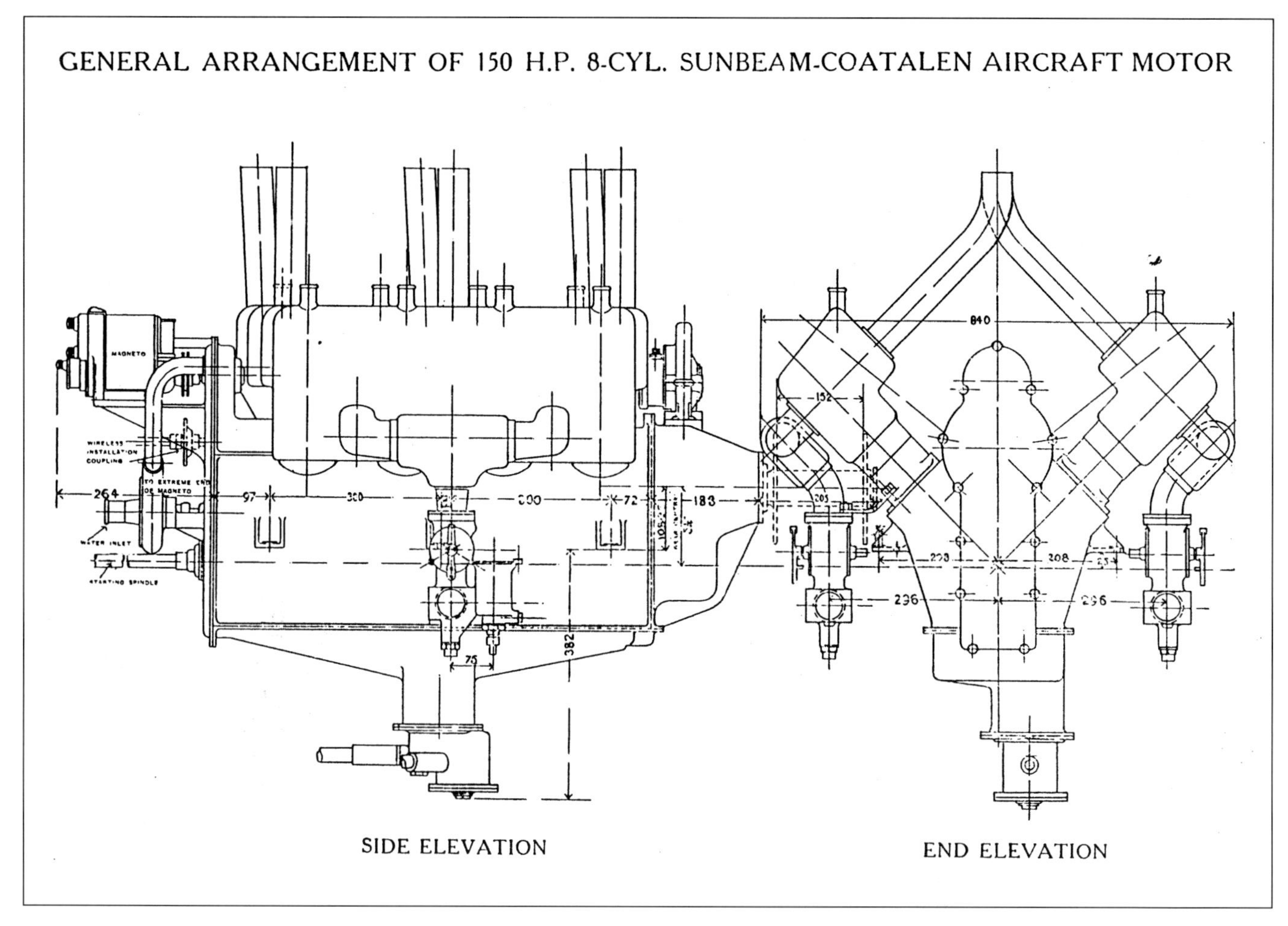

A general arrangement drawing of the Crusader showing side and end elevations.

to give 120 hp while running at 2,500 rpm, and had a fuel consumption of forty-two litres per hour.

In February 1913 M. Tollier of France took two of these new engines to install in a powerboat he was preparing for the forthcoming races at Monaco. The following month Sunbeam was ready to announce the engine, and details of it appeared in the aviation press, though mention of it had been made the previous year in *The Aeroplane*, and its existence was widely known in aviation circles.

In May it was announced that Sunbeam was to purchase a Maurice Farman biplane in which to test-fly the new engine. It was stated that the aircraft would be flown from Paris to Brooklands and might then be entered in the forthcoming Circuit of Britain waterplane competition. The next application for the V8 was actually in a Sunbeam car, however, when one was fitted to a standard 24 hp chassis to compete in the Shelsley Walsh hill-climb on 13 June, driven by C.A. Bird and Coatalen himself.

The first aircraft in which the new engine was installed was the Radley-England Waterplane No. 2. This unusual seaplane had been built originally by James Radley and Eric Gordon England with three 50 hp Gnôme rotary engines arranged in tandem on a common shaft driving a large four-blade pusher propeller, there being no single engine of sufficient power available at the time. The aircraft was in effect a twin-float seaplane, but the pilot and five passengers sat in each of the wide, punt-like floats, the pilot in the starboard one, so it was more accurately described as a twin-hulled flying boat. The engines were set between the forty-seven-foot-span wings which were held above the floats on struts. The first flight was in April 1913 and the aircraft proved very successful carrying a number of passengers aloft.

At about this time the *Daily Mail* offered a prize of £5,000 for the fastest circuit of Britain by an all-British seaplane within a period of seventy-two hours. James Radley immediately entered the Waterplane, but obviously needed to replace the French engines to comply with the all-British requirements of the prize. Unfortunately the Waterplane was wrecked on 26 May when a wing tip struck an object in the sea off Brighton as Gordon England was landing with a *Daily Mirror* photographer on board. The aircraft sank until only the top wing was visible, but the remains were salvaged and taken to Shoreham for a rebuild.

New clinker-built hulls were provided, more like boats than punts, and the new Sunbeam V8 was decided on as the powerplant, the only reasonable British alternative being the rather heavy 100 hp Green. The qualification period for the Circuit of Britain flights to take place was set between 16 and 30 August, and so there was very little time in hand for the rebuild. The engine was set between the wings, driving a 9 ft 6 in. four-blade Lang propeller with a 4 ft 7 in. pitch, and in front of it was a large square radiator and an eighty-two-gallon fuel tank, surmounted by an eight-gallon oil tank. The engine was now stated to give 150 hp at 2,200 rpm. On 6 August the Waterplane was floated on the Adur River at Shoreham, and the following day the engine was started for the first time, but ran badly. Troubles with the engine continued, and though the Waterplane was taxied it never flew. In defence of the Sunbeam much of the problem seemed to be with the new floats/hulls, the tails of which tended to bury themselves in the water making acceleration for take-off impossible. There is in fact no record of the Waterplane ever flying, though it was later sold to Noel Pemberton-Billing who planned to use it on a scheduled service between Southampton and Cowes.

Sunbeam's own Maurice Farman biplane was delivered to Brooklands late in September, and installation of the engine began. Brooklands might well have been chosen as the base for the aircraft because it was well known to Sunbeam, as their cars raced there often, and with conspicuous success. Jack Alcock was engaged as test pilot for the aircraft, and by the second week in October was able to make his first test flights in the new combination, the first time a Sunbeam aero-engine had flown. The Farman was the standard version with a forward elevator and a small two-seat nacelle. The engine was installed as a pusher driving a two-blade propeller, and the radiator panels were disposed along the sides of the nacelle, six panels on each side.

Although the flights were stated to have been successful at the time there must have been certain problems arising, because the engine was removed and a new engine (or modified old one) was not delivered for installation until the middle of December, Alcock having travelled to Wolverhampton with the old engine. He flew the aircraft several times during the third week in December, travelling well beyond the airfield, as a prelude to his stated intention of visiting the other major airfields to demonstrate the new engine to prospective purchasers.

Examples of the Crusader were also installed in one or more powerboats built by Brookes for the Smiths Financial Group. A Sunbeam mechanic, A.P. Mitchell was sent to the Seine in France to work on them.

By Sunday, 21 December Alcock was taking up passengers in the Sunbeam–Farman. On that day he took up the winner of the Brooklands weekly free flight draw, Dr Violet Turner of the Royal Free Hospital. He also made a flight of over two hours with a passenger and a flight of an hour and a half in very gusty conditions, showing a satisfying degree of reliability in the new engine.

On Friday, 2 January 1914 Alcock flew the Farman to Farnborough along with a passenger in order to deliver some engine parts, returning the same day. Throughout January he continued to test-fly the aircraft, or more correctly the engine, both with and without passengers, who included a three-year-old named Chapman from Leatherhead. After this series of tests the engine was removed, dismantled, and overhauled to

(ABOVE:)
Jack Alcock in the Sunbeam-powered Maurice Farman biplane which was the first aircraft to fly with a Sunbeam engine, firstly the 110 hp Sunbeam, and then the Crusader shown here. Note the six radiator panels along the side of the nacelle.

(BELOW):
A side view of the Crusader taken from a company brochure, with the propeller boss to the right

check its condition, which was found to be well up to expectations.

The War Office began to take an interest in the new engine. In February the Royal Aircraft Factory informed Sunbeam that it would be purchasing the engine which was then still being bench-tested at the factory. An example of the engine had been delivered to Farnborough for extensive bench testing, but the delivery date is not known, though Alcock's delivery of parts in January probably indicates that it was before then. It was stated to be the 'first modern British engine to be purchased by the Royal Aircraft Factory'. Testing showed a power output of 131 hp at 2,045 rpm with an absolute maximum of 135 hp, but it was found to suffer cracks around the flanges by which the blocks were bolted to the crankcase, and there were also fuel and coolant leaks. If these problems could be solved it was envisaged that the Crusader would make a suitable engine for military use, with a high power:weight ratio.

Alcock took the aircraft to Hendon for the first time on 13 February, carrying a passenger. He had to land at Elstree on the way because of the misty weather, but then carried on when it cleared, and returned to Brooklands in the afternoon. Testing continued through February, Louis Coatalen himself being the passenger on one occasion, and a climb to 2,400 ft had been achieved in a flight to Staines reservoir. Several flights were being made each day, 4,300 ft being the best height achieved in a flight with a passenger over Windsor above the clouds, gliding down through them on the return. Alcock was flying the aircraft in conditions so windy (gusts of up to 41 mph) that few other pilots ventured out, and he stated his admiration for the engine.

On 24 February he flew to Shoreham with a passenger, arriving over the airfield after a forty-minute flight at an altitude of 7,500 ft. He then took several passengers aloft, flying over Brighton and Worthing and well out to sea before returning to Brooklands at less than 4,000 ft, below the clouds. After many more flights during the week, he again took up the winner of the free ballot, a Mr Watson Munro of Crouch End.

On 9 March Alcock went on a long flight over Kent in the company of F.G. Clifton. He overflew Eastchurch after forty minutes, flying through a snowstorm over Chatham, and then landed at Margate for fuel after gliding down from 5,000 ft, seventy minutes after taking off. He landed for fuel again at Whitstable after running out of fuel in the air and gliding down to land in a field. On the return journey he was forced to stop at Eastchurch because of descending fog. He flew back to Brooklands the following day, after giving a demonstration flight, and the following evening went up for a night flight, taking off at 11.15 p.m. for a half-hour flight over Staines and Walton.

In March the Aero Show opened at Olympia and Sunbeam exhibited both the Crusader and the new V12 Mohawk. The V8 was now said to be of 90 mm bore and 150 mm stroke, whereas originally it had been 80 mm bore. It was also said to produce 150 hp at 2,000 rpm instead of 2,500 rpm, and had two Claudel-Hobson carburettors instead of one. The changes had increased the weight of the engine dry to 480 lb, or 630 lb in running condition. When these changes took place is not clear, but it was probably after the engine was first removed from the Farman in October 1913, with the revised engine reinstalled in December.

Sunbeam received two orders for its engines during the show, both for the forthcoming *Daily Mail*-sponsored Circuit of Britain Race. Sopwith ordered one of the new V12 Mohawks for its flying boat and Avro ordered a Crusader for its Avro 510 seaplane. These were to be the first two entries for the race, with its £5,000 prize, which was planned to take place during the first week in August.

The Avro 510 seaplane built for the 1914 Circuit of Britain Race, shown at Calshot in July 1914. A further five of these aircraft, powered by the Crusader, were built, but were not a great success.

Meanwhile, the intense testing of the engine in the Farman biplane continued from Brooklands, with flying most days, including a fifty-mile circular flight on 28 March, all at an altitude of 5,000 ft. There was continued intensive flying throughout April; Alcock was often the first up in the morning and the last down at night.

At the beginning of May the Naval and Military Aeroplane Engine Competition was due to begin at Farnborough, with an intensive series of tests on all the entered engines, which included the Sunbeam 150 hp Crusader. A prize of £5,000 was on offer to the all-British engine which most closely suited the requirements, with a promise of immediate orders worth £40,000. The main requirements were a horse power of between 90 and 200, more than four cylinders, a gross weight per horse power of not more than 11 lb, and of course a suitable layout for fitment to an aircraft. There was also a long list of desirable attributes and regulations. The trusty Green 120 hp six-cylinder inline engine was to go on to win the prize after extensive testing, though Sunbeam was awarded a consolation of £50, as were some of the other manufacturers. As with the military aeroplane competition of 1912 – in which the Cody biplane most closely suited the convoluted rules, won first prize, and was then quietly forgotten – this engine competition was the last hurrah for the reliable but far too heavy Green engine.

Jack Alcock's flying abated somewhat during May as preparations were made to enter the Aerial Derby around London on the 23rd, which was then postponed until 6 June because of bad weather. It really ought to have been postponed a second time because the weather was equally bad on 6 June, but a huge crowd had gathered so it went ahead. Jack Alcock flew over to Hendon just after midday, and had a test flight with his passenger, Harold Lane, before taking off the sixth of eleven starters. Even with the extra power of the Sunbeam engine, instead of the usual 70 hp Renault, the Farman did not have much chance of winning the race against the competition provided by the Morane-Saulnier monoplanes and two Sopwith Tabloids. This might well have been a factor in Alcock's decision to drop out; he flew back to Brooklands from the second turning point at Epsom, where one of the other competitors had already landed because of the appalling visibility.

The disappointment of his showing in the Aerial Derby may have contributed to the entry of the Sunbeam–Farman in the London–Manchester–London Race due to start on 20 June. In the meantime the intensive testing and demonstration of the aircraft continued, with flights to Epsom, Sunbury, and Shoreham, as well as many local flights. The London–Manchester Race started from Hendon and was handicapped, with a stopping point at Castle Bromwich, Birmingham, in each direction. The first 70 hp Farman had already left when Alcock took his aircraft up for a test flight. After only half a circuit he had to land with a hole in his carburettor float. The offending float was taken into the Grahame-White Works to be mended by none other than J.D. North, the chief engineer himself. By the time Alcock was able to join the race he had lost forty-nine minutes and forty-six seconds, and was one of eight starters from the original entry of eleven. Harold Lane flew as his navigator, and by the time they reached Castle Bromwich there were only four left in the field. During the half-hour compulsory stop at Birmingham they changed the faulty carburettor float, and also changed a tyre, as one had burst on take-off at Hendon. Two pilots had returned to Hendon with technical problems, and two damaged their aircraft while landing at Birmingham, one in the wrong place.

At Manchester the field was further reduced when another competitor damaged his aircraft on landing. On the return journey the American W.L. Brock reached Castle Bromwich in his Morane-Saulnier monoplane one hour, ten minutes and fifty-eight seconds ahead of R.H. Carr's similar aircraft, with Jack Alcock trailing twenty-three minutes and fifty-four seconds behind Carr, having had to land at Essington, Wolverhampton, to ascertain the way. Alcock lost even more time over the last stage when he ran into a storm the speedy monoplanes had just missed. Even though he finished third, and therefore last, the Sunbeam 150 hp Crusader had the honour of being the first British aero-engine ever to finish a long-distance cross-country race.

After the excitement of the race Alcock returned to Brooklands to continue the programme of test flights and demonstrations, and he took part in the first of Shoreham airfield's weekly flying meetings on 10 July, when he started on scratch in the circuit race and finished third. The journey to Shoreham meant the aircraft and its Sunbeam engine had clocked up a total of 30,000 miles, an excellent demonstration of reliability for prospective customers. Sunbeam lost another order for the 150 hp engine for Pemberton-Billing's PB.7 high-speed boat when it could not promise delivery in time, and he substituted a 130 hp Salmson.

Another Sunbeam-powered aircraft was being prepared to fly, however – the Avro 510 seaplane for the forthcoming Circuit of Britain Race. It was a large two-seat twin-float seaplane with an upper span of sixty-three feet, overhanging the lower by twelve feet, and with a length of thirty-eight feet. The Sunbeam Crusader drove a two-blade tractor propeller and was fitted with stub exhausts and a large frontal radiator. The aircraft was built in Manchester and then transported by rail to Calshot, where the Circuit of Britain was to commence. Fred Raynham was to make its first flight. The start of the qualifying period was postponed until 16 August.

On Tuesday, 27 July Jack Alcock flew the Farman to Wolverhampton, accompanied by Harold Lane, in order to deliver a magneto to Sunbeam. He arrived at Dunstall Park racecourse in a flying time of one hour and forty-six minutes for the 112-mile flight, not including a stop at Snitterfield, near Warwick, because of fog. While in Wolverhampton he gave exhibition flights and carried passengers, mostly for the benefit of the Sunbeam workers, who were duly proud of the aircraft which they felt exceeded the exploits of the Star aircraft built by the rival Wolverhampton car company in 1910–11.

Alcock and Lane set off for their return on the Saturday and reached Snitterfield with a gale-force wind behind them in only thirty-four minutes, and had to land because Lane had airsickness. After a respite, and a demonstration flight for the hospitable locals, they returned to Brooklands the following Monday.

In the last week before war Jack Alcock flew down to Shoreham again, once more with Harold Lane as passenger. Two Sunbeam-powered aircraft were being prepared for the Circuit of Britain Air Race, the Avro 510 with the 150 hp Crusader down at Calshot, and the Sopwith Bat Boat with the 225 hp Mohawk. All these familiar peaceful flying activities, which had developed with such increasing regularity over the previous four years, were suddenly all to come to a halt, and frantic preparations were made for a very different kind of flying.

The first military aircraft fitted with the Crusader may well have been a Royal Aircraft Factory RE.5 of the Royal Flying Corps. These large two-seat biplanes were usually fitted with 120 hp Austro-Daimler engines, but in July 1914 official records show that one of them was experimentally fitted with a Crusader, though there are no confirming records of the result of this test.

Sunbeam's own Maurice Farman was impressed in August and delivered to Hendon on the 24th. It went on to the Royal Naval Air Service at Yarmouth on 9 November but suffered an accident on the 24th and was deleted on 7 December, salvaged parts, including presumably the engine, going to Eastchurch. The Avro 510 Circuit of Britain seaplane was purchased by the Admiralty on 6 August 1914 for £2,500, a cheque being handed over on the spot. Serial no. 881 was first test-flown by the RNAS on 10 August, still at Calshot. Avro received an order for five more 510s, which were given the serials 130–4, all to be powered by the 150 hp

Crusader. The first was delivered to Killingholme on 6 December 1914, but the type did not have much success. It showed a marked reluctance to leave the water, even with only one crew member on board.

The two Sunbeam engines were stated to be the only modern British aero-engines available for production at the beginning of the war, and Jack Alcock's 150 hp Crusader was the only engine designed and built in Britain to be undertaking regular flying during 1914. Both engines were ordered by the RNAS, but production took some time to build up, only ten 150 hp Crusaders having been built by the turn of the year.

Apart from the Avro 510s, the Crusader was first fitted to six examples of the Sopwith Type 806 Gunbus, replacing 110 hp Sunbeams in Nos. 801 and 802, and being fitted new to the other four, 803–6. All six of these aircraft were built by Sopwith at Kingston, and then Robey & Co. of Lincoln received an order for thirty more Type 806s, all to be fitted with the Crusader. Only about half of these were delivered as complete aircraft, the others being delivered as spares, presumably without engines. Some of these Robey-built Type 806s were considered for palming off on the Romanian government. A few Type 806s served with the RNAS at Dunkirk during the first year of the war, but most were little used and were soon discarded in favour of better aircraft. Production of the 150 hp Crusader began to build up during 1915, with five delivered in January, two in February, and then nine in March, and this made possible orders for the aircraft which was to be most associated with the engine.

The most significant application for the Crusader was the Short Type 827 seaplane. The Short Admiralty Type 827/830 seaplane was developed from the earlier Type 166, which had proved quite successful. It had been powered by a 200 hp Salmson engine, and twenty-six had been completed, six from the parent company and the other twenty from Westland. The Type 827/830 was very similar in appearance but with slightly smaller dimensions, and was powered by two very different engines. The Type 830 was fitted with the 135 hp Salmson water-cooled radial, and the Type 827 was originally ordered with the 110 hp Sunbeam, but was eventually fitted with the 150 hp Crusader. Other than the engine installation there was very little difference between the two aircraft.

The first batch of twelve aircraft, six of each type, was ordered from Short Bros on 25 September 1914, the Type 827s being serialled 822–7 and the Type 830s 819–21 and 828–30. The type numbers were taken from the last serial of each batch, which was usual Admiralty practice at the time. The Type 830 was not called the Type 821 because the first three, 819–21, were originally ordered with the 110 hp Sunbeam, and only the last three with the Salmson.

The first Type 827 was delivered on 5 February 1915, and there was to be a total of 108 more, only thirty of which were Salmson-powered Type 830s. A second batch of ten was ordered from the parent company, serials 3063–72, the last actually being delivered with the uprated and renamed Crusader, the 160 hp Zulu. Four other firms received orders for the type 827, including Sunbeam itself which built two batches, serialled 3093–112 and 8630–49, totalling forty aircraft. Brush Electrical of Loughborough built twenty – 3321–32 and 8620–7 – and so did George Parnall & Co. of Yate – 8218–29 and 8250–7. Finally, the first aircraft ever built by the Fairey Aviation Co. at Hamble were twelve Short Type 827s, serialled 8550–61.

As related previously, the Type 827 served in East and Central Africa and in the Middle East, but also in home waters on reconnaissance and anti-submarine patrols. One Sunbeam-built example was badly damaged when the German High Seas Fleet raided Scarborough on 25 April 1916. A Mohawk-powered Type 184, 8385, actually took off to bomb the German battle cruisers as they shelled the town, but stalled and crashed from 200 ft.

One of the Fairey-built Type 827s, 8560, was actually transferred to the Royal Flying Corps and re-serialled A9920 for the School of Aerial Gunnery on Loch Doon. Its Crusader was one of the few Sunbeam side-valve engines to find its

The most successful application for the Crusader was the Short Type 827, and this one is shown operating in East Africa, a theatre where they enjoyed a great deal of success.

A Sunbeam-built Short Type 827, with a Crusader engine being manhandled down to the water at Lake Tongwe, in Belgian service.

way into the RFC, almost all of them going to the RNAS.

Production of the 150 hp Crusader to match the large orders increased dramatically in the middle of the year: after three were delivered in April and three in May, there were twenty-one delivered in June, which was to be the best month for Crusader production, and another eighty-three by the end of 1915. Most of these engines found their way into Short Type 827s, with a few going into the Sopwith 806s. With another eight-seven engines being delivered during the first six months of 1916, further applications for the Crusader could be found.

The Blackburn Aircraft Co. built two twin-engined biplane–seaplanes delivered in July 1916 and January 1917, the forerunner of the later Blackburn Kangaroo landplanes. The first was powered by two opposite-handed Crusaders, but the second was fitted with two Rolls-Royce Falcons, which not only had more power but also had outside exhausts, which enabled the exhaust pipes to run along the sides of the nacelles.

Two Avro 519 single-engined bombers were ordered by the Admiralty in 1916, and fitted with Crusaders. They were serialled 8440 and 8441 and had folding wings, one later being converted to a single-seat aircraft. They could not have been a great success as there were no more orders forthcoming, but the second aircraft was returned to Avro at Hamble in July 1916 to be fitted with one of the first 200 hp Sunbeam Afridi engines, perhaps indicating a lack of power.

At the same time that the Type 519 was being built, Avro was also building a single prototype of its Type 527 fighting reconnaissance biplane, fitted with a single Crusader. It was based on the Avro 504E with a slightly beefed-up structure and a single Lewis gun fitted to the observer's cockpit. The twin exhaust stacks of the Crusader projected straight up over the top wing, and with the radiator sited right behind them rather obstructed the pilot's forward view. At trials at Farnborough early in 1916 the rate of climb was also criticised, and doubt was expressed about the strength of the aircraft's structure with so powerful an engine.

One of the Curtiss H-4 Small America flying boats, serial 1238, which had been delivered from Hammondsport, New York, with two 100 hp Curtiss engines in March 1915, had the American engines replaced by 125 hp Anzanis in January 1916, and then had two 150 hp Crusaders fitted. The RFC decided in October 1915 to fit Crusaders to the twin-engined Curtiss Type C Canada it had just received. Two Crusaders were actually borrowed from the RNAS Depot at White City, and taken to Farnborough on the 14th. After an official change of mind the engines went back to the White City on the 27th.

Fifteen examples of another Curtiss aircraft, the R.2 tractor biplane, out of 100 ordered in 1915 and built in Toronto, were fitted with the 150 hp Crusader rather than the 160 hp Curtiss XV, or the Sunbeam 200 hp Afridi which was not yet ready. These aircraft seem to have had limited use for observer/bombing training.

At the beginning of the war the Russians were in even more desperate need of aero-engines than their Western allies, especially for their Il'ya Mouromets heavy bomber, which required four. This aircraft had first flown in 1913 fitted with four German Argus engines, but the outbreak of war ruled out this source of supply. The eighty production aircraft eventually built were fitted with a variety of engines. With more modern engines becoming available the Air Ministry released thirty Crusaders, which were delivered to the Russians and fitted to the Mark V version of the I.M. The engines were delivered on a regular weekly basis, and were erected and fitted by a Sunbeam mechanic. The Mark V had a span of 97 ft 8 in., weighed 6,500 lb empty, and was armed with two machine-guns. The Crusaders gave it a maximum speed of 76 mph at 6,500 ft, and were apparently the least liked engines available. The Russians preferred the original Argus engines, Salmsons, Renaults, or even their own RBVZs to the Crusaders. The Il'ya Mouromets-equipped units were to become the élite of the Russian Air Service, and the aircraft was highly successful, dropping over 2,300 bombs and losing only one of its number to German fighter attack.

The Crusader was also fitted to the Coastal Class of non-rigid airship, each having two engines, one at either end of the car, which was actually two Avro 510 fuselages joined together. These gave the Coastals a duration of eleven hours at full speed, which was forty-two knots. Some of the Coastals were fitted with a mixture of engines, for instance a 100 hp Berliet-Ford and a 200 hp Renault. At least eighteen of the twenty-four Coastals built had Sunbeam engines. This association with airships was to be a continuing feature of the company.

Production of the 150 hp Crusader ended in July 1916; it was replaced on the production lines by the 160 hp Zulu, which in any other company might have been known as the Crusader Mk II, being basically the same engine with the bore increased to 100 mm. Zulu production had begun in February alongside the Crusader, and was to end in November 1916.

The Coastal Class airship C.26, which was powered by two Crusaders, one pushing and one pulling. Most of the Coastals were powered by the Crusader, in some cases with only one of the two engines.

Many of the Type 827 seaplanes were still in service in 1918, but as many of them had their 150 hp Crusaders replaced by its 160 hp development, the Zulu, it is hard to say if the Crusader served right through the war, but it is nevertheless possible. The Crusader/Zulu was certainly the only British-designed engine to serve from 1914 to 1918.

Technical data

Engine type	water-cooled, eight-cylinder, ninety-degree Vee
Manufacturer	Sunbeam Motors Ltd, Moorfield Works, Wolverhampton
Horse Power	150 hp at 2,000 rpm
Capacity	7.6 litres, 90 mm bore, 150 mm stroke
Valve Type	side valves, two per cylinder
Weight	480 lb dry, 630 lb running
Dimensions	length 4 ft, width 33 in., height 29.9 in.
Propeller Nos.	AD502 (Coastal airship – tractor engine), AD581 (Coastal airship – pusher engine), S75 (Short Type 827)
Details	2 × Bosch high-tension four-cylinder magnetos, 2 × Claudel-Hobson CZ 42 mm carburettors. Prototype engine initially had 80 mm bore.
Nos. built	2+ civil pre-war (not including engines with 80 mm bore), 2+ military pre-war, 224 wartime. Total: 228+

Applications

Maurice Farman two-seat pusher biplane
- One, first flown 1913, Sunbeam's own test a/c

Royal Aircraft Factory RE.5 two-seat tractor biplane
- One, serial unknown. Tested with Crusader in July 1914

Avro 510 tractor biplane–seaplane
- Five, 130–4, delivered 6.12.14–3.4.15
- One, 881, purchased 6.8.14, Circuit of Britain a/c

Sopwith Type 806 Gunbus, pusher biplane
- Two, 801–2, replacing 110 hp Sunbeams
- Four, 803–6, delivered 5-11-14–4-1-15
- Thirty, 3833–62, built by Robey & Co., delivered 10.2.16–10.6.16 (last thirteen only as spares, probably with no engines)

Short Type 827 tractor biplane–seaplanes
- Six, 822–7, built by Short Bros, ordered with 110 hp Sunbeams but delivered with Crusaders, 5.2.15–10.4.15
- Nine, 3063–71, built by Short Bros, delivered 16.9.15–30.12.15 (3072 with 160 hp Zulu)
- Forty, 3093–112/8630–49, built by Sunbeam Motors, delivered 8.11.15–20.10.16
- Twenty, 3321–32/8230–7, built by Brush Electrical, delivered 30.4.16–24.2.17
- Twenty, 8218–29/8250–7, built by George Parnall, delivered 7.15–30.6.16
- Twelve, 8550–61, built by Fairey Aviation, delivered 28.3.16–5.16. 8560 later became A9920 in the Royal Flying Corps

Handley Page Type O, tractor biplane heavy bomber
- Two, 1372, 1373, ordered from Handley Page Ltd, 28.12.14 (later cancelled)

Blackburn GP twin-engined tractor biplane–seaplane
- One, 1415, built by Blackburn Aircraft, Leeds, delivered 7.16 with LH/RH engines

Sopwith single-seat tractor biplane bombers
- Two, 3698–9, ordered from Sopwith with special bomb-dropping gear, but later cancelled

Avro 519 bomber tractor biplane
- Two, 8440–1, delivered 2.2.16 and 28.2.16

Avro Type 527 reconnaissance tractor biplane
- One, built by Avro, Manchester

Curtiss H-4 Small America, twin-engined biplane flying boat
- One, 1238, built by Curtiss, Hammondsport, New York, delivered 11.3.15, re-engined with 150 hp Sunbeam in 1916

Curtiss R-2 tractor biplanes
- Fourteen, 3445/3447–54/3460/3463–4/3467–8, built by Curtiss, Toronto, delivered 12.15 to 11.16. Other a/c powered by Curtiss engines

Coastal Type non-rigid airship, twin-engined
- Thirteen, C1, C5, C6, C10, C16–C18, C20, C22–C24, C26, C27 (each with Crusader pusher and tractor engines. It is possible that the later Coastals were fitted with 150 hp Sunbeam Nubians)
- Three, C3, C7, C14 (each with just one Crusader tractor installation)
- Three Coastals, C11, C12, C15, engines unknown but probably Sunbeams. C12 probably became the prototype for the C Star airships which were not fitted with Sunbeams
- Six, Ca, Cb, Cc, Cd, Ce, Cf built for export to Russia and France – engines unknown

Sikorsky Il'ya Mouromets Mk V four-engined biplane heavy bomber
- Thirty engines supplied, no. of a/c fitted unknown, but probably only four

110 HP SUNBEAM

As related previously, the 110 hp Sunbeam was the early version of the side-valve V8 Sunbeam with the 80 mm bore, looked on before the war began as the same engine, but during the war entered in official records as a separate model. Records show that seven '110 hp Sunbeam' engines were delivered in 1914, two in September, four in October, and one in November, and these were quite separate entries from the 150 hp Crusader (ten of which were delivered in 1914), which was sometimes referred to by different horse powers.

A Sunbeam advertisement in a 1916 copy of *The Aeroplane* clearly states that the company built '100 hp and 150 hp eight-cylinder, and 225 hp twelve-cylinder aero-engines', and so the '110 hp Sunbeam' must be the 100 hp eight-cylinder. At a time when aero-engines of large power were in very short supply it is likely that there were examples of the earlier V8, and parts to assemble others, in the Moorfield Works, and so seven were built and delivered to the RNAS, even though the more powerful Crusader with the 90 mm bore was already available. The early applications for this engine were thus the Shelsley Walsh hill-climb car, three or four French motor-boats, the Radley-England Waterplane and Sunbeam's own Farman biplane, for its first few weeks.

After the start of the war two aircraft types had the '110 hp Sunbeam' as their specified powerplant when they were ordered, the Sopwith Type 806 Gunbus and the Short Type 827 seaplane, but only two of the former seem to have been actually fitted with engines of this designation, later being replaced by 150 hp Sunbeams.

The Sopwith Gunbus No. 1, or Admiralty Type 806 (sometimes Type 804), was derived from a seaplane built for the Greek government, and fitted with a landplane undercarriage. They were two-seat pushers with a machine-gun carried in the front cockpit. Six were ordered from Sopwith in 1914 and serialled 801–6. They were all ordered with the 110 hp Sunbeam, but only the first two seem to have been fitted with this engine. With the greater power and similar configuration of the 150 hp Crusader available, subsequent aircraft were powered with this engine, including a further batch of thirty ordered from Robey & Co. Another batch of twelve ordered with the 110 hp Sunbeam was replaced by an order for twelve Sopwith Type 860 seaplanes.

Sopwith Gunbus serial 801 was first tested at Brooklands on 6 October 1914, and then delivered to the Defence Flight at Hendon on the 11th. The second aircraft was delivered to Hendon on 28 October. Both of these aircraft were returned to Sopwith Aircraft in March 1915 for alterations, which included the fitment of 150 hp Crusader engines.

Apparently the only other type for which the 110 hp Sunbeam was specified was the Short Type 827 seaplane. Nine were ordered, serialled 819–27, to be fitted with the 110 hp Sunbeam, but in the event the first three were fitted with 135 hp Salmson engines (thereby becoming Short Type 830s), and the last six were delivered with 150 hp Sunbeam Crusaders.

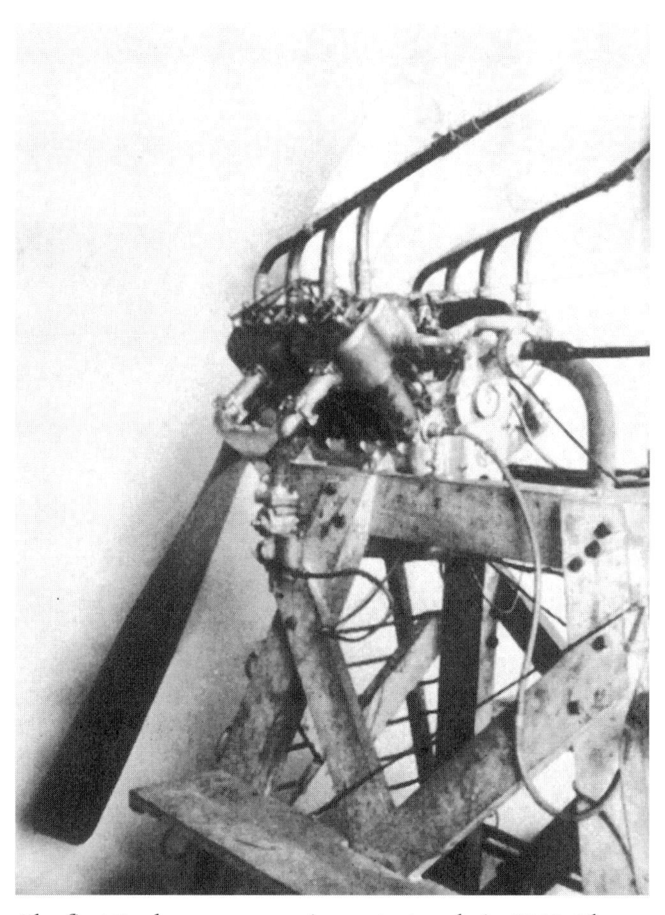

The first Sunbeam aero-engine on test early in 1913. The first example of the V8 with the 80 mm bore, i.e. the 110 hp Sunbeam, on bench-test in the Moorfield Works.

No mention is made of this engine in any surviving Sunbeam records, and it was not included in the retrospective naming of Sunbeam engines which took place in 1917, presumably because it had already disappeared from RNAS stocks.

Technical data

Engine Type	water-cooled, eight-cylinder, ninety-degree Vee
Manufacturer	Sunbeam Motors Ltd, Moorfield Works, Wolverhampton
Horse Power	110 hp
Capacity	6.03 litres, 80 mm bore, 150 mm stroke
Valve Type	side-valve
Weight	425 lb
Details	as Crusader
Nos. Built	pre-war 4+, wartime, ordered, 7, delivered 7

The first aircraft to be fitted with the 110 hp Sunbeam, the Radley-England Waterplane, on the river at Shoreham in August 1913. The Waterplane failed to fly in this form, mostly because of the design of the twin hulls, but it is the only aircraft fitted with the 110 hp Sunbeam to have been photographed.

Applications

Radley-England Waterplane No.2, twin-hulled flying boat, pusher
- One, built 1913, may never have flown

Maurice Farman, two-seat pusher biplane
- One, first flown 1913. Engine replaced 1913 by Sunbeam Crusader

Sopwith Type 806 Gunbus pusher biplanes
- Two, 801–2, built by Sopwith, Kingston, delivered 6.10.14–11.10.14
- Four, 803–6 ordered with 110 hp Sunbeams but delivered with 150 hp Sunbeams
- Twelve, 927–38 ordered with 110 hp Sunbeams, but replaced by order for Sopwith Type 860 seaplanes

Short Type 827 tractor biplane–seaplanes
- Six, 822–7, ordered with 110 hp Sunbeams but delivered with 150 hp Sunbeams

Motor-cars

Sunbeam 24 hp hill-climb car, 1913

Motor-boats

Tollier 1913 powerboat, two engines
Brookes 1914 powerboat, one engine (2+ boats)

225 HP MOHAWK

Naval interest in the 150 hp Crusader, and the search for even more power, prompted Coatalen to design a larger V12 side-valve engine, built on the same lines and giving 225 hp from 11.4 litres. It used the same cylinder sizes as its smaller V8 brother, with 80 mm and later 90 mm bore and 150 mm stroke, but the cylinders were cast in four sets of three, whereas the V8 had four sets of two, and they were arranged in a sixty-degree Vee instead of ninety degrees.

To allow for the connecting rod spacing the front starboard block of three cylinders was slightly ahead of the port three, and the rear starboard block of three was slightly behind the port three. As before the side valves were operated by rockers and push-rods, but the new engine had two Bosch magnetos and four Claudel-Hobson carburettors. Lubrication was as with the smaller engine, forced to the crankshaft bear-

Rear end view of the V12 Mohawk, showing the sixty-degree angle of the cylinder banks, and the inside exhausts.

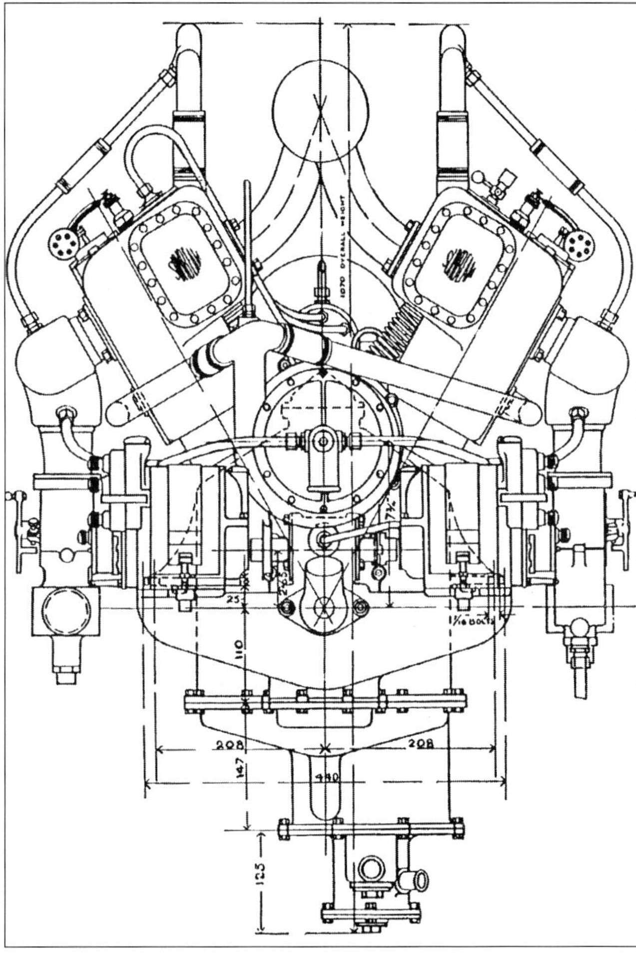

General arrangement drawing of the end elevation of the Mohawk.

ings and then splash, and the engine operated to 2,000 rpm, with a propeller geared down to 1,000 rpm. The engine was later to be named the Mohawk, but during its production and service was always known as the Sunbeam 225 hp.

When it first appeared, however, the Mohawk was a slightly smaller engine. Like the first version of the Crusader it only had an 80 mm bore, giving it a capacity of just 9.048 litres. Running at 2,400 rpm it gave 200 hp. Although this engine was designed specifically for aircraft, Coatalen saw that when fitted to a suitable car chassis it would be an excellent way of attacking many of the closed-circuit world records. At the same time running the engine in a car for long durations would be a safer and easier way of testing the engine. It was therefore installed in *Toodles V*, the fifth in a series of racing cars named after Coatalen's wife. Its first race was on 4 October, when it performed very creditably, and it subsequently broke eight world speed records.

Just like its smaller V8 stablemate, by the time the

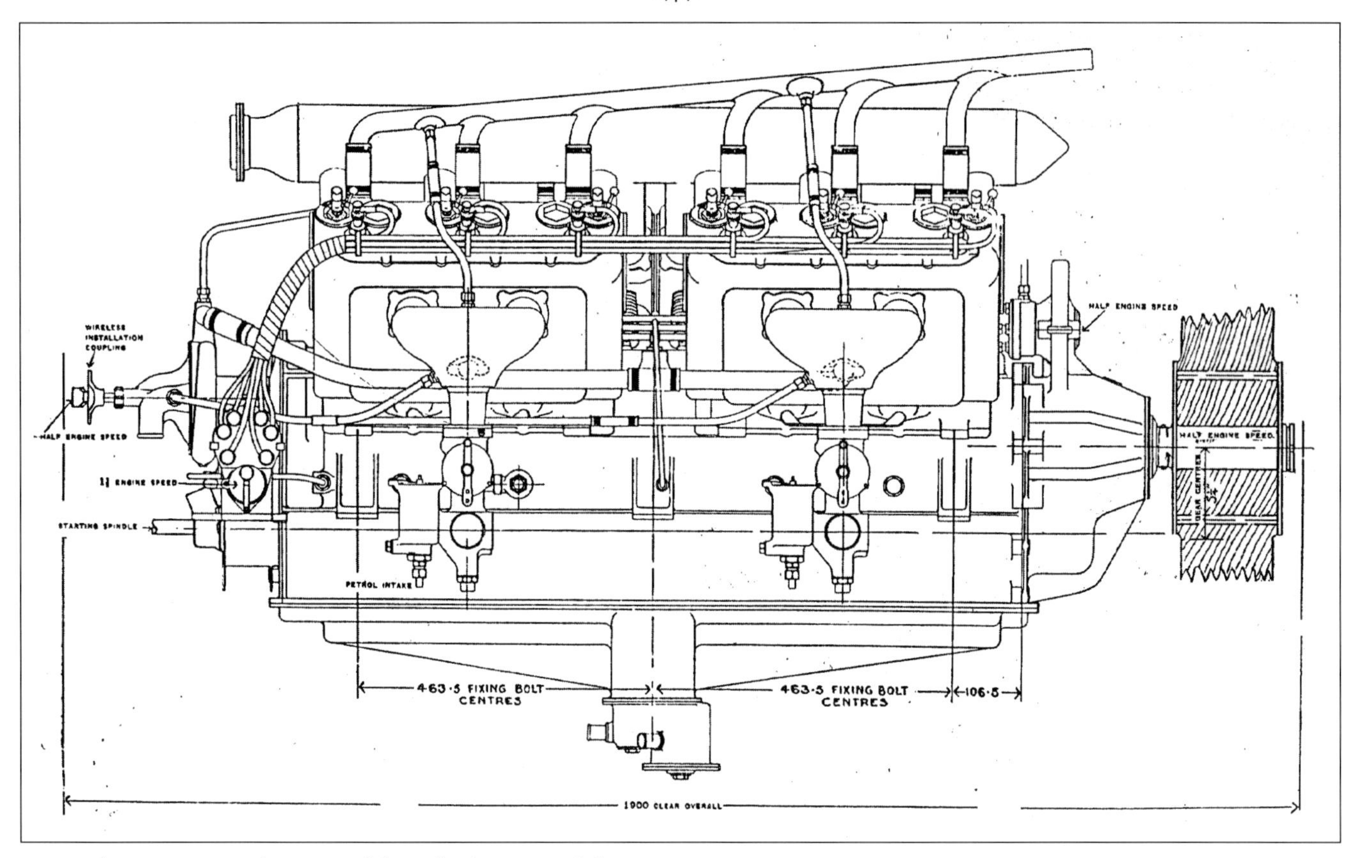

General arrangement drawing of the side elevation of the Mohawk.

Mohawk was exhibited at the 1914 Olympia Aero Show its bore had grown 10 mm to 90 mm, raising its capacity to 11.4 litres. At the same time its operating speed had been reduced to 2,000 rpm, at which it gave 225 hp. As the most powerful British engine available at the show it quickly attracted special applications. Sopwith ordered one to power their Bat Boat No. 2 for the 1914 Circuit of Britain Air Race, one of the most attractive and practical flying boats built before the war, with a two-man crew seated side by side in a boat-like hull which projected well forward of the biplane wings. The 225 hp Mohawk engine was attached to the upper wing in a pusher arrangement, driving a two-blade propeller. There were petrol and oil tanks of seventy and seven gallons respectively, giving it a range of about 180 miles.

An even more spectacular projected use for the new engine was for the Martin-Handasyde transatlantic monoplane, designed to win the *Daily Mail*'s £10,000 prize for the first non-stop transatlantic flight. The Scottish-Canadian financier MacKay Edgar had been inspired by news of the prize and offered to finance perhaps the most famous pilot of the day, Gustav Hamel, in an attempt to win it, if landfall was made in Scotland. The Brooklands firm of Martin and Handasyde, most famous for its monoplanes, were commissioned to build a suitable aircraft. The design was a sixty-six-foot-span two-seat monoplane of fairly conventional design for the day, even to the use of wing-warping instead of ailerons. The 225 hp Mohawk would drive a four-blade propeller. It was nearly completed in August 1914, with wings, fuselage, and engine mountings built, when Gustav Hamel was killed, and then events in Sarajevo ended all hopes that the attempt would take place. The final fate of the monoplane, and whether the 225 hp Mohawk was ever installed, has never been recorded.

Noel Pemberton-Billing's company, the forerunner of Supermarine, secured a German option to buy two of its projected PB.7 flying boats, each to be powered by a Mohawk driving two chain-driven pusher propellers. The PB.7 had a 'slip-wing' so that in the event of engine failure or other trouble it could land on the sea, slip its wings and tail, and proceed as an ordinary cabin boat under the power of a small marine engine. At the outbreak of war construction of the aircraft ceased, though the hulls were complete enough to be used as tenders by the company for some time.

With the advent of war the Admiralty immediately impressed the Sopwith Bat Boat, giving it the serial 879, though it seems to have had little use and was deleted in April 1915. More importantly the Admiralty saw the new engine as the powerplant for a new series of larger seaplanes able to carry a torpedo – the Short Type 184, the Wight Type 840, and the Sopwith Type 860 – all of which were ordered with the Mohawk. This type of aircraft owed its existence to Captain Murray Seuter, Director of the Admiralty's Air Department, who was a firm advocate of the concept of a torpedo-carrying seaplane. On 28 July 1914 a Short Folder seaplane, with a 160 hp Gnôme engine, had successfully dropped a fourteen-inch Whitehead torpedo, and in the same month an order was placed with Short Bros for two torpedo-carrying seaplanes to be powered by the 200 hp Salmson engine, and they were given the serials 184 and 185. These were then designated the Short Type 184, the most famous seaplane of the war. The engine requirement was soon changed to the 225 hp Sunbeam Mohawk, and the aircraft was often erroneously referred to as the 'Type 225', even when other engines were fitted later.

Production of the V12 Mohawk started up in Wolverhampton in parallel with the V8 Crusader, but only nine had been delivered during the first four months of the war. Production was stepped up rather more quickly than the smaller engine, as engines of the Mohawk's power were very scarce, and seven were delivered in December 1914, followed by eleven in January.

The first of the three new seaplanes to be delivered was the Sopwith Type 860, with the first arriving in January; the first Wight Type 840s and Short Type 184s did not arrive until April 1915, but it was the latter which was to prove the most capable aircraft of the three. A second batch of ten Type 184s, serialled 841–50, was ordered even before the first Type 184 had flown. These too originally had different engines specified – the 200 hp Canton-Unné – but again this was later changed to the Mohawk. No.184 was delivered to Grain on 21 April 1915, and was itself to become one of the most famous of the type. On 12 August 1915 this very aircraft became the first in the world to sink a ship with a torpedo. Flown solo by F/Lt G.H.K. Edmonds, as was normal when a torpedo was carried, it sank a Turkish transport off Gallipoli.

The Type 184 proved so useful a design that Short Bros received its largest contract so far, on 12 June 1915, for seventy-five of the aircraft, serialled 8031–105, all of which were powered by the Mohawk. In addition seven other manufacturers received orders for the Type 184, most initially delivering some with the Mohawk, but as time went on and more powerful engines became available they were substituted. Sunbeam's own uprated version of the Mohawk, the Gurkha, with greater bore and giving 240 hp, was fitted as new to some and replaced Mohawks in a certain number of earlier examples. The 240 hp Renault engine was fitted to some Type 184s, and later on the Sunbeam Maori became the standard engine for the type. The best estimate available indicates that 180 Type 184s were delivered new with the Mohawk.

(LEFT):
Sopwith Type 860 seaplane, serial 852, which served on HMS Ben-my-Chree *and HMS* Engadine, *and then undertook development work at Grain*

(BELOW):
A close-up of a Mohawk fitted to a Short 184 seaplane which had been captured by the Germans. It shows the way the exhaust manifold took the exhaust gases forward and then under the fuselage.

One of these was purchased by the Japanese Navy, which admired its capabilities and sent a mission to England to obtain one complete with its Mohawk engine. The aircraft, RNAS serial 8057, arrived in Japan in November 1916 and was extensively tested with a number of engines. The Japanese built a number of Short Reconnaissance Seaplanes, as they called the Type 184, at the Naval Arsenal at Yokosuka, and fitted different engines, but how many, if any, of these were Sunbeams is not recorded.

Production of the Mohawk increased rapidly until twenty-four were delivered in June 1915, and a total of 150 were delivered during that year. A further 122 Mohawks were delivered in 1916 until production completely gave way to its more powerful development, the 240 hp Gurkha, in June.

A side view of the Mohawk taken from the company's 1916 brochure; the propeller boss is to the right.

One batch of ten type 184s built by Mann-Egerton in Norwich differed significantly from the standard aircraft, and were referred to as the Mann-Egerton Type B, the Type A being the standard aircraft, of which Mann-Egerton initially delivered twelve before making changes to the design. The Type B had much longer upper wings, together with reduced span lower wings, with more rounded tips and no ailerons. The gap between the wings was increased and there were only two pairs of interplane struts.

A Short 184 seaplane fitted with the Mohawk. The radiator block on top of the forward fuselage restricted the pilot's forward vision, but he could see through it.

An urgent Admiralty need for a strategic bomber prompted a redesign of the Type 184 to a landplane able to carry a reasonable bomb-load against the Royal Navy's priority targets, which were the German airship sheds and surface ships. As the Type 184 was able to lift a naval torpedo, albeit only just, it seemed a landplane derivative would be eminently suitable. A solitary prototype was ordered from Short Bros and first flew in 1915, powered by a Mohawk, but it was found to be unsatisfactory. Changes were made, with an increase in wing-span of twelve feet, an extra bay being incorporated, and the Mohawk being replaced by one of the new Rolls-Royce Eagles. Production orders were placed for the revised aircraft, all to be powered by the Eagle, except for an order placed with Sunbeam.

Sunbeam received an order for twenty Short Bombers and was allowed to fit its own engines. It has generally been supposed that these were Mohawks, but the last production Mohawk had been delivered in June 1916, a month before the first Sunbeam-built Short Bomber flew. The Gurkha had replaced the Mohawk on the production line, and it is almost certain that it was this engine which powered the aircraft. Only fifteen of the order were actually built, serialled 9356–70, the other five being cancelled as the more capable Handley Page 0/100 bomber was becoming available.

Another single-engined bomber fitted with the Mohawk was the Avro Type 519, the only type to have been fitted with both the Crusader and its larger V12 brother. Four Type 519s were ordered, two single-seaters for the Admiralty with the smaller engine and two two-seaters for the RFC with the Mohawk. The first, Serial 1614, was delivered during 1916, but had a poor performance, thought to be due to the large radiator on the forward fuselage. The second aircraft, 1915, was then fitted with equal span wings, unlike 1614, and was delivered on 1 November 1916, but no useful purpose for the type could be found.

The main rival to the Short Type 184 was the Wight Type 840, built by J. Samuel White & Co. at East Cowes. An initial batch of ten aircraft was ordered from the parent company on 2 September 1914, and serialled 831–40, the type number deriving from the last of these serials, as was Admiralty practice. The aircraft was also capable of carrying the fourteen-inch Whitehead torpedo, which weighed 810 lb, but was normally used on anti-submarine patrols from Felixstowe, Scapa

The second of four Avro Type 519s, serial 8441, a type which started with the 150 hp Crusader, and was still underpowered when the 225 hp Mohawk was introduced on 8441.

Flow, and Gibraltar. The first aircraft was delivered on 2 January 1915, and proved satisfactory; another batch of twenty aircraft was ordered from the parent company on 8 February, also powered by the Mohawk, and serialled 1300–19, followed by 4 more serialled 1351–4.

Orders for the Wight type 840 were placed with two other companies, all to be powered by the Mohawk. J. Beardmore & Co. of Dalmuir received orders for two batches of twelve and twenty respectively, serialled 1400–11 and 9021–40, but the last twelve were delivered without engines as spares. Portholme Aerodrome Ltd of Huntingdon also received an order for twelve, serialled 8281–92, but the last seven were only delivered as spares without engines. Thus the total number of Wight Type 840s delivered with their Mohawk engines seems to have been fifty-nine.

The third torpedo-carrying biplane ordered, powered by the Mohawk, was the Sopwith Type 860, an initial batch of ten being contracted in late 1914, serialled 851–60. The first production aircraft, 851, had an inauspicious start when it went out of control during very rough weather on its first flight. Sopwith's chief designer, Mr Alston, was drowned in the resulting crash. The aircraft was salvaged after an operation lasting six days and rebuilt. The first batch was followed by another batch of twelve, serialled 927–38. This may well have been an order for the Sopwith Type 806 changed to one for the new aircraft. Only nine of this batch were actually built, and the first aircraft – serial 927, plus two others, 932 and 934 – were retained by Sopwith for some reason and never delivered. The Type 860 was clearly a less capable aircraft than the two rival seaplanes and none of the type seems to have survived beyond 1915, the year of their manufacture.

One type 860 was actually used to test a variable-pitch propeller, or 'Admiralty aileron propeller' as it was referred to in an Advisory Committee for Aeronautics Specification. The jigs for it were made by Lang at Addlestone, followed by tests at the National Physical Laboratory. The propeller was made by Sunbeam at Wolverhampton during 1915, and fitted to the Mohawk in a Type 860 at the Isle of Grain. As there was no subsequent development it cannot have been a great success.

The other main recipient of the Sunbeam Mohawk was a number of Bréguet biplanes ordered by the RNAS during 1916. Twelve Bréguet de Chasse tractor biplanes – serialled 1393, 1394, 3209–13, and 3883–7 – had Mohawks, other aircraft in the order having different engines. A solitary Bréguet de Bombe, serial 3888, also had a Mohawk, a second

A Beardmore-built Wight Type 840 seaplane, serial 1400, passing through the last lock on the Forth–Clyde canal.

aircraft of the type being cancelled, and two Bréguet Type V Concours tractor biplanes were ordered with Mohawks, but were fitted with Rolls-Royce Eagles.

One RE.7 biplane was fitted with a Mohawk at the Royal Aircraft Factory, one of a number of such trial engine installations in what was normally a seriously underpowered aircraft with its usual 120 hp Beardmore.

When finally supplanted on the Sunbeam production lines in June 1915 by the more powerful Gurkha, 287 Mohawks had been delivered since the start of the war. Installations for 266 aircraft have been traced, and this is probably near to the correct total, given that engines of the period were frequently changed in service. This seems to have been particularly the case with Coatalen's side-valve engines, none of which was a model of reliability, and all of which were very difficult to start. Nevertheless, the Mohawk and its smaller V8 brother the Crusader were the only large British aero-engines in production during the first months of the war, and completed many thousands of hours of service installed in the Short and Wight seaplanes of the RNAS.

As a postscript to the story of the Mohawk, after the outbreak of war the Mohawk-powered racing car *Toodles V* had been shipped to the United States, where of course racing was continuing unaffected by events in Europe. There it won a match race against a Peugeot and a Blitzen Benz at the racetrack at Sheepshead Bay, Long Island, and was then the cause of one of the worst disasters in motor-racing history. In a race on a dirt track at Kalamazoo the driver lost control and the car swerved across the track creating a pile-up with eight other cars, causing ten deaths. Apparently the remains of the car were acquired by the Packard Motor Co., and after examining the Mohawk engine the company developed the world's first production twelve-cylinder motor-car engine, something on which Sunbeam had been working when the war intervened.

At the end of hostilities aero-engines were available at ridiculous prices, and a number of prospective racing drivers were attracted by the idea of high horse power for minimal cost. One of these was Harry Hawker, the famous Sopwith test pilot, who acquired two Mohawks and modified a Mercedes 35 hp chassis to take one of them. Hawker did the work himself at his home in Hook, and though he had originally intended to race the car, and did test it at Brooklands, a lack of adhesion for the rear wheels may have been the reason he converted it into a four-seat tourer, though he did claim it was only capable of 110 mph and therefore no use to him as a racing car.

Another Mohawk was installed in a Napier chassis by Cyril Bone of Sussex, but much later on, in 1925. The car with a new home-built two-seat body was entered for two meetings at Brooklands in 1926, but failed to achieve any success in very inexperienced hands.

Technical data

Engine Type water-cooled, twelve-cylinder, sixty-degree Vee
Manufacturer Sunbeam Motor Car Co., Moorfield Works, Wolverhampton
Horse Power 225 hp at 2,000 rpm
Capacity 11.8 litres, 90 mm bore, 150 mm stroke
Valve Type two poppet side valves per cylinder
Weight 905 lb dry
Dimensions length 74.8 in., width 30.7 in., height 42 in.
Propeller Nos. AD501M & AD565 (Short Type 184)
Details cylinders, en-bloc threes, cast-iron; geared propeller (0.5:1) LH tractor/RH pusher, four Claudel-Hobson CZ 40 mm carburettors, two high-tension six-cylinder magnetos
Nos. Built 4 pre-war civil orders, 1 delivered, plus 1 for Sunbeam racing car; 287 wartime orders, 287 delivered

Applications

Martin-Handasyde transatlantic monoplane
One, unfinished
Sopwith Bat Boat No. 2 biplane flying boat
One, 879, Circuit of Britain a/c, delivered 7.8.14
Pemberton-Billing PB.7 pusher flying boat biplane
Two, ordered but not completed at outbreak of war
Short Type 184 tractor biplane seaplanes
Eighty-seven, 184–5/841–50/8031–105, built by Short Bros, delivered 21.4.15–1.8.16 (some re-engined with Gurkha). 8083 and 8084 transferred to the French, and 8057 to Japan. 8357 later fitted with Renault-Mercedes engine
Thirteen, 8001–13, built by S.E. Saunders Ltd, East Cowes, delivered 2.3.16–14.7.16 (remainder of order for thirty fitted with Gurkha)
Twelve, 8344–55, built by Mann-Egerton Ltd, Norwich, delivered 11.15–1.6.16 (Mann-Egerton Type A)
Ten, 9085–94, built by Mann-Egerton with revised wings, delivered 1.8.16–11.16 (Mann-Egerton Type B)
Twelve, 8356–67, built by Westland Aircraft, Yeovil, delivered 23.1.16–11.5.16
Twelve, 8368–79, built by Phoenix Dynamo, Bradford, delivered 13.1.16–11.6.16
Twenty-one, 8380–91/9065–71/9081–4, built by Frederick Sage & Co., Peterborough, delivered 17.11.15–12.10.16 (9072–81 fitted with Gurkhas)
Ten, 9041–5/N1260–4, built by Robey & Co., Lincoln, delivered 12.6.16–6.5.17. Further a/c in order fitted with Gurkhas, and last seven, N1265–71, probably fitted with 240 hp Renaults
One, N1240, built by J. White & Co., East Cowes, to improved design, delivered 30.4.17
Short Bomber tractor biplane landplane
One, 3706, built by Short Bros, delivered 3.4.16 (later re-engined with Eagle)
Wight Type 840 tractor biplane–seaplane
Thirty-four, 831–40/1300–19/1351–4, built by J. Samuel White, East Cowes, delivered 2.1.15–1.16
Twenty, 1400–11/9021–8, built by J. Beardmore, Dalmuir, delivered 12.9.15–8.5.16 (twelve more delivered as spares with no engine)
Five, 8281–5, built by Portholme Aerodrome Ltd, Huntingdon (remaining seven on order delivered as spares with no engine)
Sopwith Type 860 tractor biplane–seaplane
Nineteen, 851–60/927–35, built by Sopwith Aircraft, Kingston, delivered 24.3.15–7.15 (three more on order cancelled)
Avro Type 519 two-seat tractor biplane
One, 1614, built by Avro Manchester, delivered 1916
Avro Type 522 (Type 519A) two-seat tractor biplane
One 1615, built by Avro Manchester, delivered 1.11.16
Bréguet de Chasse tractor biplane
Twelve, 1392/1394/3209–13, built by Bréguet, Villacoublay, delivered 1915 – 2.4.16 3883–7
Bréguet de Bombe tractor biplane
One, 3888, built by Bréguet, Villacoublay (second a/c cancelled)
Royal Aircraft Factory RE.7 tractor biplane
One, serial unknown. One Mohawk was tried in an RE.7

Motor-cars

Sunbeam 1913 racing car *Toodles V* (early engine with 80 mm bore)
Harry Hawker's 1919 Sunbeam-Mercedes
Cyril Bone's 1926 Sunbeam-Napier

160 HP ZULU

During 1915 Louis Coatalen developed the V8 Crusader by increasing the bore from 90 mm to 100 mm, while maintaining the 150 mm stroke, thereby increasing the capacity from 7.6 to 9.4 litres. All other aspects of the engine remained the same, except that the reduction gear ratio was changed to 1.86:1, and in this form it gave 160 hp at 2,000 rpm. When the Sunbeam engines were retrospectively named in 1917, instead of calling this engine the Crusader Mk II, as most manufacturers would have done, Sunbeam chose to give it a new name, Zulu.

Throughout its service it was referred to as the 160 hp Sunbeam, and the name Zulu was hardly ever, if at all, used, remaining somewhat obscure to this day. To begin with it was put into small-scale production alongside the 150 hp Crusader, the first four being delivered in February 1916, followed by three, two, six, and eight over the following four months. Then in June production of the 150 hp Crusader ceased altogether and the 160 hp Zulu completely replaced it on the production line, nineteen being produced that month. The Zulu remained in production until November when the last five of a total of seventy-five were delivered, the last five side-valve aero-engines to be delivered by the Sunbeam Motor Car Co.

In service the Zulu was mainly used to replace 150 hp Crusaders fitted to Short Type 827 seaplanes in service, for instance 3111 and 8251. A very small number was fitted to new Short 827 aircraft, for instance 3072, the last of a batch of ten built by the parent company at Rochester and delivered on 30 December 1915, and the first two of a batch of eight Short 827s built by Brush Electric, 8230 and 8231. The 160 hp Zulu was in all likelihood fitted to the others in the batch.

Just one aircraft had the Zulu as its sole powerplant. In 1916 Avro designed a twin-engined bomber powered by two opposite-handed Zulu engines in a pusher arrangement, the Type 523 Pike. The sole prototype, N523, was delivered to Farnborough in January 1917. Although having a good performance on only 320 hp, the Handley Page O/100 was already offering an even better performance and the Type 523 was not proceeded with.

Technical data

Engine Type	water-cooled, eight-cylinder, ninety-degree Vee
Manufacturer	Sunbeam Motor Car Co., Moorfield Works, Wolverhampton
Horse Power	160 hp at 2,000 rpm
Capacity	9.4 litre, 100 mm bore, 150 mm stroke
Valve Type	side-valve, two per cylinder
Weight	similar to Crusader, exact figures unknown
Dimensions	length 49 in., width 33 in., height 29.9 in.
Propeller Nos.	AD566 (Short Type 827), AD581 (Coastal Airship – pusher engine)
Details	As with Crusader, 2 × Bosch high-tension four-cylinder magnetos, 2 × Claudel-Hobson CZ 42 mm carburettors
Nos. Built	75 ordered, 75 delivered

Applications

Avro Type 523 Pike twin-engined pusher biplane bomber
One, N523, built by Avro, Hamble, delivered 29.1.17

Short Type 827 biplane–seaplanes
Fitted in place of 150 hp Crusaders as new and in service, e.g. a/c serials 3072, 3111, 8231, 8232, and 8251; total number unknown

Coastal Class airships
Fitted in place of 150 hp Crusaders; number unknown

The Avro 523 Pike. The first of a series of twin-engined Avro biplanes, it was one of the few aircraft fitted from the outset with the Zulu, opposite-handed in a pusher arrangement.

240 HP GURKHA

At the same time that Coatalen increased the bore of the V8 Crusader to produce the 160 hp Zulu, he increased the bore of the 225 hp Mohawk from 90 mm to 100 mm, raising the capacity from 11.66 litres to 14.14 litres, and the power to 240 hp. As with the V8 engine the reduction gear ratio was reduced from 2:1 to 1.86:1. Thus both the main production lines at Moorfield Works continued to feature engines with identical cylinders. As with the Zulu the new engine was known as the 240 hp Sunbeam in service, but was retrospectively given a new name, Gurkha, rather than being called the Mohawk Mk II which would have been the logical step, as all other aspects of the engines remained the same, only the size of the bore changing.

The first Gurkha was apparently bench-run in October 1914, but did not go into production until early in 1916. Probably the desperate need for engines mitigated against disrupting the production line at an earlier date. Alongside the Zulu the first Gurkha was delivered in February 1916, and production continued in small numbers, never more than three per month, until the Mohawk was phased out in June with the last two being delivered, eighteen Gurkhas being delivered that month. It remained in production for only four more months with the last five delivered in October, a month before Zulu production ceased. A total of eighty-three 240 hp Gurkhas was delivered in all, but unlike the Zulu most of them found their way into new aircraft. It was installed in new Short Type 184 seaplanes being built by Robey & Co. at Lincoln, S.E. Saunders at East Cowes, Frederick Sage at Peterborough, and J. Samuel White at East Cowes, a total of fifty-three new aircraft being fitted with Gurkhas.

In addition Gurkhas were fitted as replacements to 225 hp Mohawks as they were removed from Short 184s. The most famous example of this is 8359, the Short 184 which flew at the Battle of Jutland on 31 May 1916. This aircraft was fitted with a Mohawk at Jutland, but the engine was later replaced by a 240 hp Gurkha, probably at Dundee in March 1917, and that is the engine which is now to be seen in the remains of the aircraft, little more than the front fuselage, on display in an unrestored condition at the Fleet Air Arm Museum at Yeovilton. It is the last surviving Sunbeam side-valve aero-engine.

In February 1917 the Rear-Admiral Commanding the East Coast complained that the 225 hp Mohawk-powered Short seaplanes stationed at Killingholme and South Shields had made repeated attempts to get airborne carrying the standard fourteen-inch torpedo, all of which failed because of the sea states prevailing and the age of the aircraft. He requested their immediate replacement by 240 hp Gurkha-powered seaplanes. He was told the following month that the Gurkha would be supplied when available, but that the units operating over the English Channel had priority. In the event a different solution was found to the problem, and the torpedos were

A close-up of the Gurkha installed in the Short 184, serial 8359, in the Fleet Air Arm Museum at Yeovilton. The aircraft and engine are displayed in completely unrestored form, the last surviving Sunbeam side-valve aero-engine.

(LEFT):
A Short 184, serial 9048, fitted from new with the 240 hp Sunbeam Gurkha. This aircraft was a Type D single-seat bombing version built by Robey & Co. and delivered in August 1916. It took part in a number of bombing attacks on German naval installations in Belgium.

(BELOW):
The second of fifteen Short Bombers built by Sunbeam, serial 9357. It is shown on Dunstall Park racecourse, Wolverhampton, with a full load of bombs. It was delivered to the RNAS by lorry on 20 July 1916. All Sunbeam-built bombers were fitted with the Gurkha.

withdrawn from the North Sea seaplane units.

Another aircraft was also fitted new with the 240 hp Gurkha. The prototype Short Bomber biplane had been fitted with the 225 hp Mohawk, but production examples were ordered from a number of manufacturers with the Rolls-Royce Eagle, the exception being twenty Short Bombers ordered from Sunbeam. The Mohawk had ceased production before the first of the bombers, 9356, was delivered on 27 July 1916, so 240 hp Gurkhas were fitted to all the fifteen Short Bombers built. The last five in the order were cancelled as the RNAS was by then receiving the far more capable Handley-Page O/100 bomber. The Sunbeam-built Short Bombers are often quoted as being powered by the 225 hp Mohawk, but this probably results from confusion arising from the fact that the prototype had been Mohawk-powered.

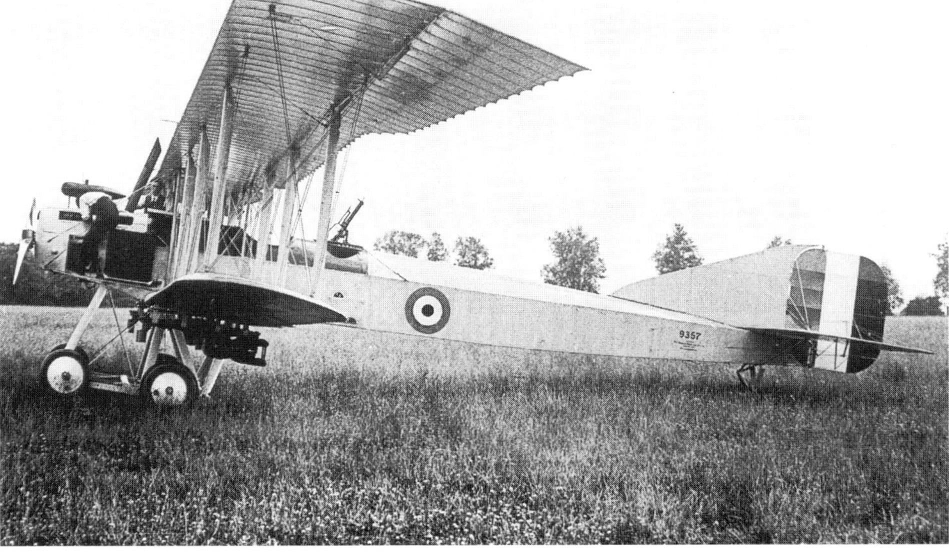

The Gurkha was also installed about June 1917 in the sole Beardmore WB.1 long-range biplane bomber, which had first flown with the 230 hp Beardmore Adriatic engine, driving a 10 ft 6 in. four-blade propeller.

Technical data

Engine Type water-cooled, twelve-cylinder, sixty-degree Vee
Manufacturer Sunbeam Motor Car Co., Moorfield Works, Wolverhampton
Horse Power 240 hp at 2,000 rpm
Capacity 14.14 litres, 100 mm bore, 150 mm stroke
Valve Type two poppet side valves per cylinder
Weight 960 lb
Dimensions as Mohawk: length 74.8 in., width 30.7 in, height 42 in.
Propeller Nos. AD501M (Short Type 184, SD557 (Short Bomber))
Details as Mohawk, with increased bore
Nos. Built 83 ordered, 83 delivered
Applications

Short Admiralty Type 184 tractor biplane seaplanes
- One, 8003, built by S.E. Saunders & Co. at East Cowes, delivered 1.4.16 with Mohawk, later refitted with Gurkha
- One, 8004, built by S.E. Saunders & Co. at East Cowes, delivered 4.16
- Seventeen, 8014–30, built by S.E. Saunders & Co. at East Cowes, delivered 24.6.16–28.2.17
- One, 8048, built by Short Bros at Rochester, delivered 18.1.16 with Mohawk, later refitted with Gurkha, subsequently fitted with a Maori
- One, 8101, built by Short Bros at Rochester, delivered 14.7.16, rest of batch of seventy-five had Mohawks
- Fifteen, 9046–60, built by Robey & Co. at Lincoln, delivered 17.8.16–3.2.17 (first five in order fitted with Mohawks)
- One, N1086, built by Short Bros at Rochester; most of batch of twenty had Renault engines; delivered 5.4.17
- One, N1149, built by Short Bros at Rochester; other nine in a batch of ten had Renault engines; delivered 3.7.17
- Three, N1262–4, built by Robey & Co. at Lincoln, fitted with Mohawks later replaced by Gurkhas
- Nine, 9072–80, built by Frederick Sage & Co. at Peterborough, delivered 29.6.16–6.10.16 (9079 may have been fitted with a 260 hp Maori)
- Nine, N1241–8, built by J. Samuel White & Co. at East Cowes, delivered 3.7.17–16.8.17

Short Bomber tractor bomber
- Fifteen, 9356–70, built by Sunbeam Motor Car Co. at Wolverhampton, delivered 27.7.16–30.1.17 (five more a/c cancelled)

Beardmore WB.1 tractor biplane bomber

310/320 HP COSSACK

At the beginning of the war the Admiralty was demanding engines with more and more power, with two basic ends in mind. Captain Murray Seuter was advocating a very large aircraft capable of bombing the German fleet or strategic targets such as the industrial factories which supplied the German fleet. His technical adviser, Harris Booth, preferred a seaplane as the most suitable for naval operations, and sketched out a huge three-engined biplane which J. Samuel White on the Isle of Wight was asked to build. At the same time Frederick Handley Page called at the Admiralty to ascertain the sort of aircraft they were looking to order. Informed of Commander Samson's famous demand for a 'bloody paralyser' of an aircraft, Handley Page immediately sketched out his Type O, with a 114 ft wing-span and two Sunbeam 150 hp Crusader engines, the most powerful then available.

A side view of the 320 hp twin overhead camshaft Cossack with the propeller boss to the right.

It also became clear that even the best of the three torpedo-carrying seaplanes ordered, the Short Type 184, was underpowered with the Sunbeam 225 hp Mohawk, and could only just lift the standard fourteen-inch torpedo when new, if only the pilot and a minimal fuel supply were carried. An engine of 300 hp was called for, and Rolls-Royce was brought in to aero-engine production with just that in mind.

Louis Coatalen's response was to design a brand-new engine which would be the first of a family of engines. He chose to abandon the side valves of his early aero-engines, and used the overhead camshaft layout of his 1914 racing-car engines. He had already built a 150 hp V8 OHC engine, which would be called the Nubian, but this was experiencing technical troubles. A V12 brother of the Nubian was also developed, the 200 hp Afridi, but his new 300 hp V12 engine was of completely different design. This was later named Cossack.

The twelve cylinders were set in a sixty-degree Vee and had a bore of 110 mm and a stroke of 160 mm, giving a total capacity of 18,246 cc. There were twin overhead camshafts operating four valves per cylinder by rocker arms with exposed valve springs. The connecting rods were articulated which gave a good big end bearing surface area without being too long, though this layout was hard to balance. The engine gave 310 hp at 2,000 rpm in its initial form, and had a running weight of 1,372.5 lb. The propeller was driven through a 2:1 reduction gear. The four Claudel-Hobson C2S 42 carburettors were sited outside the banks and the engine had two BTH twelve-cylinder magnetos. This large engine had a length of 61.8 inches, a width of 37.8 inches, and a height of 38.89 inches. The blocks were cast-iron, in groups of three with integral cylinder heads.

Large orders were placed for the Cossack engine, the first two being delivered in March 1916, and for a while the engines were hand-built and only delivered at roughly one per fortnight; in fact only eleven were delivered during the first six months. With the phasing out of Gurkha production, which ended in October 1916, the production of the Cossack built up rapidly, with twelve delivered in September, sixteen in October, twenty-three in November, and twenty-eight in December. Production continued at this rate until the Cossack was phased out in December 1917 when the last one of a total of 350 was delivered. The final thirty-two ordered were suspended, and then cancelled.

The first urgent application for the Cossack was in the Admiralty Seaplane Type AD.1000, designed by Harris Booth at the Air Department of the Admiralty to operate as a strategic bomber or torpedo carrier. Construction of it was entrusted to J. Samuel White at East Cowes, who received orders for eight in February 1915, originally to be fitted with the 225 hp Mohawk. Availability of the more powerful Cossack switched the order, and the seaplane was powered by no fewer than three, two fitted as tractors in the nose of each of the twin fuselages and one as a pusher, set between the 155-foot-span wings at the rear of the crew cabin.

The first aircraft, serial 1358, was being delivered to Grain on 31 May 1916 when it unfortunately suffered engine failure en route, and force-landed. It was still being repaired in August 1916, and the decision was taken to refit it with the more powerful 475 hp Sunbeam Viking engines. Finally, by 17 March 1917 the first AD.1000 was deleted. The second and last aircraft completed, serial 1000, was delivered to Felixstowe in June 1916, but was not ready for trials until January 1917, and was deleted at the end of the year. The Handley Page O/100 had fulfilled the requirements for a strategic bomber, and the AD.1000 was only notable as the biggest and most powerful British aircraft of its day.

The availability of the Cossack, 50% more powerful than engines hitherto produced, enabled Short Bros to design a larger, more capable torpedo-carrying seaplane than the Type 184, which had only marginal ability to lift the Whitehead torpedo. The largest Short seaplane of the war, the aircraft was most widely known as the Type 310, after the horse power available from its Cossack I engine, but it was also known as the Short 320, reflecting the horse power of the Cossack II. In fact it was produced in two versions not related to the engine used. The Type A, which was the torpedo carrier, was referred to as the Type 310-A, able to carry an eighteen-inch torpedo, and the Type B, referred to as the Type 310-B, was the reconnaissance and anti-Zeppelin patrol aircraft. The main difference was that the Type B had three-bay equal-span wings, whereas the Type A had longer-span upper wings. Two prototypes of each were ordered early in 1916, serialled 8317–8 and 8319–20 respectively.

The first Type A was delivered to the Isle of Grain on 26 July 1916, and the first Type B followed on 26 September. The latter was not ordered into quantity production, the first aircraft, 8319, being used for trials with the 6 lb Davis gun, but the Type A, with small modifications to the float struts, as the Short Type 310-A4, received an order for ten in November, serialled N1150–9.This order was followed by another for twenty, serialled N1300–19, all fitted with the 310 hp Cossack.

Development of the engine by Sunbeam had continued producing the Cossack II, which had four magnetos instead of two for dual ignition, and an air or hand starter. The unreliability of the early British magnetos had created a requirement for dual ignition, especially for seaplanes which undertook long patrols. The ratio of Cossack Is and IIs produced is unknown, but the vast majority were probably Cossack IIs. The Cossack II produced 320 hp, and was fitted to subsequent Type 310s. Short Bros received an order for forty-five more aircraft with the Cossack II, serialled N1390–409 and N1480–504. Sunbeam had received an order for thirty Short Type 310s in December 1915, serialled N1360–89, and these were all fitted with the Cossack II.

The Sunbeam-built aircraft were delivered from September 1917 to January 1918, by which time a second order for twenty aircraft had been received, serialled N1690–709, and the last of these was delivered in June 1918, to give a final total of 119 Cossack-powered Type 310s. After this the Admiralty began to place greater emphasis on the development of carrier-borne torpedo bombers which was to result in the Sopwith Cuckoo. A number of Short Type 310s was sent to Japan, including the five Sunbeam-built examples N1697–701. Others went to the United States Naval Air Service, operating mostly from Killingholme on south Humberside, including the Sunbeam-built examples N1373, N1375, N1696, N1702, and N1704–6.

The Cossack also powered at least twelve of the Handley Page 0/400 bombers, though six of these were really a half-way house between the earlier 0/100 with only some of the fuel system modifications which denoted the later 0/400s. The Handley Page Type O, originally ordered in 1914, had been designed around two 150 hp Sunbeam Crusaders, but the availability of the 250 hp Rolls-Royce Eagle caused a substitution to be made and the aircraft became the Type O/100, a reference to its wing span. One O/100, serial 3117, was fitted with 310 hp Cossack Is for a twenty-hour test flight programme, and then a series of other engines, before fitment with 320 hp Cossack IIs.

The six production O/100s powered by the Cossack came about when Handley Page had a production gap in their works caused by the non-arrival of drawings for twenty-two Felixstowe F.3 flying boats it was to build, twenty with two 320 hp Cossack engines, and two with folding wings. Therefore Handley Page suggested an extra order for six or twelve O/100s powered by any available engine, and the six aircraft ordered were B9446–51. The Cossacks were housed in cylindrical nacelles with frontal radiators. The Felixstowe flying boats were never built, and though the prototype Felixstowe F.3, N64, was fitted with Cossacks, production aircraft were all powered by Rolls-Royce Eagle VIIIs.

Other aircraft for which the Cossack was specified but which were never built were the Norman-Thompson twin-engined cruiser flying boat, two of which were ordered and then cancelled, and the single-engined Handley Page Type

The second Sunbeam-built Short Type 310-A4 seaplane, fitted with the 320 hp Cossack, photographed at Grain on 29 September 1917, twenty-eight days after it had been delivered by road.

(ABOVE):
A Short Type 310-A4, with wings folded, showing the radiator block mounted on the forward fuselage.

(BELOW):
A Cossack complete with nacelle ready for installation in one of the interim batch of six Handley Page O/100 bombers, B9446–51, with some of the fuel modifications of the O/400. It is believed to be shown outside the Moorfield Works.

P/320 raiding triplanes, two of which were also ordered and then cancelled.

The Cossack was one of the few British engines to find its way into a French aircraft during the war. The Etablissement Tellier at Argenteuil built a biplane flying boat late in 1917 and fitted a Cossack beneath the upper wing driving a four-blade pusher propeller. The aircraft was put through severe tests by French Naval Aviation at St Raphael. With a load of 1,050 kg it climbed to 2,000 metres in nineteen minutes and thirty seconds, and with 1,530 kilos it took twenty-eight minutes and twenty-five seconds. The engine consumed 18.4 gallons of petrol and 7.2 gallons of oil per hour.

The aircraft was ordered for anti-submarine patrol work, and was to make many flights from France to Corsica. A total of 150 Cossacks was ordered by France; not all were delivered by the Armistice. Tellier was taken over by Nieuport-Delage after the war and on 22 February 1921 James Todd, the chairman of STD Motors, announced that Monsieur Delage had joined the board of STD Motors in France, and at the same time there had been an important French order for large Sunbeam aero-engines. Whether these were further Cossacks for the Tellier flying boat or the latter part of the order for 150 is not known. It is believed the delivery of the order of 150 was completed but the number of aircraft to which they were fitted is not known.

As early as November 1916 the Sterling Engine Company of Buffalo, New York, announced it was to build the

A Sunbeam Cossack ready for test at the Sterling Engine Co., Buffalo, New York. A manufacturer of marine engines, Sterling also acquired the rights to Sunbeam's side-valve engines, but there are no records of how many Sterling-Sunbeams were built.

Cossack under licence, and that the engines would be known as Sterling-Sunbeams. Sterling was a large manufacturer of petrol engines from 10 hp to 300 hp, mostly for use in boats, the most widely used engine being a V8 200 hp. In November 1916 Sterling had stated that it expected to complete the first prototype Cossack within three months, and a picture exists of one engine being readied for test, but there appears to be no evidence of any more being built or any being delivered to Great Britain. At the same time the company had taken out a licence for the Crusader and the Mohawk, but the Cossack was the first it intended to build, and it is not known whether the others ever were. At the end of the war there was still a contract (No. 34a/1478/C1392) for thirty-two Cossacks outstanding, none having been delivered by 18 November. This contract must have been in suspension because Cossack deliveries had ended the previous year.

Post-war, the Cossack found a new lease of life as an airship engine, being fitted to three new rigid airships, the R.36, R.37, and R.38. As built for airships the engines were known as Cossack IIIs. Sunbeam not only built the engines but also the complete power cars for these airships. One of them, the R.37, never flew, being cancelled and scrapped at Short Bros' Cardington Works when 95% complete. Sunbeam had already delivered the engines which were in four single cars and one double. The R.38, which was also built by Short Bros alongside the R.37, had slightly different power arrangements as the six Cossacks were in three double cars.

The other airship in the class, R.36, was built by Beardmore & Co. Ltd. It was originally intended to have three Cossack engines and two Maoris, but when completed the

(BELOW):
Side view of the Cossack III for airship use showing the flywheel to the left and the engine controls at the rear to the right.

(Below):
A front view of the Cossack III showing the flywheel which served as a clutch so that the engine could be kept running without the propeller turning, for manoeuvring purposes.

(Above):
A rear view of the Cossack III for airships showing the magnetos and the engine controls, which had of course to be available to the mechanic within the airship car.

(Centre Left):
The airship R.36, G-FAAF, one of three similar airships to be powered by the Cossack, this one with three Cossacks and two Maybach engines.

(Above):
The starboard wing car of the R.37, complete with its Cossack engine, outside Moorfield Works. This airship was to be powered by six Cossacks but was scrapped when 95% complete.

(Left):
A complete airship gondola with its Cossack engine, built by Sunbeam, probably for the R.37, and showing the propeller boss well to the rear of the engine.

Maoris had been superseded by two 260 hp Maybach water-cooled six-cylinder engines taken from the Zeppelin L.71. Construction of R.38 began in 1917 but it did not fly until 1921, and had only eighty hours in the air when it suffered a mooring accident at Pulham on 21 June 1921, and was broken up.

The R.38 was at the time of its completion the largest airship then built, being 672 feet long and eighty feet in diameter. She had been built as a high-flying airship, suitable for strategic bombing, and was therefore of the lightest possible construction. Unfortunately she was too light, as subsequent events proved. She was sold to the United States and became the ZR.2. On only her third flight, on 24 August 1921, with a mixed American/British crew on board, she took off on a proving flight from Howden. On her return she was seen to make much too sharp manoeuvres in the dense air low over the Humber and broke up, most of those on board dying in the subsequent crash and fire.

The Cossack was one of the Sunbeam's most successful engines, performing well on long overseas patrols in Short seaplanes and Tellier flying boats, but none has apparently survived.

Technical data

Engine Type	water-cooled, twelve-cylinder, sixty-degree Vee
Manufacturer	Sunbeam Motor Car Co., Moorfield Works, Wolverhampton; Sterling Engine Co., Buffalo, New York
Horse Power	(Cossack I) 310 hp (Cossack II) 320 hp at 2,000 rpm (torque 919 lb/ft)
Capacity	18.246 litres, 110 mm bore, 160 mm stroke
Valve Type	OHC, four valves/cylinder, articulated connecting rods
Weight	1372.5 lb (running)
Dimensions	length 61.8 in., width 37.8 in., height 38.9 in.
Propeller Nos.	AB586 (Felixstowe F.3 prototype), AD569 (Handley Page O/400), AD586 (Curtiss H12), S170 (Short Type 310)
Details	four Claudel-Hobson C2S 42 carburettors, outside banks, 2:1 geared propeller, (Cossack I) two magnetos, air starter, (Cossack II) four magnetos, air and hand starter
Nos. Built	UK 382 ordered, 350 delivered (32 cancelled); France, 150 ordered, 150 delivered; US 1 licence-built (possibly more), (Cossack III) 14

Applications

A.D. Admiralty Type 1000 three-engined biplane–seaplane
  Two, 1000/1358, built by J. Samuel White, East Cowes, delivered 4.6.16 and 13.5.16 (six others cancelled – serials 1355–7 and 1359–61)

Short Type 310-A torpedo carrier, tractor biplane–seaplane
  Two, 8317–8, built by Short Bros, Rochester, first delivered 26.7.16

Short Type 310-A4 tractor biplane–seaplane (310 hp Cossack I)
  Thirty, N1150–9/N1300–19, built by Short Bros. Rochester, delivered 24.3.17–11.12.17

Short Type 310-A4 (sometimes Type 320) tractor biplane–seaplane (320 hp Cossack II)
  Forty-five, N1390–409/N1480–504, built by Short Bros, Rochester, delivered 19.12.17–13–4–18
  Fifty, N1360–89/N1690–709, built by Sunbeam Motor Car Co., delivered 29.9.17–20.6.18

Short Type 310-B reconnaissance and Zeppelin-patrol tractor biplane–seaplane (310 hp Cossack I)
  Two, 8319–20, built by Short Bros, Rochester, delivered 26.9.16–10.17 (8320 converted to Type 310-A4)

Porte Baby FB.2 tractor/pusher biplane flying boat
  Three, 9800–2: 9800 built by May, Hordern & May at Felixstowe, delivered 20.11.15 (3 × 310 hp Cossacks, then pusher engine replaced by RR Eagle, then the 310 hp Cossacks replaced by 320 hp Cossacks); 9801 delivered 23.5.16 (two Cossacks as tractor engines and 260 hp Green, and then RR Eagle as the pusher); 9802 delivered 2.8.16 (two Cossacks as tractor engines, and RR Eagle as pusher)

Felixstowe F.3 twin-engined tractor biplane flying boat
  One, N64, built at Felixstowe as an F.2c. Converted to F.3 prototype late 1917, when Cossacks were fitted

Handley Page Type O/100 twin-engined tractor biplane heavy bomber
  One, 3117, built by Handley Page at Cricklewood fitted with 310 hp Cossack Is, later replaced with 260 hp RAF 3a engines, then four 200 hp Hispano-Suiza engines in tandem, finally with 2 × 320 hp Cossack IIs

Handley Page O/400 twin-engined tractor biplane heavy bomber
  Six, B8803/B8806/B8810–3, built by Royal Aircraft Factory at Farnborough for RNAS (a seventh a/c, B8807, had Rolls-Royce Eagles, and five more in the batch may have had either engine), delivered 8.18–10.18

Handley Page O/400 twin-engined tractor biplane heavy bomber
  Six, B9446–51, built by Handley Page Ltd, at Cricklewood, delivered 7.1.18–23.2.18

Tellier pusher biplane flying boats
  No. unknown, built by Etablissement Tellier, Argenteuil (taken over by Nieuport-Delage)

HM Airship R.36, built by Beardmore at Inchinnan, three Cossack IIIs (plus two Maybach M6 engines)

HM Airship R.37, built by Short Bros at Cardington after frame constructed by Vickers Ltd at Barrow, six Cossack IIIs (airship scrapped when 95% complete)

HM Airship R.38, built by Short Bros at Cardington, six Cossack IIIs in three power cars

155 HP NUBIAN

In March 1916, in response to promptings from the Admiralty, Louis Coatalen began to develop an all-new aero-engine, featuring for the first time the twin overhead camshafts and four valves per cylinder of his 1914 Grand Prix and TT racing cars, the layout which had been copied from the 1913 Peugeot Grand Prix car. The new engine was a V8 with the cylinder banks set at an angle of sixty degrees, and with cylinders of 95 mm bore and 135 mm stroke giving a capacity of 7.685 litres. The engine gave 155 hp with the propeller geared at 0.615:1, and weighed 684 lb. It was 41.4 inches in length and a low 30.1 inches high.

The engine was later to be called the Nubian, and fifty were ordered, with the intention of using them to power the new single-engined AD biplane flying boat, which had been designed by Harris Booth at the Admiralty's Air Department, to be built by Supermarine. Unfortunately the Nubian suffered tremendous teething troubles, and so a 150 hp Hispano-Suiza was used in the AD flying boat instead. The Nubian was completely redesigned to get over the problems, and re-emerged as an engine with a ninety-degree Vee, the configuration of Sunbeam's original V8, the Crusader. In this form it became the Nubian II.

This delay meant the first four Nubians were not delivered until October 1917, by which time it had been rather superseded by Sunbeam's own 200 hp V8 Arab and the Hispano-Suiza 200 hp V8. Production of the fifty ordered continued in a desultory fashion until July 1918, by which time thirty-six had been completed. The remaining fourteen were cancelled. Amazingly one of the thirty-six Nubians built is one of the handful of Sunbeam aero-engines which still survives, on display in the Science Museum in London for some years, and now held in their store at Wroughton, Wiltshire.

(ABOVE):
The Nubian II in the Science Museum at South Kensington. This rare engine is now in the Science Museum's store at Wroughton.

(BELOW):
The Saunders T.1, the only aircraft definitely powered by the Nubian, which was probably installed because the more capable Hispano-Suiza was unavailable.

Over the years, according to many publications, the Sunbeam Nubian is supposed to have powered many different aircraft, but in most cases the engine actually used must have been the Sunbeam Crusader. Both were 150 hp ninety-degree V8 engines, and both were referred to as 150 hp or 155 hp Sunbeams during their service/production life, so the mistakes were easy to make. The confusion may hide the fact that some of these aircraft (and airships) may indeed have been re-engined with Nubians, after the first was delivered in October 1917, or may have had Nubians fitted to late delivered models. Two examples of the twin-engined Blackburn GP biplane–seaplane are usually quoted as being powered by Nubians. As the first, serial 1415, was delivered in July 1916 and the second, 1416, in January

1917, this cannot be so; the engine used must have been the Crusader, until the aircraft was re-engined with Rolls-Royce Falcons.

The only design which can positively be identified as having been powered by the Nubian was the sole Saunders T.1, special serial X14. This aircraft was the first original design produced by S.E. Saunders Ltd (later Saunders-Roe) at East Cowes. The designer was H.H. Thomas, and the T.1 was a single-bay two-seat biplane with unstaggered, unequal-span folding wings. The rear observer had a Scarff ring-mounted Lewis gun and there was a synchronised fixed forward firing gun, but the exact purpose Thomas had in mind for the aircraft is not clear. He hoped to power it with the 200 hp Hispano-Suiza V8, but those were in short supply, and so a Sunbeam Nubian (serial 5530) was fitted driving a four-blade propeller, and the aircraft first flew in late 1917. No orders were forthcoming for the aircraft, and the Nubian was removed in 1918.

There are indications that a number of Nubians was supplied to Russia, possibly as replacements for the Crusaders in the Il'ya Mouromets heavy bombers, but as such deliveries are bound to have coincided with the Russian revolution, they were probably few in number and may explain the cancellation of the last fourteen engines in the order for fifty.

Clearly Coatalen's first OHC aero-engine was not a success, but its V12 cousin was to become his most successful aero-engine.

Technical data

Engine Type water-cooled, eight-cylinder, sixty-degree Vee (Nubian I), ninety-degree Vee (Nubian II)
Manufacturer Sunbeam Motor Car Co., Moorfield Works, Wolverhampton
Horse Power 155 hp
Capacity 7.658 litres, 95 mm bore, 135 mm stroke
Valve Type twin overhead camshafts, four poppet valves per cylinder
Nos. Built 50 ordered, 36 built (14 cancelled)
Applications
Saunders T.1 two-seat tractor biplane
One, X14, built by S.E. Saunders at East Cowes, 1917

200 HP AFRIDI

The Afridi was the second V12 of the two families of overhead camshaft engines Coatalen designed during 1915/1916, the other being the Cossack. The Afridi and Cossack had nothing in common, other than the V12 layout, the Afridi being much smaller with a length of 55.9 in., width of 33.5 in., and a height of 33.9 in. The Afridi had a bore of 92 mm and a stroke of 135 mm, which gave it a capacity of 11.476 litres, the two banks of cylinders being set at sixty degrees. It had twin overhead camshafts per block, driven by a train of gears and four valves per cylinder, giving 200 hp at 2,000 rpm. It had two Claudel-Hobson carburettors on the outside of the blocks, four magnetos, inside exhaust valves, and drove a geared propeller. The Afridi was probably the V12 counterpart of the V8 Nubian, though the latter had a bore of 95 mm and a stroke of 135 mm.

The Afridi was conceived and built to replace the side-valve Crusader/Zulu on the production lines, while the Cossack replaced the larger Mohawk, though production of the Afridi overlapped that of the side-valve Zulu by a period of five months. The first two Afridis were delivered in July 1916 and production built up slowly to twenty-six delivered in December, by which time all side-valve production had stopped. Production of the Afridi then exceeded the total side-valve production achieved in any month when fifty-one were delivered in January 1917 and fifty-five the following month. Production continued to June by which time it was supplanted on the Sunbeam production lines by its larger capacity, dual-ignition successor, the Maori. The Afridi was just coming into production as the Air Board decreed that all new engines should have dual ignition, hence probably the limited applications found for it.

No known photograph of an Afridi exists but this picture of the Maori II shows the general configuration of its predecessor, with twin overhead camshafts and inside exhaust valves. One hundred Afridis were converted to Maori Is by increasing the bore and fitting dual ignition, becoming practically identical to the Maori II.

Short seaplane Scout Type S.313 No. 1, powered initially by the 200 hp Afridi, but later modified and re-engined with a Maori.

Short seaplane Type S.364 Scout No. 3, also initially with the Afridi but found to be underpowered and refitted with the Maori.

The Afridi supplanted some Sunbeam side-valve engines in both the Sopwith Type 860 and Wight Type 840 seaplanes, as well as some of the landplane versions. It also found its way into a number of one-off designs, replacing a Crusader in the second Avro 519 bomber, the change being undertaken by Sunbeam itself. It also powered the solitary Short N.2A seaplane scout in January 1917, though it was later itself replaced by a Maori, because the aircraft was seriously tail-heavy and underpowered.

The main application found for the Afridi seems to have been eighty-five Curtiss R-2 biplanes supplied from America with 160 hp Curtiss XV engines. These were replaced by the Afridi in the first thirty aircraft, the next fifty-five being delivered to store without engines, though a number are known to have subsequently flown with the Sunbeam fitted. Many of the early Curtiss R.2s went to 3 Wing at Luxeil as bombers, though one, serial 3464, went as far as Mudros in the Aegean. Most of the later ones served as gunnery trainers at Eastchurch and Cranwell.

As with the side-valve engines Coatalen increased the power of the Afridi by increasing the bore, from 92 to 100 mm, though this was probably not unrelated to the need to convert it to dual ignition, and in this form the engine developed 250–260 hp, and in the Sunbeam fashion was then given a new name, the Maori. One hundred of the 299 Afridis built were then converted to Maoris before delivery, becoming Maori Mk Is. The last one of the order of 300 was cancelled and production ceased in June 1917, totally supplanted by the Maori.

Technical data

Engine Type water-cooled, twelve-cylinder, sixty-degree Vee
Manufacturer Sunbeam Motor Car Co., Moorfield Works, Wolverhampton
Horse Power 200 hp at 2,000 rpm
Capacity 11.4 litres, 92 mm bore, 135 mm stroke
Valve Type two overhead camshafts per block, four poppet valves per cylinder
Weight 745 lb
Dimensions length 55.9 in., width 33.5 in., height 33.9 in.
Propeller No. AD598 (Curtiss R.2)
Details four Claudel-Hobson carburettors, four magnetos, inside exhaust valves, geared propeller
Nos. Built 300 ordered, 299 delivered (100 converted to Maoris)

Applications

Curtiss R.2 tractor biplanes
Eighty-five, 3445–529, supplied by Curtiss with Curtiss 160 hp XV engines which were replaced with '200 hp Sunbeams', probably Afridis. Most if not all of first thirty delivered with Sunbeams, next fifty-five just delivered to store, possibly with no engines; some flew including No. 3510 with 200 hp Sunbeam. Last fifteen of order not delivered

Avro 519 tractor biplane
One, 8441, built by Avro Manchester, delivered with a Sunbeam Crusader. Refitted with an Afridi by Sunbeam after 18.7.16

Short Improved Navyplane patrol pusher biplane–seaplanes
Two, N20, N21, ordered from Short Bros, 2.17, with Afridi engines, then cancelled

Short S.364, N.2A biplane tractor seaplane scout No.1/2
One, N36, built by Short Bros, Rochester, delivered 2.1.17, later fitted with Maori

Short N.2A biplane tractor seaplane scout No.3
One, built by Short Bros, Eastchurch

Short Day Bomber tractor biplanes
N507, N508 ordered from Short Bros 9.16 and cancelled 12.16

Armstrong-Whitworth fighter/reconnaissance tractor biplane
N515, built by Armstrong-Whitworth at Gosforth, delivered 8.3.17, but not accepted

160 HP AMAZON

The second engine in the Cossack family of engines was the straight six, 160 hp Amazon. It was basically half a Cossack, with the same cast-iron cylinders in two groups of three with a bore of 110 mm and a stroke of 160 mm giving a total volume of 9.2 litres, retaining the twin overhead camshaft design with four poppet valves per cylinder. It was fitted with two 42 mm Claudel-Hobson BZS carburettors. Two magnetos were fitted to the Amazon I, and it was fitted with a compressed air starter. It gave 160 hp at 2,000 rpm through a geared propeller, which was the same power output as the Beardmore straight six, a development of the well-established 120 hp Beardmore, and a copy of the pre-war Austro-Daimler engine. The Beardmore had been ordered in large numbers, most notably to power the FE.2b, but the Amazon offered the same power for a smaller size, being only 9.2 litres against the Beardmore's 16.6 litres.

A side view of the 160 hp Sunbeam Amazon with the propeller boss to the left. No aircraft applications for this engine have ever been found.

A second version of the Amazon was also developed, the Amazon II for non-aviation use, with a hand or air starter and a single magneto. The mark numbers for the single- and dual-ignition Amazons were the opposite of those for the Cossack, which suggests that the Amazon was first developed after the dual-ignition Cossack II, and then the single-ignition Amazon II was offered as an afterthought. The numbers of each mark of Amazon built are not known. The Amazon was 55.29 in. long, 19.09 in. wide and 38.58 in. high, which was shorter, slightly narrower, but taller than the Beardmore. Its running weight was 747 lb, and empty weight 530 lb.

Though developed initially in 1916 it had a lower priority than the Cossack, and when an order for 100 Amazons was placed, the first six were not delivered until July 1917. Production continued at a slow rate, never more than thirteen per month until April 1918, when the last nine of a total of seventy-seven had been delivered, the remainder being suspended. A Ministry of Munitions survey at the end of the war indicated, however, that of 100 Amazons ordered under Contract CP138965, eighty had been delivered, and the rest suspended and finally cancelled. By contrst 2,556 of the 160 hp Beardmores were delivered by the time production ceased at the end of the war. It may well be the Sunbeam Amazon was one 160 hp straight six engine too many.

No applications for the Amazon have yet been discovered, but there are indications that a number of Amazons were delivered to the Russian Air Service, which might explain the lack of use of the engine in this country and the suspension of the contract after the revolution.

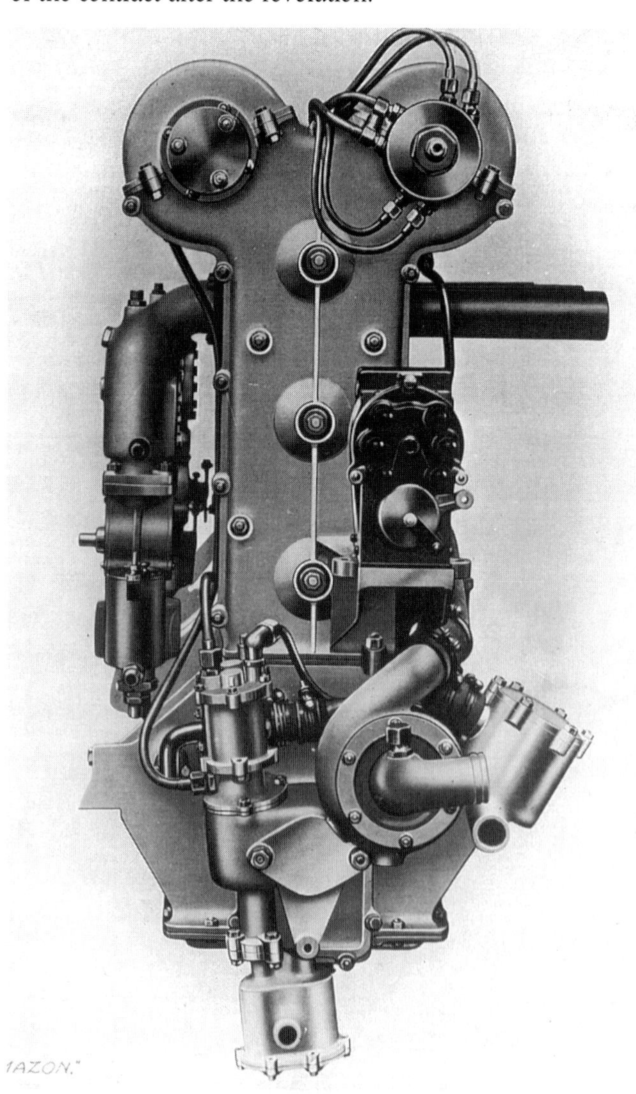

A rear view of the Amazon II showing the single magneto. Most of the production engines were probably dual-ignition Amazon Is.

A front view of the Amazon showing the twin overhead camshafts and the slim lines of the engine.

Technical data

Engine Type water-cooled, inline straight, six-cylinder
Manufacturer Sunbeam Motor Car Co., Moorfield Works, Wolverhampton
Horse Power 160 hp at 2,000 rpm
Capacity 9.2 litres, 110 mm bore, 160 mm stroke
Valve Type twin OHC, four valves per cylinder
Weight 530 lb empty, 747 lb running
Dimensions length 56.3 in., width 19.1 in., height 38.6 in.
Details 2 × Claudel-Hobson 42 mm BZS carburettors, (Amazon I) geared propeller, air starter, two magnetos, (Amazon II) geared propeller, hand starter, one magneto
Nos. Built (Contract CP138965) 100 ordered, 77 delivered, 23 cancelled
Applications Unknown; possibly Coastal airship C-14

450 HP VIKING

The third engine in the Cossack family, the eighteen-cylinder Viking, was basically three Cossack blocks in a 'W' or broad-arrow layout, the first such engine to run. It had 110 mm × 160 mm cast-iron cylinders, cast in blocks of three with twin overhead camshafts and four poppet valves per cylinder. The outside banks were at an angle of sixty degrees, the same as the Cossack, with the third bank squeezed between them. The centre bank had the master connecting rod, with two articulated connecting rods attached from the side banks, enabling three pistons and connecting rods to operate on a single crank throw. The engine operated a left-hand drive in tractor form, with the propeller geared to 900 rpm. Its capacity was a massive 33.6 litres and it had no fewer than six magnetos and an air and a hand starter.

It was a massive engine weighing 1,430 lb and giving 450 hp at 1,800 rpm, the most powerful British engine of its day. It was 63 in. long, 46.5 in. wide, and 44.5 in. high, and its sheer size and weight seem to have limited it to use in boats, with the single exception of an aircraft of equally massive proportions, the AD.1000. A total of seven of these strategic bombing seaplanes was ordered from J. Samuel White, serialled 1355–61, but only one, 1358, was completed. Originally fitted with three 225 hp Mohawks, it failed to fly, and was then fitted with three 320 hp Cossacks, but suffered damage after a crash. When the aircraft was rebuilt it was fitted with three 475 hp Vikings, and apparently flew well early in 1917, but by then its capabilities had been exceeded by the Handley Page O/100 landplane and the Felixstowe F.2B flying boat, and the aircraft was deleted later in the year.

A total of fifty Vikings was ordered and the first delivered in February 1917 for the AD.1000. Production then continued at the desultory rate of about one per month until the last three were delivered in August, making a total of nine, the final forty-one being suspended. However, at the end of the war the Ministry of Munitions noted that up to 18 November

(LEFT):
The aviation version of the 475 hp Sunbeam Viking with the propeller boss to the right.

(BELOW):
The motor-boat version of the Viking with direct drive, which was fitted to a number of Thorneycroft Coastal motor-boats and 'explosion rammers'.

A rear view of the motor-boat version of the engine showing six six-cylinder magnetos. The naval version of the engine also had dual ignition.

1918, thirteen Vikings had been delivered against an order of twenty-five (Contract No. CP116175), the remainder being suspended. It is also probable that five Vikings were sold to the French, but whether this was a different contract or not is not clear.

Some of the British engines were fitted to two classes of naval motor-boat. The 60 mph Coastal motor-boats made by John I. Thorneycroft & Co., as inshore submarine chasers, were fitted with the Viking, as were radio-controlled 'explosion rammers'. It is not known what the French did with their engines.

In a lecture to the Royal Aeronautical Society in 1917, Louis Coatalen showed a picture of a Viking which had six six-cylinder magnetos, and so it is possible that at least one of the Vikings was fitted with dual ignition, and in the same way that the Cossack I became the Cossack II with dual ignition, this engine would have been the Viking II.

The Viking layout showed the way for the Napier Lion which came two years later. However the Lion, a broad-arrow engine designed from a blank sheet of paper, as opposed to the Viking which was adapted from a V12 engine, gave the same horse power for only 960 lb, as against the Viking's 1,430 lb.

Technical data

Engine Type water-cooled, eighteen-cylinder, 'W' layout, outside banks at sixty degrees
Manufacturer Sunbeam Motor Car Co., Moorfield Works, Wolverhampton
Capacity 33.6 litres, 110 mm bore, 160 mm stroke
Valve Type twin overhead camshafts, four poppet valves per cylinder
Weight 1,430 lb (running)
Dimensions length 63 in., width 46.5 in., height 44.5 in.
Details six magnetos, air and hand starter, propeller geared to 900 rpm
Nos. Built 50 ordered, 9 delivered (possibly 13; 5 to France). Remainder cancelled

Applications

Admiralty AD.1000 seaplane
1358, built by J. Samuel White at East Cowes, delivered 13.5.16 with Mohawk then Cossack engines, refitted with three Vikings from February 1917

MOTOR-BOATS

J.I. Thorneycroft Coastal motor-boats
Experimental 'explosion rammers'

A front view of the motor-boat version of the Viking with the substantial exhaust manifold partially hiding the broad-arrow arrangement of the three-cylinder banks, with their twin overhead camshafts.

250/275 HP MAORI

As with his side-valve engines, Coatalen increased the power of his V12 Afridi engine by enlarging the bore in this case by 8 mm to 100 mm, retaining the same stroke of 135 mm. The new engine was given the name Maori, and it was Sunbeam's most successful engine. The prime movement in its development had been the Admiralty's insistence on a switch to dual ignition. Before the war all magnetos had come from Germany, and after the outbreak of war both France and Britain had not only to start to make their own, but first to learn how to. Not surprisingly, early examples were unreliable, and the solution was dual ignition with two sparking plugs per cylinder.

(ABOVE):
Side view of the Maori II, basically the Afridi with increased bore and dual ignition. The Maori was to become Sunbeam's most successful engine.

(LEFT):
Rear view of the Maori II showing the four six-cylinder magnetos, fitted when the Admiralty insisted on dual ignition for its aero-engines.

Apart from the adoption of dual ignition the capacity went up to 12.27 litres and the power had been increased to 250 hp at 2,000 rpm, driving a geared propeller, but most of the technical aspects of the engine were the same as those of the Afridi. It featured the same twin overhead camshafts, driven by a train of gears from the crankshaft, and operating four valves per cylinder, with the exhaust valves on the inside and the four Claudel-Hobson BZS.38 carburettors on the outside of the cylinder banks. There were four magnetos with covers, and the engine weighed 1,065 lb in running condition.

The Maori began to supplant the Afridi on the production lines in April 1917, when the first thirteen were delivered, though the last 100 Afridis were retrospectively converted to Maoris, redesignated Maori Mk 1s. The last Afridi was delivered in June, by which time Maori deliveries had reached fifty-five per month, with a high of seventy-two in August. The new-build Maoris were designated the Mk II.

Through the last half of 1917 the Maori was the major production engine at the Moorfield Works, and most of them went into the seaplanes formerly powered by Sunbeam's side-valve engines, especially the Short Type 184. At least 537 Type 184s have been identified as being powered by the Maori, together with twenty-seven of the rival Wight 'converted' seaplanes, and from April 1918 a total of 130 of the new family of Fairey seaplanes: the Campania, the IIIA, and the IIIB.

These Fairey seaplanes began with the Campania, a seaplane especially designed to operate from the decks of HMS *Campania* and other such ships. Most Campanias had Rolls-Royce Eagle engines, but twenty-six had the Maori, though these were operated normally from shore stations. They were followed by two experimental seaplanes with folding wings, usually referred to by their serials N9 and N10. The former started its life with a Rolls-Royce Falcon, but was later fitted

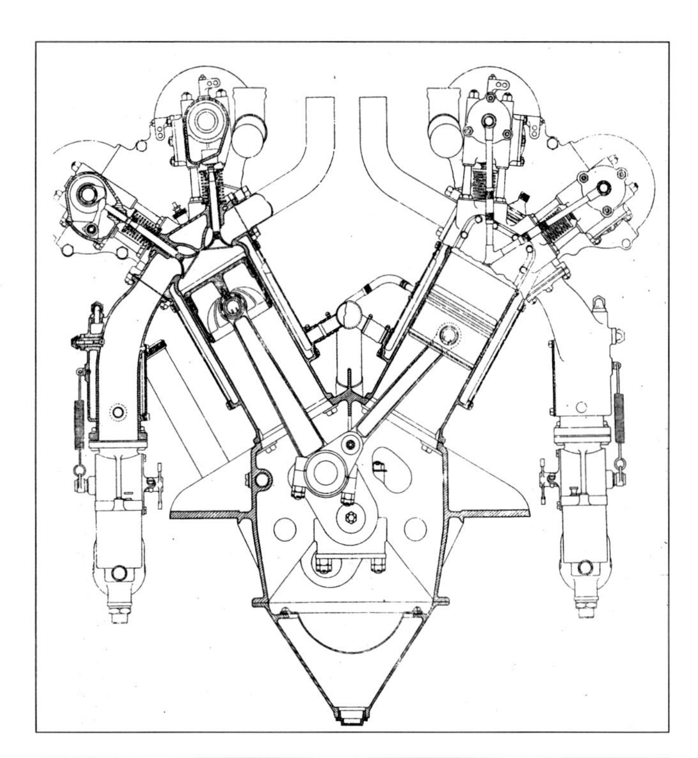

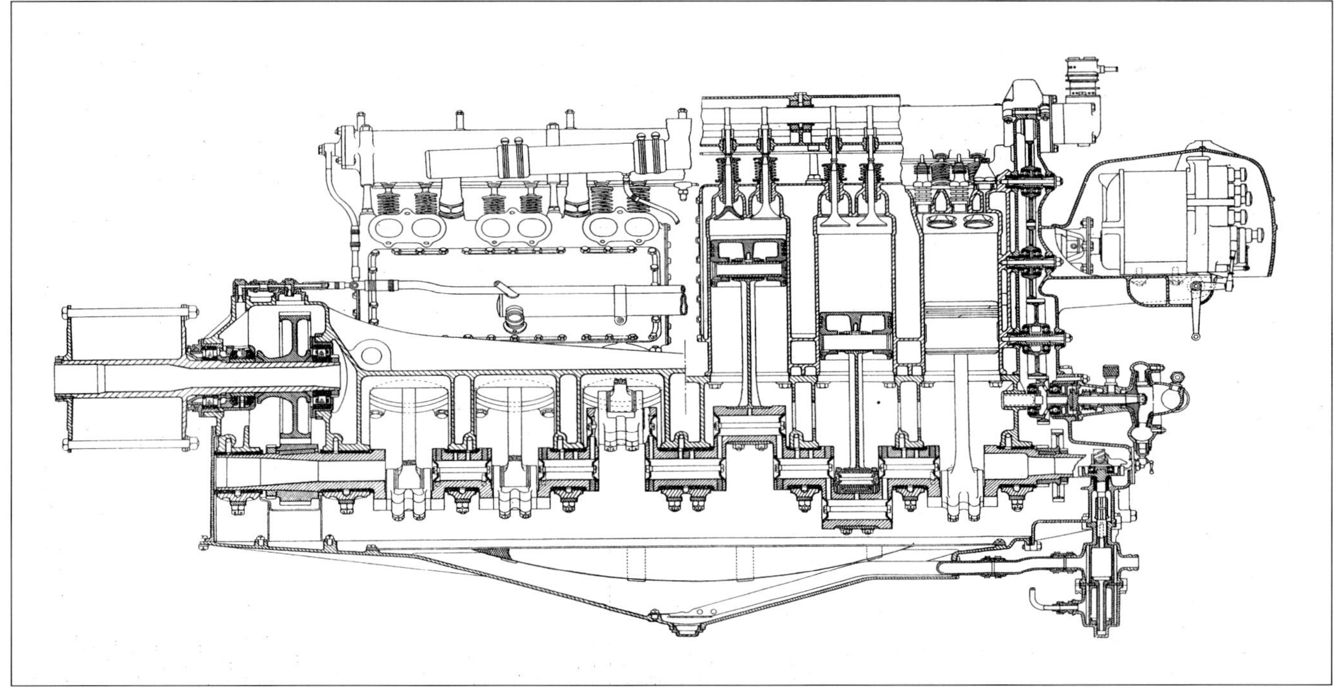

(ABOVE): *Longitudinal and transverse sections of the Sunbeam Maori I/II engine.*

(LEFT): *Short Type 184, serial 8076, fitted with a Maori I or II as shown by the central exhaust stack. This aircraft served with the experimental flight at Grain.*

(LEFT): *A close-up of the engine installation on Short Type 184, 8076, taken on 20 November 1917, when it had broken engine bearers. After repair it was fitted with a Maori II.*

(BELOW): *Maori-powered Short Type 184, N9089, on the 'tram-traverser' at the Brush Electric Works, Loughborough, in October 1918.*

(BELOW LEFT): *A close-up of the Sunbeam Maori I/II installation in a Fairey F.22 Campania seaplane.*

(BELOW RIGHT): *The Fairey F.22 Campania with the engine cowlings fitted.*

(BELOW):
The Fairey III, N10, as first completed with side radiators for the Maori II engine

(RIGHT):
A close-up of a subsequent version of the Fairey III, N10, with a frontal radiator, fitted with experimental blinds, shown closed. The aircraft has also now been fitted with a wheeled undercarriage.

(BELOW):
A close-up of a Maori I/II installed in a Handley Page O/400 bomber, with the cowlings removed.

with a Maori, and a Maori engine was fitted to N10 from the outset. Initially N10 had side radiators, but was later fitted with a frontal radiator which had experimental radiator blinds. At the same time N10 was fitted with a wheeled undercarriage. The two aircraft, N9 and N10, differed fundamentally, but led to the ubiquitous Fairey Type III, over 100 of which were powered by Maoris.

One rather obscure aircraft which was fitted with the 250 hp Maori I was the Avro Type 528 Silver King, a single-engined 'bomb-dropping' biplane for the Admiralty. The sole prototype suffered persistent engine trouble and was not accepted by the RNAS.

Development of the Maori continued, and though the Mark II version of the engine, basically the new-build Maori, was usually quoted as giving 260 hp, and the converted Afridis, the Maori Mk Is, quoted at 250 hp, the two versions were not markedly different. A much more radical change came with the Mark III, which had the exhaust valves on the outside of the cylinder banks, instead of the inside, and the carburettors inside the Vee. This version gave 275 hp, and though records of the different marks delivered have not survived, it was probably the one most widely produced.

The Maori was fitted experimentally to a number of aircraft, including four RE.8s, which thereby became RE.9s, and the single Parnall Zeppelin Strafer, which was destined never to fly, condemned as unsafe, overweight, and dangerous. Two Curtiss H-12 'Large America' flying boats built in Canada were fitted with a pair of Maoris but not delivered to Great Britain, and the Short Type N.2B seaplane scout also had a Maori. The sole flying boat design produced by the Royal Aircraft Factory, the CE.1 (Coastal Experimental 1) was built with two different engines, serial N97, had a 200 hp RAF.3a, and N98 a 260 hp Maori. With the Felixstowe F.2 becoming available, the CE.1 was not needed, but the two prototypes were extensively used in collecting data for hull design.

The other major application of the Maori was to be the Handley Page O/400 heavy bomber. A single O/100, serial 3142, was fitted with Maoris in January 1918. It had been built originally for the Russian government and fitted with Fiat engines, but events over there led to the order being cancelled and it was assigned to the Testing Squadron at Martlesham Heath, where it suffered a crash. The rebuild was fitted with Maori engines by Handley Page personnel. O/400s were ordered from both Handley Page at Cricklewood and the Birmingham Carriage Co. in Smethwick to be fitted with the Rolls-Royce Eagle, the Liberty, or the Maori, as available. The Maori was apparently only fitted when the other engines were not available, and there is no record of how many of the 150 aircraft ordered were Sunbeam-powered.

The Handley Page O/400, 3142, was tested at Martlesham Heath fitted with the two Maoris (Nos. 19325 and 19320) and was then fitted with Fiat engines again for comparison. Despite having a higher loaded weight of 10,170 lb against 9,961 lb, when Maori-engined the aircraft had a better climb rate, taking 4.8 minutes to 2,000 feet against 6.2 minutes, 13.8 minutes to 5,000 feet against 17.2 minutes, and 40 minutes to 10,000 feet against 53.5 minutes. The Maori was also fitted to the second Vickers Vimy prototype, B9953, together with Vickers N98/97 four-blade propellers. In comparison with the Eagle-engined aircraft it was found that B9953 could not maintain altitude on one engine, and was in fact written off during flight tests after engine failure.

Throughout 1918 the Maori remained in large-scale production, alongside the troubled Arab. The only other engines in production were a few Nubians and Amazons early in the year. Delivery requirements for the Maori had been set at ninety per month late in 1917, but production was deliberately cut back to try to help the build-up of Arab production which remained seriously behind schedule. Only 152 Maoris were delivered in the five months from February to June 1918, and then production was built up again, with sixty-six in each of the following two months.

A Handley Page O/400 fitted with Maori I/II engines at Tern Hill. The straight-through exhaust above the engine nacelle can be seen.

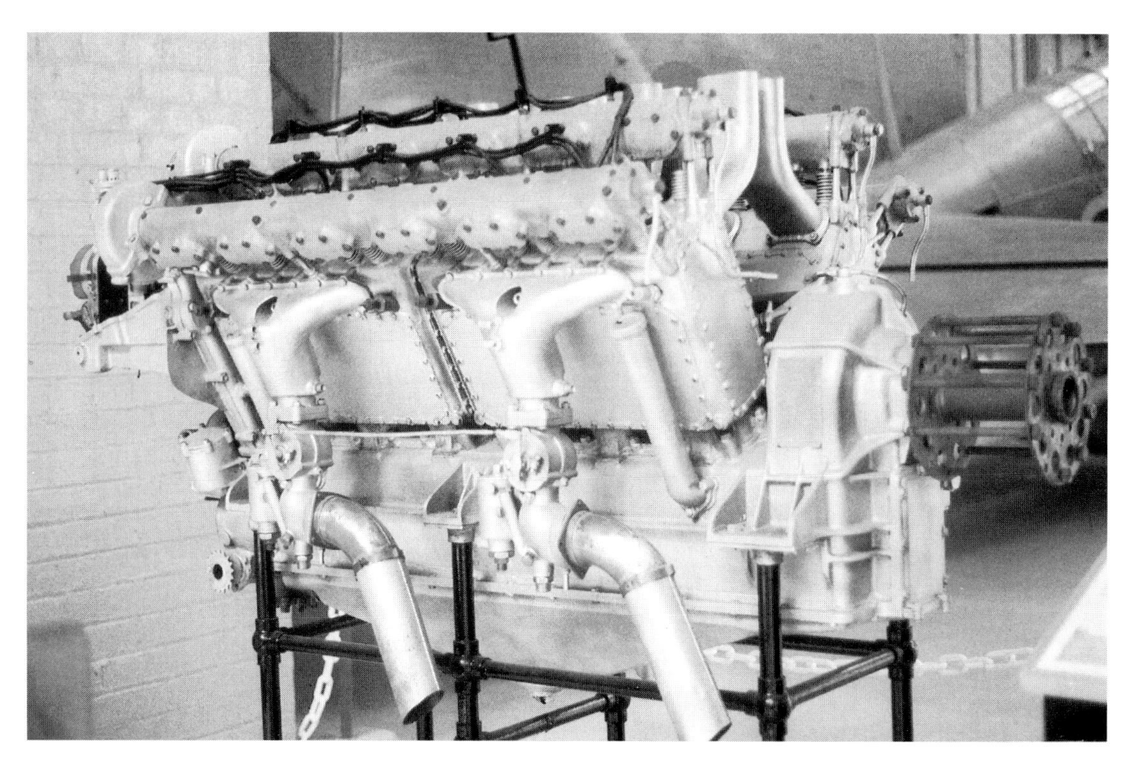

(LEFT): *The Maori II engine in the Imperial War Museum at Duxford, before restoration paid for by IMI Marston of Wolverhampton.*

(BELOW): *Installation drawing for the Maori I/II engine.*

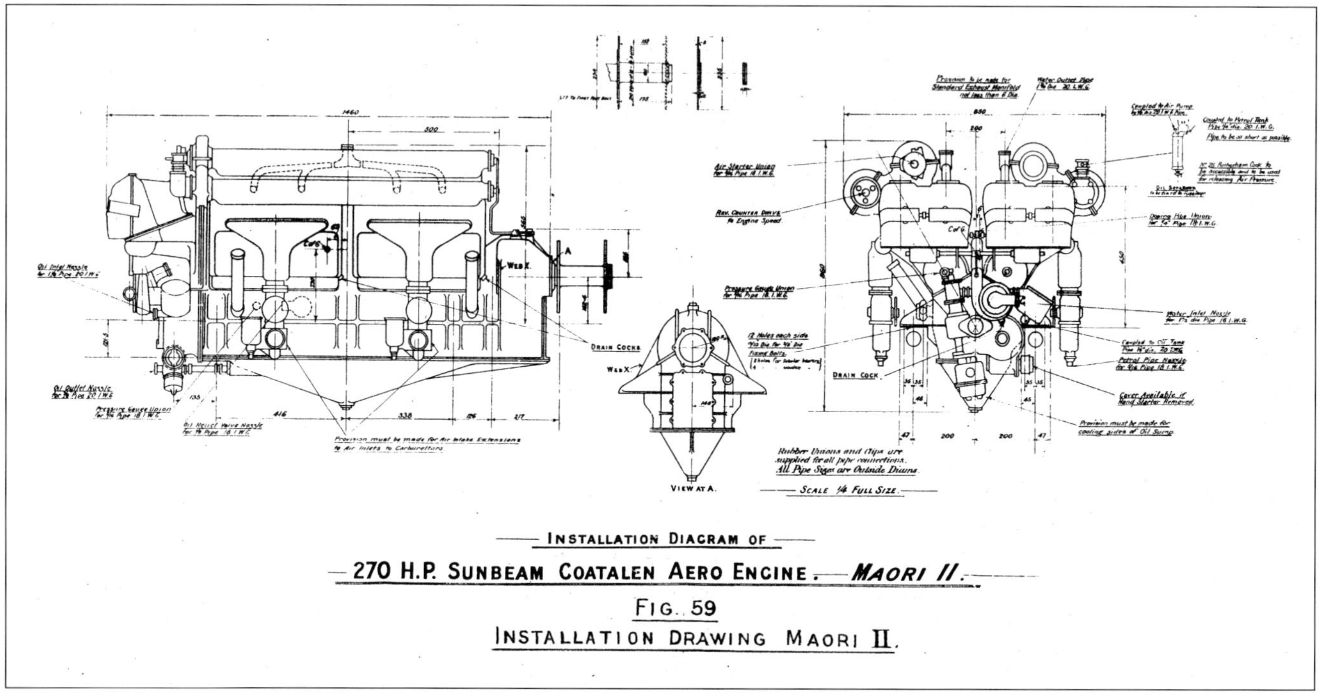

On 28 October 1918 it was reported that Maori production was being held up because of a shortage of carburettors. The Claudel-Hobson carburettors were also being built in Wolverhampton by H.M. Hobson Ltd, at the Accuracy Works only a couple of hundred yards from The Sunbeam, so liaison between the two companies must have been easy. At the time the cost of a Maori engine FOR from Wolverhampton was £1,215. By then Maori requirements were anticipated to be fifty-one per month in December. By the end of the year a total of 974 Maori engines had been delivered from total orders of 1,063. Of a total of 360 ordered under Contract No. AS29772, forty were to be delivered as Manitous, an improved version of the Maori with bore increased yet again to 110 mm. There remained a balance of forty-nine engines to be delivered, but these were placed on four months' notice of cancellation.

An unusual application for the Maori came just before the end of the war in the three-engined Grahame-White E.IV Ganymede heavy bomber. This was a twin-fuselage design with a tractor Maori III at the forward end of each fuselage, with an additional central nacelle housing the pilot and a pusher Maori III. This was a large aircraft with an 89 ft 3 in. span and a length of 49 ft 9 in., and the 275 hp Maoris gave it a top speed of 105 mph at low altitude. It had been designed with the 400 hp Liberty engine in mind, with which a top speed of 120 mph was hoped for, but these were not available. Three prototypes were ordered, C3481–3, but only the first was finished.

Short Type 184s powered by the Maori continued to be built well into 1919 by several contractors, and many of these

Head-on view of the Maori III, showing the twin overhead camshafts and the carburettors moved to the centre of the sixty-degree Vee.

Rear view of the Maori III showing the covers over the magnetos.

were sent on the ill-fated military expeditions against the Bolsheviks in Russia. Among the Maori-powered Type 184s used by Siren Force in the very north of Russia were N9024, N9029, N9034, and N9045 built by Robey & Co., N9119 built by J. Samuel White, and N9190–2 built by Supermarine. Operating in the Baltic were N9046, N9055, N9057, and N9303 built by Robey & Co., N9065, N9070, N9079–80, and N9269 built by Brush Electric, and in southern Russia on the Black Sea were N9125 and N9131 built by J. Samuel White, N2835, N9012, N9164, and N9296 built by Robey & Co., and N9260, N9276–7, and N9076–7 built by Brush Electric. Many of these aircraft were lost and some were handed over to the White Russian forces. A substantial number of Maori-powered Fairey IIIBs were also used in Russia, N2233 going to north Russia and N2231–2, N2236, N2241, N2243, N2249–50, and N2253 going to south Russia.

Other Maori-powered Type 184s were exported after the war, including N9128, N9265–6, and N9268 to Chile, a number to Japan and Greece, and nine to Estonia, including N9127, N9129–30, N9132, and N9134. Two of these – N9132, coded '40', and N9134, coded '41' – were still being operated by the Estonian Air Force in November 1933, when '40' crashed in the Gulf of Finland, and the other was retired.

Five Maori-powered Type 184s came onto the civil register, operating joy flights in the main. They were the J. Samuel White-built N9118 (G-EBBN), N9286 (G-EAJT), N2996 (G-EBFG), N2998 (G-EALC), and the Brush-built N9096 (G-EBBM). One Maori-powered Fairey IIIA also went onto the civil register when N2876 became G-EADZ registered to the Navarro Aviation Co., but it was subsequently sold and re-engined with a Rolls-Royce Eagle.

The most famous application of the Sunbeam Maori came after the war, and it was for a new version, the Mark IV, designed specifically for the R.33 and R.34 airships. This version ran at 2,100 rpm and gave 275 hp, driving the propeller directly, with a flywheel fitted. It also had an enlarged water-cooling system, which also cooled the exhaust pipes. A governor, which came into operation at 2,500 rpm or when the oil pressure fell below 20 lb/sq. in., was also fitted. It had a dry weight of 920 lb.

The Maori IV was fitted to the two most successful British airships of all time, the R.33 and the R.34. These two ships were based on the German Zeppelin L.33 which had come down in this country in September 1916 and had not been destroyed by fire. Air Ministry experts spent months examining the surviving structure, and the result was the design of a new class of British airship, each to be powered by five Maori IVs.

R.33 was built by Armstrong-Whitworth at Selby in Yorkshire, and R.34 by Beardmore Ltd at the Inchinnan Works on the Clyde. Both were 645 ft long and 78 ft 9 in. wide with a volume of 1,950,000 cu.ft. The engines were disposed in four cars, the forward one being at the rear of the control car driving a 17 ft diameter propeller. Two coupled together in the rear car drove a single 19 ft 6 in. propeller. The other engines were in midships gondolas driving 16 ft diameter propellers, and were equipped to operate in reverse for manoeuvring purposes. The starboard engine had a plate welded to the exhaust pipe for heating kettles and saucepans.

R.33 made its first flight on 27 May 1919 with a seven-hour trip over the North Sea, with the R.34 following shortly afterwards. German plans to make a transatlantic flight in a Zeppelin prompted the Air Ministry to plan a similar flight,

(ABOVE):
Side view of the Maori IV designed especially for airships, and used in the R.33 and the R.34.

(BELOW):
Rear view of the Maori IV, showing engine controls fitted for operation in the power cars.

(BELOW):
Front view of the Maori IV showing the flywheel, which operated the propeller by direct drive, and was also fitted with a governor.

A Maori IV installed in one of the power cars of either the R.33 or the R.34, which were the most successful of all British airships.

and R.34 was the chosen airship. Just two weeks after Jack Alcock made the first non-stop Atlantic flight with his navigator Arthur Whitten Brown, engines made by his former employer powered the first non-stop east–west crossing, and then the first double crossing.

R.34 took off from East Fortune on Wednesday, 2 July 1919 at 02.48 hrs carrying 4,900 gallons of petrol for its five Maoris. By six a.m. R.34 was cruising at 1,500 ft at thirty-eight knots on four engines at 1,600 rpm, the forward engine being rested. By eleven a.m., the rear two engines had also been stopped, reducing speed to thirty knots in dense fog. This was the airship's most efficient speed as the two engines consumed only twenty-five gallons an hour at 1,600 rpm. By 3.15 p.m. the three centre-line Maoris were being used, resting the two wing engines, and 49 mph was being achieved. Adverse weather caused all five Maoris to be run by seven p.m., and by 8.30 p.m. their rpm had been increased to 1,800. The first engine trouble did not take place until around two p.m. the following day.

The starboard Maori developed a tiny water leak. One of the small set screws which held the flat aluminium plate water jacket in place, and also held a clip supporting a copper pipe, worked loose. The mechanic tightened it up, but in doing so broke off the head of the screw, causing a leak of the order of one drop a minute. He repaired it by placing a small plate over the hole, held down by the adjacent screws, and in a small piece of inspiration took the chewing gum from his mouth and placed it beneath the plate as an extra sealant. This was incorrectly reported in the airship's log as having been a cracked water jacket repaired using copper sheet and the entire ship's supply of chewing gum!

The flight continued in a relatively uneventful manner, but by 12.30 a.m. on the fourth day, 5 July, they were beginning to become worried by the fuel supply. With 500 miles to go to New York they calculated that they would have just enough petrol flying on two engines, with occasional help from a third. They finally arrived at Hazlehurst Field, Long Island, at 1.54 p.m. GMT, 7.54 p.m. local time, on Sunday, 6 July, after a journey of 108 hours and twelve minutes.

The return journey began at 11.55 p.m. on 9 July, with 4,900 gallons of fuel, but without Ballantyne, the stowaway on the outward journey. They crossed the American coast with four engines running, the other resting. Things went well until 4.20 a.m. on 11 July when the forward engine in the aft car broke down. It seemed that bolts had sheared resulting in connecting rod fractures and a badly notched crankcase, and repair in the air was impossible. By six a.m. on the 12th they were running on three engines, as the aft Maori had broken valve springs, which had to be replaced.

On Sunday, 13 July they arrived over Pulham Air Station at 6.20 a.m., and at 6.47 a.m. they had landed, having completed the first two-way crossing of the Atlantic by air, following the first east–west crossing. Captain J.T. Irving of the Sunbeam Motor Car Co. was waiting at Pulham to examine the engines, and went straight to the starboard car to investigate the famous chewing-gum incident. He was relieved to find such a minor repair, and not pounds of chewing gum holding the engine together as might have been expected by reports in the popular press. The problem with the forward Maori in the aft car had probably been caused by the mechanic accidentally falling on the clutch lever, thereby de-clutching the engine and causing it to over-rev. This caused the failure of the studs of the connecting rod big-end bearings.

The five Maoris had contributed about 900 hours' running time during the double journey, having already run about 300 hours before the flight. On the R.34's return to its Scottish base at East Fortune it flew over Wolverhampton as a tribute to the men of the Sunbeam Motor Car Co. who had built the Maori engines and propellers, and also the men of John Marston Ltd who had made the radiators, and the men of H.M. Hobson Ltd who had made the carburettors.

If the R.34 had performed the most famous flight of all British airships, her sister ship was to become the most successful in terms of longevity. On 30 April 1919 she was able to get all five Maoris running within seventy seconds of the signal being given, and then did a test flight of four and a half hours at up to 60 mph, and on the day R.34 took off for New York R.33 flew over London trailing banners exhorting people to buy Victory bonds. She became the first true British civil airship early in 1920 when she was registered G-FAAG, and was used to test various schemes for the use of airships, for example the carriage of aircraft by airships, dropping Sopwith Camels while in flight. She was also used to examine night-flying facilities on the civil air routes, to test mooring masts, and was even used for traffic control by the Metropolitan Police. The R.34 crashed into a hill on 28 January 1921 and was taken to Howden and broken up, but R.33 continued flying until August 1923 when she was stored at Cardington.

She was refitted in 1924 in connection with the Imperial Airship Programme and made her first flight after this on 2 April 1925. After suffering severe damage later in the month she was repaired and once again took part in a programme of releasing aircraft in flight, DH.53s and then Gloster Grebes. She made her last flight on 23 November 1926, the last time Maori engines flew in an airship, and was broken up in 1928. The control car still survives, unfortunately without the rear engine compartment, and is on display in the RAF Museum, Hendon.

The only examples of Maoris to survive are a Maori II in the Musée de l'Air in Paris, another Maori II in the Imperial War Museum at Duxford, and a Maori in Hamilton, New Zealand. Duxford's Maori was restored in the 1980s by an outside contractor, the cost covered by IMI Marston Ltd in exchange for the long-term loan of Duxford's Sunbeam Manitou, the Maori's successor, which is now on display in IMI Marston's private museum. The third Maori II turned up in New Zealand where Straight 8 Restorations, a vintage car restorer, obtained one and set about restoring it to run in a scratch-built car, built on the lines of a 1922 Sunbeam eight-cylinder racer, but of larger dimensions. This engine had possibly been fitted to a speedboat as the double row of inside exhausts pointed straight up.

The R.33, which was fitted with five Maori IV engines, as well as Sunbeam-supplied gearing, transmission, and propellers. This was the longest-lasting British airship.

The R.34, which was the first aircraft to cross the Atlantic

Technical data

Engine Type water-cooled, twelve-cylinder, sixty-degree Vee
Manufacturer Sunbeam Motor Car Co., Moorfield Works, Wolverhampton
Horse Power 2,000 rpm; Maori I 250 hp, Maori II/III 260 hp, Maori IV 275 hp
Capacity 12.27 litres, 100 mm bore, 135 mm stroke
Valve Type twin overhead camshafts, four valves per cylinder
Weight (running) 1,065 lb (Maori I), 1,080 lb (Maori II/III/IV)
Dimensions length 63.5 in., width 33.5 in., height 34.4 in.
Propeller Nos. AB706–7 (LH/RH Short Type 184, Wight Type 840, Fairey Campania), AB716 (Short Type N.2B and Type 184), AB6932–4 (Handley Page O/400), AB7062/4 & AB7073–5 (Short Type 184), AD707 (Wight SP), AD718 (Short Type 184), FA4441 (Fairey IIIB), FA4475M (Fairey IIIA/B), FA4476 (Fairey III/IIIA)
Details four Claudel-Hobson CZS 38 mm carburettors, four BTH magnetos, compression ratio Maori II 5.3:1, Maori III 5.2:1, Maori IV 5:1. Maori I/II: inside exhaust valves, geared propeller; Maori III: outside exhaust valves, geared propeller; Maori IV: outside exhaust valves, governed with flywheel, water-cooled exhaust
Nos. Built 1,063 ordered, 1,023 delivered (40 to be built as Manitous)

Applications

Royal Aircraft Factory CE.1 patrol tractor biplane flying boats
One, N98, built at Farnborough, delivered 3.18 (a previous prototype had been powered by a RAF.3a)
Parnall Zeppelin Strafer, or Night Flyer Scout
One, N505, built by Parnall at Bristol, delivered but not flown (condemned as unsafe, dangerous, and overweight)
Avro Type 529 Silver King, tractor biplane bomber
One, no serial, built by Avro, Manchester, tested 19.12.16
Fairey F.2A Patrol tractor biplane flying boats
Two, N88–9, order later cancelled (275 hp Maori III)
Fairey Campania tractor seaplane
One, N1006, built by Fairey & Co. at Hayes, delivered 10.17 (250 hp Maori I); nine others in this order fitted with RR Eagles
Twenty-five, N2375–99, built by Fairey & Co. at Hayes. delivered 23.3.18–16.6.18 (260 hp Maori II); first fifteen a/c built with RR Eagles
Fairey III tractor biplane–seaplanes
Two, N9–10, built by Fairey & Co. at Hayes, experimental seaplanes leading to design of Type III
Fairey IIIB shipboard bomber tractor biplane–seaplanes
Fifty-four, N2230–45/N2247–54/N9230–59, built by Fairey & Co at Hayes, delivered 16.8.18–30.6.19 (six in first batch fitted with RR Eagles). 260 hp Maori II and 275 hp Maori III
Fairey IIIA shipboard reconnaissance tractor biplane–seaplanes
Fifty, N2850–99, built by Fairey & Co. at Hayes, delivered 30.4.18–22.8.18. N2876 became G-EADZ on civil register then re-engined with Eagle
Wight 'converted' tractor biplane–seaplanes
Two, 9845/9853, built by J. Samuel White & Co., East Cowes, delivered 17.3.17 & 8.9.17. 9845 delivered as landplane, later converted to seaplane
Ten, N1280–9, built by J. Samuel White & Co., East Cowes, delivered 6.10.17–1.18 (first three with 250 hp Maori I, rest with 260 hp Maori II)
Fifteen, N2180–96, built by J. Samuel White & Co., East Cowes, delivered 25.1.18–30.3.18 (five more delivered as spares, N2195–9, and thirty more cancelled), 260 hp Maori II
Curtiss H.12 (Improved H.8) 'Large America' twin-engined tractor biplane flying boats
Two, N1160, N1174, built in Canada but not delivered
Short Type 184 tractor biplane–seaplanes
Four, 8048/8065/8075–6, built by Short Bros at Rochester, with Mohawk, later refitted with Maori
Five, N1086/N1089/N1096–8, built by Short Bros at Rochester, delivered 5.4.17–7.7.17 (others in batch of twenty may have had Maoris or 260 hp Renaults), 250 hp Maori
Short Type 184 (Improved) tractor biplane–seaplanes
Five, N1250/N1256–9, built by J. Samuel White & Co., East Cowes, delivered 8.9.17–19.12.17 (rest of batch had Renaults), 250 hp Maori
Eighty-six, N2950–99/N9100–35, delivered 4.4.18–24.10.18 (260 hp Maori II) N9135 type trials with Sunbeam Manitou; fifty, N9400–49, cancelled; four to civil register – N9118 (G-EBBN), N9286 (G-EAJT), N2996 (G-EBGF), N2998 (G-EALC); N9128 given free to Chile, N9127, N9129, N9130, N9132, N9134 sold to Estonia

One, 9079, built by Frederick Sage at Peterborough, rest of batch of twenty had Mohawks
Twenty-seven, N1593–9/N1780–99, built by Frederick Sage at Peterborough, delivered 11.17–15.3.18 (first three a/c built had Renaults), 260 hp Maori II
Nineteen, N1621–4/N1760–74, built by S.E. Saunders at East Cowes, delivered 9.11.17 – 23.2.18 (Maori II)
Twenty-seven, N1653–9/N1740–59, built by Phoenix Dynamo at Bradford, delivered 24.10.17–29.3.18 (first twenty-three a/c built had Renaults), 260 hp Maori II
One hundred and eighteen, N1672–89/N2630–59/N2790–819/N9060–99 built by Brush Electrical at Loughborough, delivered 10.17–5.12.18 (first twelve a/c had Renaults), Maori II (thirty, N2600–29, cancelled)
Twenty, N9260–79, built by Brush Electrical at Loughborough, delivered 30.1.19–3.20, 275 hp Maori III (ten more cancelled). N9096 to civil register as G-EBBM. N9265–6 and N9268 free to Chile
One hundred and ninety-eight, N1827–39/N2820–49/N2900–49/N9000–59/N9140–69/N9290–304, built by Robey & Co. at Lincoln, delivered 12.17–3.20 (first twelve a/c built had Renaults), 260 hp Maori II. N9012 to Russian Aviation Corps. Next forty-five in last batch cancelled
Thirty, N9170–99, built by Supermarine at Woolston, delivered 12.9.18–25.3.20

Short N.2B tractor biplane–seaplanes
Two, N66–7, built by Short Bros at Rochester, delivered 22.9.17–16.3.18 (N67 fitted with RR Eagle for a time)

Royal Aircraft Factory RE.9 tractor biplane
Two, A3542/A3561, built by Daimler & Co. at Coventry, converted from RE.8s with installation of the Maori
Two, A4600/A4609, built by Standard Motors at Coventry converted from RE.8s with Maori

Handley Page O/100 twin-engined tractor biplane heavy bomber
One, 3142, built by Handley Page, Cricklewood for Russian government with Fiat engines. Not delivered, fitted with Maoris after rebuild following a crash

Handley Page O/400 twin-engined tractor biplane heavy bombers
Fifty, C3381–430, built by Handley Page at Cricklewood and fitted with Eagle, Liberty, or Maori engines as available
One hundred and fifty, C9636–785, built by Handley Page at Cricklewood and fitted with RR Eagle/Liberty/275 hp Maori III as available
Fifty, D8301–50, built by British Caudron Ltd and fitted with Eagle, Liberty, or Maori engines as available

Vickers FB.27 Vimy twin-engined tractor biplane heavy bomber
One, B9953, built by Vickers at Bexley (second prototype, first and third fitted with Hispano-Suiza and Salmson engines), 275 hp Maori III

Grahame-White E.IV Ganymede three-engined biplane day bomber
One, C3481, built by Grahame-White Co., Hendon, 2 × tractor engines, 1 × pusher, two more prototype cancelled

HM Airship R.33, built by Armstrong-Whitworth at Selby, five Maori IV engines

HM Airship R.34, built by Beardmore Ltd at Inchinnan, five Maori IV engines

MOTOR-CARS

Scratch-built 'Sunbeam-type', being built Hamilton, New Zealand, 1996 – on.

200 HP ARAB

The Sunbeam Arab may well have been the first Sunbeam engine referred to by its name from the outset. The huge demand for aero-engines which built up in 1916 placed tremendous strains on the British aero-engine manufacturers, and the War Office attempted to ease the problem of production by standardising on engines of about 200 hp. In January 1917 they had a look at four new 200 hp designs, the Hispano-Suiza V8, the BHP straight six, the Sunbeam Saracen straight six, and a new V8 engine Sunbeam had under development.

It had cast aluminium cylinder heads and blocks, die-cast aluminium pistons, and developed 208 hp from 12.3 litres, weighing only 550 lb. It has often been said that the Arab was a copy of the 200 hp Hispano-Suiza 8B engine, and certainly they were very similar. Marc Birkgit had designed a 150 hp V8 engine at Hispano-Suiza with a bore of 120 mm and a stroke of 130 mm, but a relatively low compression ratio of 4.7:1. By fitting longer pistons, giving a higher compression ratio of 5.3:1, the engine gave 200 hp despite being almost unchanged in other respects. It had two cast aluminium blocks with screwed-in steel liners, single overhead camshafts, and three valves per cylinder.

A Sunbeam Arab from the propeller end showing its clean lines and the aluminium monobloc cylinder banks.

The rear of the Arab showing the two magnetos.

The Arab too was a V8 with two cast aluminium blocks and cylinders of 120 mm bore and 130 mm stroke, each with a single overhead camshaft driving three valves per cylinder. It gave 200 hp, and also had a compression ratio of 5.3:1. As in the case of the Peugeot OHC Grand Prix cars of 1913, it is clear Louis Coatalen was not averse to copying other designers' features, but there were fundamental differences between the two engines. The Arab's steel liners were pressed in with large flanges to hold them in position, and the valve seats were screwed in. It also had Coatalen's normal articulated connecting rods, rather than the Hispano-Suiza's forked rods, and the crankcase was very different, with the Arab's crankshaft held completely in the upper half on seven die-cast white metal bearings.

After the initial failure of Coatalen's own V8 overhead camshaft engine, the Nubian, it may well be that he sought inspiration elsewhere, but to what extent the Arab was based on the French engine will never be completely known. Certainly there is no evidence that Coatalen 'acquired' a Hispano-Suiza for examination, as he had the 1913 Peugeot racing car.

The first Arab had been bench-run in the latter part of 1916, and by the end of the year four or five had been tested. The design was then submitted to the Internal Combustion Engine Committee of the National Advisory Committee for Aeronautics, along with the Sunbeam Saracen. The Saracen was considered already out of date, though 2,000 of the rival straight six BHP engines were ordered.

Both the Arab and the Hispano-Suiza engine received large orders, the latter from Wolseley Motors as well as the parent company. Even though the test results of the bench-run engines were not likely to be very accurate, it was the Arab which accrued the lion's share of the orders. In March 1917 Sunbeam received an initial order for 1,000 Arabs, and this was increased to 2,000 in June, with deliveries to be completed by March 1918 on the understanding that no alterations would be made to the design of the first 500, and eight weeks' notice would be given of any changes required in subsequent engines. Contracts were also placed with Austin Motors, Lanchester, Napier, and Willys Overland in the United States for 1,000, 300, 300 and 560 engines, and Sunbeam immediately began work with these to produce production drawings.

The progress of these drawings was held up when the engines under test began to show defects which required alterations, and it was not until August/September 1917 that the technical department was able to approve a complete schedule of working drawings, though Austin Motors was already in bulk production. Further production problems arose when difficulties in obtaining satisfactory cylinder castings were discovered, and by the end of the year only eighty-three Arabs had been delivered.

Possibly the first aircraft in which the Arab was installed, the Martinsyde F.2 fighter. Sunbeam completed the installation itself, but the engine was later removed and installed in a SE.5a.

The first Sunbeam-built Arab was delivered in May 1917, with three more the following month, then there were no more until eight were delivered in September. One of the first Arabs was fitted to the new Martinsyde F.2 two-seat fighter/reconnaissance aircraft, which had first been flown in May 1917 with an Hispano-Suiza engine. The French engine was removed and an Arab fitted by Sunbeam, but on 7 July the aircraft was still at Wolverhampton having the exhaust pipes and oil tank altered. On 21 July it was reported to have been badly damaged undergoing maker's trials at Wolverhampton, and would not be ready for another ten days. It was finally despatched by road and arrived at Martlesham Heath on 11 August. Tests were complete within a week, and Sunbeam's representative at Martlesham began overhauling the engine and carrying out alterations to the water system, these being completed by 15 September. Engine tests took place the following week and then the aircraft flew to Wolverhampton on 1 October with the intention of taking the engine out and fitting it to an SE.5a. The Martinsyde F.2 was not ordered into production because the Bristol F.2b Fighter filled the role for which it was intended.

The Arab removed from the Martinsyde was sent to the Royal Aircraft Factory at Farnborough to be fitted to SE.5a B609, but was still awaiting parts in mid-November. On 24 November the engine was run, but it was found the propeller boss was heating up, and there would be a further long delay while this was sorted out. Meanwhile the rival 200 hp Hispano-Suiza had already been fitted to an SE.5a and this had now been sent on to Martlesham Heath.

By that time there were 400 SE.5s held in store awaiting engines, and the only ones in service had Hispano-Suiza engines, though the Wolseley Viper, an ungeared version of the Hispano-Suiza, would shortly be introduced. Because of a shortage of Rolls-Royce Falcons it was decided in December 1917 that Corps Reconnaissance Bristol Fighters were to be fitted with the Sunbeam Arab, and two rebuilt airframes, B8914 and B8915, were hastily fitted with Arabs, so hastily they retained their Falcon engine bearers and radiators. They were flown to France for evaluation, and so great was the vibration in one of them that five exhaust stubs fell off! Nevertheless, six more Bristol Fighters, C4657–9 and C4662–4 were likewise equipped with Arabs at the No.3 Repair Depot, retaining their Falcon engine bearers and radiators. They too were sent to France and experienced alarming vibration problems.

Sunbeam had developed the Arab II with an ungeared propeller which was 2.6 inches shorter without the gearing and 13 lb lighter. By 18 January 1918 one of these Arab IIs was at Farnborough to be fitted to another SE.5a, B4898. This aircraft, together with a Bristol Fighter with an ungeared Arab, B3990, arrived at Martlesham at the end of January. Tests proceeded and another Arab-powered Bristol Fighter, B8915, arrived on 8 February. On the 16th B3990 suffered an engine failure, and a new Arab was sent by Sunbeam.

Another Bristol Fighter, B1204, this time with a geared Arab, was sent from Bristol on 23 February, but the following week B8915 had engine trouble and a new one had to be fitted. The SE.5a then went back to Farnborough on the 17th, while the three Bristol Fighters carried on their testing programme at Martlesham. Another Arab-powered aircraft arrived in March, the first of four Grain Griffins, N100–3, tractor biplanes built by the RNAS at Grain. It returned to Grain for modifications in April.

A second Bristol aircraft was also fitted with the Arab, the Scout F. Originally designed to take the Hispano-Suiza, when the contract for two prototypes was issued on 4 June 1917 it specified Sunbeam Arabs, as the rival engine would not be available. The Scout F was a purposeful-looking fighter and the first of two prototypes, B3989, was ready for test-flying in March 1918. It proved to have a remarkable performance with a top speed of 138 mph at sea level and 128

(RIGHT): *The Arab installation in a Bristol Fighter. This installation suffered from severe vibration problems, and was to involve the company and the RAE in months of work in fruitless attempts to find a solution.*

An Arab removed from a Bristol Fighter and installed in a test rig, with No. 8 Squadron.

mph at 10,000 feet, and many fighter pilots who tried it rated it a better aerobatic aircraft than the SE.5a. However, it was roundly condemned because of the Arab engine, and was never ordered into production, though a third prototype was built with a 300 hp Cosmos Mercury radial engine.

A contemporary fighter, the two-seat Avro 530, was also fitted with an Arab because of supply difficulties with the Hispano-Suiza engine. Built as a rival to the Bristol F.2b, the first Avro 530 had the French engine, but the second, B3953, was fitted with the Arab and flew in 1918. The aircraft was inferior in performance to the Bristol design, and there were no orders.

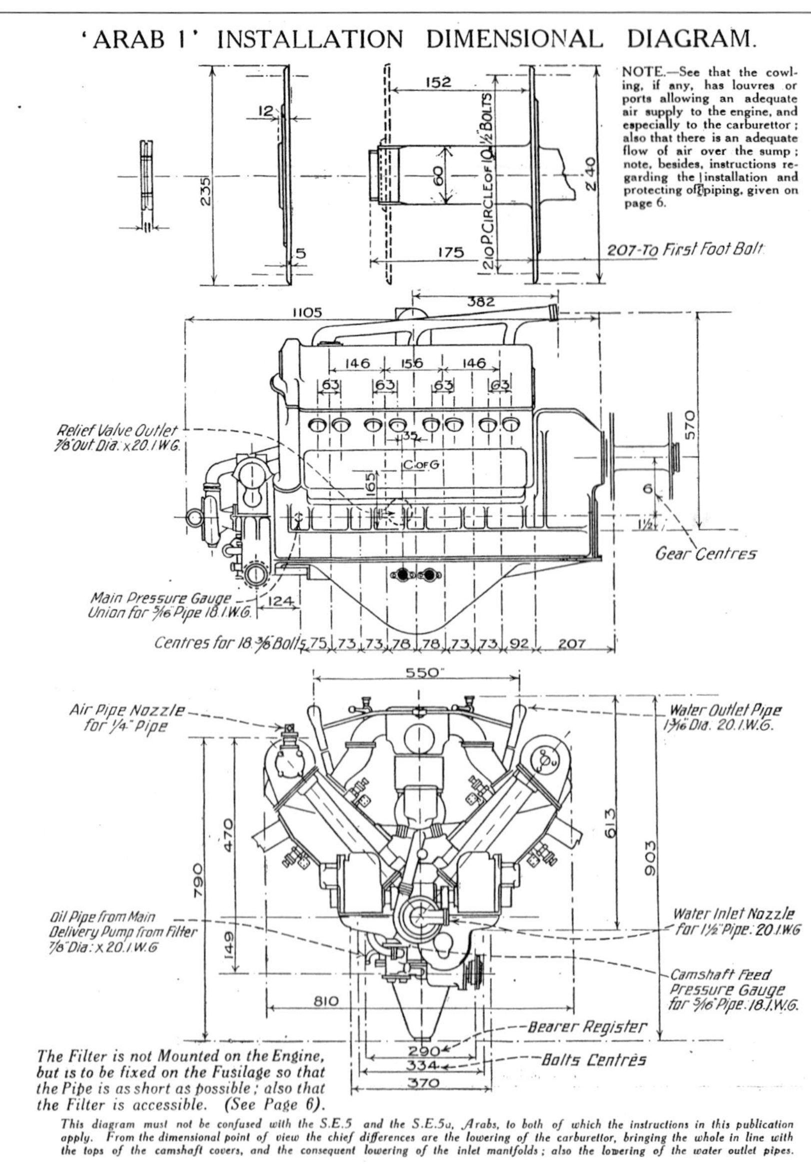

The installation drawing for the Arab with side and end elevations.

(LEFT): *A Grain Griffin, N102, one of a small number of these aircraft powered by the Arab, and shown at Grain in July 1918.*

(BELOW): *The single-seat Bristol Scout F, B3989, another solitary prototype powered by the Arab, an aircraft which would have been excellent with a better engine.*

(LEFT): *The second prototype Avro 530 two-seat fighter, B3953, fitted with an Arab instead of the 200 hp Hispano-Suiza in the first aircraft.*

Once the Arab began to be tested in the air, further problems began to arise. By 21 March 1918 the delay in production of the Arab by Austin Motors for the Bristol Fighter was such that Captain Verney was sent to Sunbeam by the Air Council, to reside there to sort out all difficulties which arose. Similar difficulties were becoming apparent at the other contractors, and at Willys Overland the first engines had only just passed their tests, allowing production to commence.

While at Martlesham Heath the Arab-powered Bristol had its performance compared with an Hispano-Suiza-powered Bristol, and it was found that it had an increase in time to 15,000 feet of one minute, and a decrease in its top speed at 15,000 feet of 3.5 mph.

The three Arab-powered Bristol Fighters at Martlesham were joined by three more on 20 July – D7965, D7968, and D7971 – which were to do tests with different engine mountings to try to find a solution to the terrible vibration problems. Different combinations of modified engines, standard Sunbeam mountings, and new mountings designed at Lanchester, Bristol, and Martlesham itself were all tried in a programme which was still on-going in January 1919, and involved five further Bristols – C9880, C9883, C9842, D7807, and D7910. One feels for those Martlesham Heath test pilots as they flew aloft day after day in aircraft which threatened to shake apart. The vibration problem was largely caused by the connecting rod layout which Coatalen had used, with a master and articulated rod on each pair of pistons, resulting in a greater stroke for the pistons driving the articulated rods, and thus out-of-balance forces. The lightly built crankcase was sometimes split by these vibrations, and because of the layout of the main bearings and the engine bearings, the latter often broke.

At the time of the Armistice the four British manufacturers had delivered only 1,026 Arabs, and most of these had been allocated to Bristol Fighters being built by various contractors other than British & Colonial. The first Arab built by Willys Overland in America was fitted to a Bristol Fighter, D7968, at Martlesham Heath on 31 August 1918. A total of 689 Bristol Fighters have been positively identified as being fitted with Arabs, though there may have been more.

The Arab found its way into a number of prototype aircraft, including Sunbeam's own Type 7 Bomber which finally arrived at Martlesham Heath for performance tests on 18 July 1918 after a protracted delay. It was also fitted to the single Supermarine Baby pusher flying boat, N59, the Norman-Thompson N.2C twin-engined pusher biplane flying boat, N82, the Sage 4b tractor biplane–seaplane, N116, and the Armstrong-Whitworth two-seat biplane fighter, N514.

One of the most unusual aircraft powered by the Arab was the Royal Aircraft Factory's last design, the A.E.3 Ram, a two-seat armoured ground attack aircraft. It was to have been powered by a 200 hp Hispano-Suiza, but the continued non-availability of that engine meant two of the three prototypes (B8781–2) were fitted with the Arab in a pusher installation. The aircraft was armed with two forward firing Lewis guns and one on telescopic mounting for rear defence. The crew's nacelle was heavily armoured and they were supplied with no fewer than thirty-two double Lewis gun drums. The first Arab-powerered AE.3 flew for the first time on 28

(ABOVE): *The sole Sage 4b seaplane trainer, N116, powered by the Arab, replacing an earlier 150 hp Hispano-Suiza.*

(LEFT): *The first Arab completed under licence by Willys Overland in Toronto.*

(LEFT): *The Norman-Thompson NT.2B flying boat trainer was powered by an Arab in a pusher installation. This is a close-up of N2294, one of ninety-four such Arab-powered aircraft.*

(BELOW): *Arabs awaiting shipment from the Moorfield Works near the end of the war. In the background there are also a number of Maoris.*

March 1918, with the second at the end of May, a few days after a third BR.2-powered prototype, designated the Ram II, took to the air. The AE.3 found little favour with the Royal Air Force and there were no production orders.

The other main recipients of Arabs in significant numbers were both post-war aircraft. The Norman-Thompson NT.2B biplane training flying boats each had a pusher Arab. A total of seventy-nine of these was delivered with Arab engines, beginning on 18 November. After the war a number of these was exported, three going to Norway – N2260, N2275, and N2288 – the latter two becoming N-12 and N-13 respectively. One each went to Japan (N2283), Peru (N2293), and Chile (N2284), the latter being exhibited at the Atlantic City Air Exposition of 1919 on the way to Chile. Two went to Estonia and one went on to the British civil register as G-EAQO, before being exported to Canada and becoming G-CACG. Up to 160 Sopwith Cuckoo torpedo-bombers may also have been fitted with Arabs, rather than the rival Wolseley Vipers.

By December 1918, of the 6,160 Arabs ordered from five manufacturers only 1,311 had been delivered, and 2,350 had already been cancelled, the remainder being 'settled'. Very shortly afterwards they were being sold off cheaply by the Aircraft Disposals Board, but there were few takers.

In 1921 one Arab found its way into a racing car. A wine importer named Phillip Rampon had acquired one of the Humber racing cars which had been vanquished by the sixteen-valve Sunbeam at the 1914 Isle of Man TT Race. After endless trouble with its engine he decided to fit an aero-engine and acquired an Arab. The work was done by his mechanic, Ernest Martin, and Rampon called the resulting car the Martin-Arab. The car was entered for a number of race meetings during 1921, but either did not start or did not do very well, and was broken up shortly afterwards. Nevertheless, it might have the dubious distinction of having the last Sunbeam Arab to run.

There is little doubt that the Sunbeam Arab was one of the worst engines of the First World War. The government made the huge mistake of ordering it in vast quantities after only a handful of hand-built prototypes had been bench-run at the factory. They also then planned much of the country's aircraft production against the expected deliveries. Once the engine was tested in the air the terrible vibration problems which were to beset it came to light. These problems were never to be solved, but attempts to do so held up production for many months. Perhaps this is the one good thing about the whole sorry saga. By the time the Arab was received in substantial numbers the war was almost over.

Technical data

Engine type water-cooled, eight-cylinder, ninety-degree Vee
Manufacturer Sunbeam Motor Car Co., Moorfield Works, Wolverhampton; Austin Motor Car Co., Northfield, Birmingham; Lanchester Motor Co., Birmingham; D. Napier & Sons, Acton; Willys Overland, Toledo, Ohio, USA
Horse Power 208 hp at 2,000 rpm
Capacity 11.771 litres, 120 mm bore, 130 mm stroke
Valve Type single overhead camshafts, three poppet valves/cylinder (one inlet, two exhaust)
Weight (dry) Arab I 530 lb, Arab II 517 lb
Dimensions Arab I length 43.5 in., width 31.9 in., height 35.5 in.; Arab II length 40.9 in., width 31.9 in., height 35.5 in.
Propeller Nos. AB6625/9 (Bristol F.2b), AB8162 (Sage Seaplane), AB8210 (Bristol F.2b Cuckoo), AB8212 & AB8224 (Cuckoo), AB9180 (Bristol F.2b), AD646 (Sunbeam Bomber), D1465 (Norman-Thompson NT.2B), IPC2411 (Supermarine Baby), P3041 (Bristol Scout F)
Details (Arab I) geared spur, 0.6:1 LH tractor/RH pusher; (Arab II) direct drive, RH tractor/LH pusher, outside exhausts, one Claudel-Hobson HC.7 carburettor, two AV.8 or Dixie magnetos
Nos. Built 6,110 ordered, 1,311 built (to 18.12.18)
Applications

Martinsyde F.2 Fighter
One, fitted with Arab I at Sunbeam Motor Car Co., Wolverhampton, delivered to Martlesham 11.8.17
Royal Aircraft Factory SE.5a tractor biplane fighter
One, B609, built by Vickers at Weybridge, fitted with geared Arab I
One, B4898, built by Royal Aircraft Factory, Farnborough, fitted with ungeared Arab II
Bristol Scout F tractor biplane fighter
Two, B3989–90, built by British & Colonial at Bristol
Grain Griffin tractor biplane
Four, N100–3, built by RNAS at Grain, delivered 9.3.18–19.9.18, later re-engined with 230 hp BHP
Short Improved Navyplane pusher biplane patrol seaplane
Two, N20–1, ordered but later cancelled
Supermarine Patrol biplane–seaplanes
Two, N24–5, ordered but later cancelled
Supermarine Baby pusher flying boat fighter
One, N59, delivered 2.18, second a/c serial N60 as spares only, third a/c serial N62 cancelled
Royal Aircraft Factory A.E.3 Ram biplane pusher ground attack
Two, B8781–2, first flown 28.3.18 and end of May 1918. A third prototype was powered by BR.2 rotary (B8783)
Fairey N.2A tractor biplane–seaplanes
Six, N76–81, ordered and later cancelled
Norman-Thompson N.2c Type twin-engined pusher biplane flying boat
One, N82, built by Norman-Thompson Ltd at Middleton-on-sea, delivered 1.8.18 (second a/c, N83, not completed)
Fairey F.2a tractor biplane flying boats
Two, N88–9, ordered with Sunbeams or Eagles, but later cancelled
Norman-Thompson School flying boats
Three, N107–9, ordered with Arab or Hispano-Suiza, but later cancelled
Sage 4B School tractor biplane–seaplane
One, N116, built by Frederick Sage & Co., Peterborough, delivered 30.6.16, as Sage 4 (with Hispano-Suiza), converted to Sage 4b with Arab and delivered 13.5.18
Short day bomber, tractor biplane
Two, N507–8, ordered but later cancelled
Armstrong-Whitworth fighter/reconnaissance tractor biplane
One, N514, built by Armstrong-Whitworth at Gosforth, delivered 8.3.18
Sunbeam Bomber (Admiralty Type 7) (D Type) tractor biplane
One, N515, built by Sunbeam Motor Car Co., Moorfield Works, Wolverhampton, delivered 19.7.18, later given new serial H4424 (second a/c N516 cancelled)
Norman-Thompson NT.2B pusher flying boat biplane trainers
Sixty-seven, N2260–95/N2400–29/N2578–9, built by Norman-Thompson Ltd, Middleton-on-sea, delivered 2.11.18–30.1.19 (sixty-five more cancelled, another twenty-two delivered with Hispano-Suiza engines). Sold to Norway N2260, N2275 ('N-12'), N2288 ('N-13'). Sold to Japan N2283, sold to Chile N2284, sold to Peru N2293, sold to Estonia N2286–7, to civil register N2290 (G-EAQO), then to Canada (G-CACG). Four others 'exported'
Fifteen, N2500–N2514 built by S.E. Saunders, East Cowes, delivered 21.11.18–1.1.19 (nine more cancelled)
Fifteen, N3300–14, built by Supermarine at Woolston (no evidence of engine type) but never delivered
Sopwith Cuckoo T.1 tractor biplane torpedo bomber
One hundred and eighteen, N6900–9/N6911–25/N6927–9/N6950–70/N6972–96/N6998/N7150/N7156–92/N7194–9, built by Blackburn at Leeds, three more in batch had Wolseley Vipers, delivered 10.10.18–6.19. Some were Mk IIs with Wolseley Viper engines (thirty-two, N7980–8011, ordered with Arab but delivered with Wolseley Viper)
Three, N6930–2, built by Pegler & Co., Doncaster, delivered 24.10.18–12.18 (seventeen more not delivered/partially completed/cancelled)
Thirty-nine, N7000–38, built by Fairfield Eng. at Glasgow, delivered 8.8.18–30.1.19 (eleven more still at makers on 30.1.19, fifty others cancelled)
Bristol F.2b Fighter tractor biplanes
Built by British & Colonial Aircraft at Bristol
One, B1204, sole identified Arab-powered of batch B1101–350 with various engines, but largely Falcons
One, B3990, test aircraft at Martlesham Heath
One, B4898, test aircraft at Martlesham Heath
One, B8915, test aircraft at Martlesham Heath
One, C1025, one of batch of C751–1050, the rest with Falcons
Five, D6965/D7968/D7971/D7807/D7910, fitted with Willys Overland Arab, these aircraft all at Martlesham Heath for tests with different engine mountings
Fifty, E5259–308, ordered originally from Standard Motor Co., but order was transferred
One, F4631, from batch F4271–970, the rest with Falcons
Built by National Aircraft Factory No.3 at Aintree
One, D2132, of batch D2126–625, the rest with Falcons
Built by Marshall & Sons, Gainsborough
One hundred and fifty, D2626–775
One, F9549, possibly built from spares
Built by Sir W.G. Armstrong-Whitworth at Gosforth
Two hundred and fifty, E1901–2150, E2058 became G-EBCU
Built by Standard Motors at Coventry
Seventy-four, E5179–E5252 (next six in batch sent to Bristol to be fitted with Pumas), E5219 became G-EBDB
Built by Gloucestershire Aircraft Co.
Three, C9842/C9880/C9883
One hundred and fifty, E9507–656
Avro Type 530 two-seat tractor biplane fighter
One, B3953, built by Avro at Hamble, second prototype

MOTOR-CARS

Martin-Arab racing car, 1921

200 HP BEDOUIN

In later years it was common for aero-engine manufacturers to redesign their inline or Vee engines to run upside down, at least to begin with, so as to increase the forward visibility from a single-engined aircraft's cockpit. Louis Coatalen was one of the first to do this when he redesigned the Arab in this way, producing the A8, or inverted Vee, Bedouin.

Few details of the engine have survived, other than its similarity to the Arab with eight 120 mm × 130 mm cylinders, three valves per cylinder, and what would best be described as single underside camshafts. There were still two magnetos and outside exhausts, and the engine apparently still produced 200 hp, with a direct drive propeller. The method he chose to lubricate the engine in this form has not survived however.

The scheme was obviously not seen as being successful enough to proceed with, and there is no evidence that the Bedouin was ever fitted to an aircraft.

Technical data

Engine Type	water-cooled, eight-cylinder, inverted ninety-degree Vee
Manufacturer	Sunbeam Motor Car Co., Moorfield Works, Wolverhampton
Horse Power	200 hp at 2,000 rpm
Capacity	12.3 litres, 120 mm bore, 130 mm stroke
Valve Type	three valves per cylinder (one inlet, two exhaust), single camshafts
Details	two magnetos, outside exhausts, direct drive
Nos. Built	prototypes only
Applications	none

325 HP MANITOU

The successful Maori engine spawned a more powerful successor named the Manitou. Basically the same as the Maori III, it had aluminium blocks instead of cast iron, and the bore was increased from 100 mm to 110 mm, the stroke remaining the same at 135 mm, raising the capacity from 12.3 litres to 15.395 litres. This was the second time this V12 engine had been increased in volume, as the original Afridi had a 92 mm bore and a capacity of 11.4 litres.

Head-on view of the Manitou which followed the Maori on the production lines. With the same configuration as the Maori III it featured a greater use of aluminium and an increased bore.

The cylinder blocks were cast in aluminium in groups of three, as before, and arranged on the crankcase in two rows of six set in a sixty-degree Vee. There were twin overhead camshafts, driven by trains of gears from the crankshaft, for each bank, and these operated four valves per cylinder, two inlet and two exhaust. There were the usual 'H' section articulated connecting rods, and a hollow crankshaft was carried on eight die-cast white metal bearings. The propeller was driven directly through 1.54:1 gearing to the propeller shaft, which was mounted, with the thrust bearing, on an extension of the crankcase cast on the engine.

The weight of the engine dry was 845 lb, and 1,050 lb in running condition, which was 30 lb lighter than the Maori IV, because of the aluminium blocks, and yet the engine gave twenty-five more horse power, 300 hp at 2,000 rpm, later rising to 325 hp. There were two Claudel-Hobson HC7 carburettors set inside the Vee, and two BTH AV12 type magnetos driven from the train of gears at 3,000 rpm. Both electric and hand starters were fitted to the engine.

Despite the change from cast iron to aluminium there was so little difference between the Maori and the Manitou that the same handbook was used for each engine, noting only the changes between them. Coatalen had striven to make the engines as identical as possible, given that the Maori was his most successful design.

Forty Manitous were initially ordered under Contract AS29772, replacing forty Maoris, and then further orders of 500 and 300 were placed under Contract 34a/247/C209. Only one Manitou was delivered before the end of the war, with two more before the end of November 1918, followed by ten in December as the Manitou started to replace the Maori on the production lines. Maori/Manitou production had actually been cut back slightly to ease production difficulties with the Sunbeam Arab, and in May 1918 it had even been proposed to cancel 200 Maori/Manitou from existing contracts.

The only aircraft known to have been fitted with the Manitou was the Short Type 184, serial N9135, which had

A rear view of the Manitou showing the two magnetos. Only a single Short Type 184 has ever been traced as being powered by the Manitou.

been built by J. Samuel White at East Cowes and delivered to Grain in March 1919. It carried out the type trials on the Manitou.

As an example of the reliability and servicing of state-of-the-art water-cooled engines at the end of the First World War, the Manitou's manual reveals the following recommendations. After ten hours' running the oil and air filters were to be cleaned and checked, the spark plugs cleaned, the water pump greasers packed with thick lubricant, and a few drops of special oil put into the magneto bearings. After twenty-five hours' running the oil and water had to be changed and the petrol system cleaned, with the valves and plugs being checked. After 100 hours' of running the engine was to be removed from the aircraft for a complete overhaul either at the maker's or at a properly equipped workshop. There was obviously one particular problem with the Manitou, and presumably with the Maori before that, of defective cooling of the upper corner of the cylinder casting immediately above the exhaust valves. The manual recommended keeping this area clean and painted to detect the problem if there was incomplete water circulation.

The Manitou was to feature at all the post-war aero shows for many years, and it was to be one of the four engines – the other three were the 800/900 hp Sikh, the 400 hp Matabele, and the 100 hp Dyak – Sunbeam continued to promote long after it had dropped mention of the majority of its wartime types. The company's lack of success in selling the engines was shown by an advertisement in January 1922, when brand-new Manitous held in store at the Moorfield Works were offered for sale at £395, against a normal list price of £1,250.

Although the Manitou did not find its way into many aircraft, it did have one application which was to become world famous. Coatalen decided to repeat the success of the pre-war Mohawk-engined *Toodles V* racing car. He built a special single-seat chassis to take a version of the Manitou engine. Apparently he did not take a Manitou out of store, as many racing-car drivers were doing with dirt-cheap war-surplus aero-engines, but built an engine especially for the car. In doing so he gave it an increased bore of 120 mm and quoted the average stroke as 138.5 mm instead of 135 mm, apparently because one block had the standard stroke of 135 mm but the other was 142 mm, giving a total capacity of 18,322 cc. There were also three valves instead of four, one inlet and two exhaust, driven by a single camshaft on each bank. Apparently the Arab valve gear had been used, made possible by increasing the bore to 120 mm, the same as that of the Arab. In this hybrid form the engine gave around 355 bhp, up from the 325 hp of the standard Manitou, though the car was initially always known as the 350 hp Sunbeam.

The car made two inauspicious appearances at Brooklands during 1920, driven by Harry Hawker, Sopwith's famous test pilot. On the first occasion a tyre burst and he crashed through a fence, and on the second he stalled it on the start line and was unable to get away. The car had better success on the track in 1921 and 1922, but it was on 18 May 1922 that it had its first real success, breaking the first of many world records. Standing- and flying-start records were set for the half mile, kilometre, and mile, and a flying-start record only for two miles, the best of these being 136.05 mph for the half mile. The following day world records were set for the five miles and ten miles, and a new Brooklands lap record of 121.54 mph was set, before tyre trouble intervened.

Malcolm Campbell took an interest in the car and persuaded Coatalen to let him compete in it at the Saltburn Speed Trials of 1922, setting the fastest time at 127.1 mph and beating the time for the flying kilometre at 134.07 mph, though this was not recognised as a world record because of the timing method used. Campbell was certain that the car could go much faster, and begged Coatalen to sell it to him. Two weeks before the Danish International Speed Trials at Fanoe Beach Coatalen relented, and parted with the 350 hp Sunbeam for a considerable sum. With his trusty mechanic Leo Villa, Campbell rushed to get the car ready. Again his best mean speed bettered the record for the kilometre at 137.72 mph, but it was not recognised because of the timing apparatus.

Campbell had a year to prepare for the next meeting and turned to Boulton & Paul Ltd, the Norwich aircraft manufac-

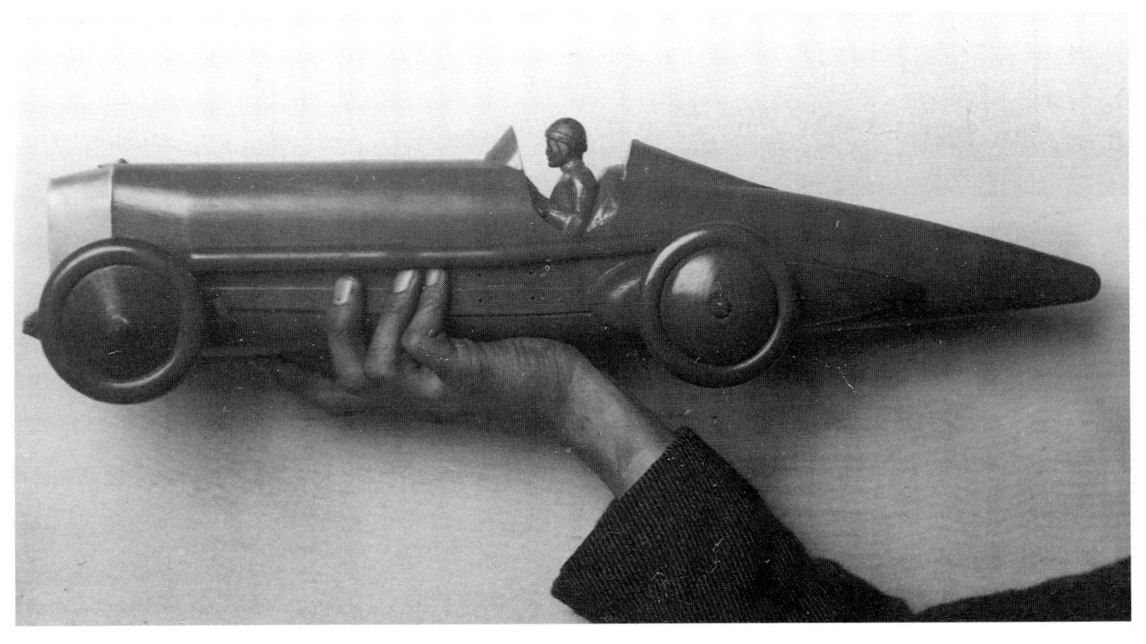

A model of the 350 hp Sunbeam produced by Boulton & Paul in Norwich after wind tunnel tests. In this form the Manitou-powered car became the first in the world to exceed 150 mph.

(LEFT): *Sir Malcolm Campbell in the 350 hp Sunbeam, on Pendine Sands where he broke the record.*

(BELOW): *The Manitou engine as installed in the 350 hp Sunbeam. It was especially built for the car with Arab valve gear and one larger than normal block.*

turer, to improve the aerodynamics of the car. Using their wind tunnel extensively, they designed a new long tail for the car, together with a streamlined driver's head-rest, streamlined covers for the side chains, and other improvements. With these modifications, the 350 hp Sunbeam was once more ready to attack the world record, and the Danes installed approved timing apparatus. After his best timed run of 139.81 mph a tyre came off the car, bouncing into the crowd and killing a small boy, and the meeting was abandoned. Campbell then took the car to Pendine Sands in South Wales, and on 24 September 1924 he set a mean speed of 146.16 mph, a new world record for the flying kilometre, in effect the land-speed record.

It was clear that the magic figure of 150 mph was possible, and new high-compression pistons were supplied by Sunbeam, and a longer radiator cowl, and other minor streamlining improvements were fitted. Campbell returned to Pendine and on 21 July 1925 set new records of 150.87 mph for the kilometre and 150.76 for the mile, the first car in the world to exceed 150 mph. This car, together with its Sunbeam Manitou engine, is now preserved in the National Motor Museum at Beaulieu in Hampshire.

The powerboat fraternity, like the road racers, also found aero-engines a convenient source of relatively cheap high power. Edward Mackay Edgar commissioned two aero-engined powerboats from S.E. Saunders of the Isle of Wight.

One, *Maple Leaf VI*, was powered by two 600 hp Rolls-Royce Condor engines, and the other, *Maple Leaf V*, was powered by four Sunbeam Manitou engines giving it 1,400 hp. This boat was to continue Harry Hawker's association with Sunbeam-powered devices, for he was to be the driver/pilot.

The Manitou was a good engine for the day, slightly smaller and less powerful than the latest versions of the Rolls-Royce Eagle, and apparently of course untried. If Sunbeam had called it the Maori Mk V, it might have been seen by the aviation fraternity as an engine with many thousands of hours on long sea patrols behind it, and been slightly better received.

Technical data

Engine Type water-cooled, twelve-cylinder, sixty-degree Vee
Manufacturer Sunbeam Motor Car Co., Moorfield Works, Wolverhampton
Horse Power 325 hp at 2,000 rpm
Capacity 15.395 litres, 110 mm bore, 135 mm stroke
Valve Type twin OHC, four poppet valves/cylinder
Weight 845 lb dry, 1,050 lb running. With six hours' fuel, 1,838 lb
Propeller No. AB8900 (Short Type 184)
Details two Claudel-Hobson HC.7 carburettors, two BTH AV12 magnetos or two Remys ignition sets, outside 1.57:1 geared propeller, compression ratio 5.2:1
Nos. Built 840 ordered, thirteen delivered, 827 cancelled, special Manitou built for 350 hp Sunbeam car post-war

Applications

Short Type 184 (Improved) tractor biplane–seaplane
One, N9135, built by J. Samuel White & Co. at East Cowes, delivered 3.19, Type Trials with Manitou, first a/c fitted with Manitou

MOTOR-CARS

350 hp Sunbeam – world land-speed record-holder (a specially built engine with modified valve gear, single overhead camshafts and three valves/cylinder, possibly Arab in origin)

POWERBOATS

Maple Leaf V – four Manitou engines

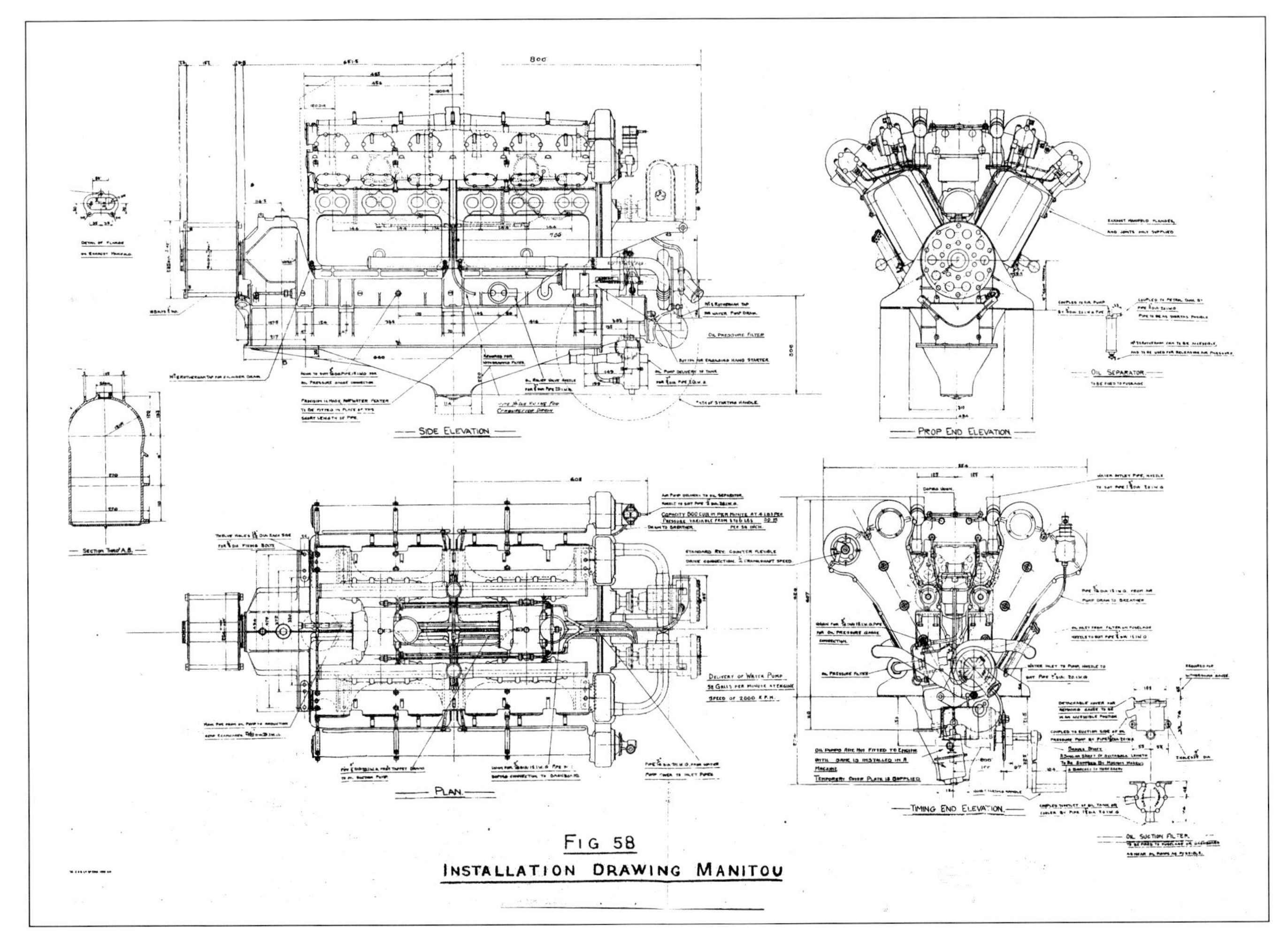

Installation drawing for the Maori III/Manitou engine showing the change to outside exhaust valves.

200 HP SARACEN

In 1916 Coatalen did for his Cossack family of engines what he had done for his side-valve engines. He increased the bore, thereby creating a basically similar range of engines, but giving them different names. He also changed the cylinder block construction from cast iron to aluminium, but otherwise attempted to keep the engines as identical as possible. The first of these was the Saracen, which was derived from the straight six Amazon.

He increased the bore from 110 mm in the Amazon to 122 mm, the stroke remaining the same at 160 mm, thereby increasing the capacity from 9.13 litres to 11.23 litres. Other than this the two engines were fundamentally the same, having cylinders cast in groups of three, with twin overhead camshafts operating four valves per cylinder. The Saracen had two magnetos, an air starter and gave 200 hp at 2,000 rpm, with a 2:1 geared propeller.

In January 1917 the Saracen was submitted for consideration to the Internal Combustion Engine Committee of the National Advisory Committee for Aeronautics, along with another new 200 hp V8 engine Sunbeam was bench-testing, the Arab. The committee also considered two other 200 hp engines, the Hispano-Suiza V8 and the BHP Straight Six. Both the V8 engines received huge orders, the BHP orders for 2,000, but the Sunbeam Saracen was rejected as being already obsolete, which is rather strange, as its lower-powered brother the Amazon did receive a small order. The decision probably had more to do with freeing Sunbeam's production capacity for the Arab, which seemed likely to be, at the time, one of the most important engines of the war.

Technical data

Engine type	water-cooled, six-cylinder inline
Manufacturer	Sunbeam Motor Car Co., Moorfield Works, Wolverhampton
Horse Power	200 hp at 2,000 rpm
Capacity	11.23 litres, 122 mm bore, 160 mm stroke
Valve Type	twin overhead camshafts, four poppet valves per cylinder
Weight	740 lb
Dimensions	probably similar to Sunbeam Amazon
Details	two magnetos, air starter, geared propeller
Nos. Built	prototypes only
Applications	none

200 HP SPARTAN

Between 1913 and 1918 Louis Coatalen designed an amazing total of ten V12 aero-engines. Of course a number of them were only earlier ones with increased bore, such as Mohawk/Gurkha, Afridi/Maori/Manitou, and Cossack/Matabele, but even so there were six quite distinct Sunbeam V12 engines during the war years. Easily the most obscure of these was the Spartan.

The few surviving details list it has having a bore of 105 mm and a stroke of 130 mm, which might suggest it was a Maori with a 5 mm increased bore, except that its power output is listed at only 200 hp against the Maori's 275 hp. It is described as having only single overhead camshafts, which might immediately suggest a relationship with the V8 Arab, but the Spartan had four valves per cylinder whereas the Arab had only three, and the Arab had a completely different cylinder size of 120 mm × 130 mm.

The secret of its low power output of only 200 hp from an engine of 14.03 litres capacity may lie in the two very interesting words used in the few details set against the Spartan in surviving records: 'air-cooled'. If the Spartan was Louis Coatalen's one and only attempt to produce an air-cooled engine, the V12 layout was a very strange one to choose. There were V8 air-cooled engines, most notably the ubiquitous Renault 70/80 hp, but a V12 air-cooled would probably make it unique, because of the obvious difficulties in cooling the rearmost cylinders, though the Napier Dagger did feature a twenty-four-cylinder air-cooled 'H' layout in the 1930s.

An Air Board report in late 1917 mentions that the erection of a 'Sunbeam Air-Cooled Engine' was proceeding. The crankshaft was bedded, and the connecting rods, pistons, and cylinders were fitted, but the cam gear was not yet finished. The only other surviving details of the engine were that it had two magnetos and a geared propeller. One thing is also clear, however: the Spartan was not a success.

Technical data

Engine Type	air-cooled, twelve-cylinder Vee
Manufacturer	Sunbeam Motor Car Co., Moorfield Works, Wolverhampton
Horse Power	200 hp
Capacity	14.03 litres, 105 mm bore, 135 mm stroke
Valve Type	four valves per cylinder, single overhead camshaft
Details	two magnetos, geared propeller
Nos. Built	prototypes only
Applications	none

400 HP MATABELE

The Sunbeam Matabele was the last development of the successful Cossack family of engines, being basically a Cossack with aluminium instead of cast-iron blocks and a bore increased from 110 mm to 122 mm, thereby increasing the overall capacity from 18.2 litres to 22.45 litres. The related straight six engine the Saracen was developed in the same way from the Amazon, and was basically the port bank of the Matabele, but the sequence of the designs is not clear. Whether the Matabele was developed from the Cossack, and the Saracen then produced by taking half a Matabele, or whether the Saracen was developed from the Amazon first, or at the same time as the Matabele, is lost with the Sunbeam records, but a list of names prepared by Sunbeam for its engines includes the Saracen but not the Matabele, suggesting the straight six engine was first.

Like the rest of the Cossack family, the Matabele had cylinders cast in groups of three and twin overhead camshafts, driven by trains of gears from the crankshaft, which operated four valves per cylinder. The crankshaft was carried on eight die-cast white-metal bearings. The two banks of cylinders were set at sixty degrees, with the two Claudel-Hobson HC.7 carburettors between them. The pistons were aluminium and there were articulated connecting rods. Ignition was by four magnetos, two having a clockwise rotation and two anti-clockwise, and two spark plugs per cylinder. The Matabele developed 420 brake horse power at 2,000 rpm and the propeller was geared down to 1,225 rpm, i.e. a 1.63:1 gearing. The engine weighed 1,000 lb empty, 1,091 lb with water, and 2,548 lb with oil and fuel for six hours. It was fitted with air or hand starters.

(ABOVE RIGHT): *A head-on view of the Matabele showing the carburettors inside the sixty-degree Vee, and the propeller boss.*

(RIGHT): *A side view of the V12 Sunbeam Matabele, the last development of the Cossack range of engines, with a greater use of aluminium and a larger bore.*

The engine was developed in two versions, the Matabele I as described above, and the Matabele II, which only had two magnetos and direct drive, for non-aeronautical use. For testing the Matabele the RNAS acquired a DH.4, A8083, from the RFC on 16 February 1918, and this was delivered to Castle

A rear view of the Matabele showing the four magnetos. The only aircraft known to have been powered by the Matabele was a single DH. 4.

Bromwich for fitment of the engine. The aircraft was delivered thus equipped to Hendon on 5 May 1918, travelling the distance in only thirty-five minutes, which equated to 150 mph over the ground, with very little wind. The fuel consumption proved to be only 0.52 pints per hp per hour. The aircraft then went to Farnborough on 27 June. It was tested at the Central Flying School from 16 to 31 December 1918, and then on 11 January 1919 went to Martlesham Heath for performance tests.

With the Matabele the DH.4 had a top speed of 122 mph at 10,000 ft, a figure higher than any other engine tested, the best of the rest being the 325 hp Rolls-Royce Eagle at 118 mph and the 400 hp Liberty at 117 mph. Top speed at 6,500 ft was 108 mph. Time to climb to 10,000 ft was only eight minutes and thirty-five seconds, no other engine coming within five minutes of this time, except the Eagle Mk VIII which managed nine minutes. The time to 15,000 ft was even more outstanding at exactly sixteen minutes, again only the Eagle Mk VIII even coming close. The service ceiling of the Matabele-powered DH.4 was 21,000 ft, bettered only by the Eagle Mk VIII which could take the aircraft up to 22,000 ft.

By 15 February all the tests were described as 'washed out', and the engine was to be returned to the Sunbeam works. This was the only known time the engine was fitted to an aircraft, though it was still being advertised in aviation magazines as late as 1923, and by then was quoted 'As supplied to the French Government'. How many Matabeles the French bought, and what they did with them, is not known. It may be a coincidence that at about the same time Sunbeam took a number of close-up photographs of the Bréguet 19b, J7507, which the RAE had acquired for evaluation. These include pictures of the engine and the engine bay with the original engine removed. The French did buy Cossack engines which they fitted to Tellier flying boats, but whether the Matabele was seen as a replacement is also unknown.

The Matabele found some fame when fitted to powerboats such as those produced by Victor Despujols in France, the Sunbeam–Despujols IV and V, which could do 76 mph powered by a single Matabele geared up to 3,000 rpm and started by compressed air. The Matabele's exhaust manifold was of a special design which acted as an efficient water-cooling arrangement.

On 4 August 1920 the Matabele was fitted to three powerboats taking part in elimination trials to represent Great Britain in the International Trophy. The Sunbeam–Despujols I had a single Matabele, its sister boat the Sunbeam–Despujols II had two Matabeles, and the *Maple Leaf VII* had four, arranged in two pairs and giving the boat a massive 1,800 hp, and on test in the Solent it proved capable of over 80 mph. Not surprisingly *Maple Leaf VII* was one of the three boats selected, with the Sunbeam–Despujols I. The other Matabele-engined boat failed to start because of a drowned magneto.

During unloading in Canada, where the International Trophy was to take place, the *Maple Leaf VII* was accidentally dropped, which threw the hull out of line, something which proved to be her downfall. On the second lap of the race she started to break up when doing 85 mph and began to sink. She was towed ashore and salvaged, and the Matabele engines went back to Wolverhampton to go into store, but they were to be seen again.

The Matabele was one of the engines displayed by Sunbeam at the Paris Salon of December 1919, and at Olympia in 1920, and was to be advertised for a number of years, but without much success in the aeronautical world.

Like the Manitou the most famous application of the Matabele was in a land-speed record-breaking car. The 350 hp Sunbeam had been the first car to exceed 150 mph in 1925, but its record was beaten several times over the next two years, firstly by another Sunbeam with a specially built engine driven by Henry Segrave, then by Parry Thomas's Liberty-engined *Babs*, and finally by Malcolm Campbell, this time in his own Napier Lion-engined *Bluebird*, setting a speed of 174.883 mph at Pendine Sands.

The magic mark of 200 mph was approaching, and when Henry Segrave talked to him about a new attempt at the record, it was clear to Coatalen that more power was the answer. No one aero-engine could provide sufficient power, but Coatalen devised a simple and inexpensive solution to the problem. In the stores at Moorfield Works were the Matabeles which had been removed from the ill-fated *Maple Leaf VII* powerboat. Rated at 435 hp at 2,000 rpm, two of these would give more than enough power to drive a car through the 200 mph barrier.

Coatalen, and the car's designer Captain Jack Irving, devised a layout which sited the driver between the engines, each of which had its own cooling system, and encased the entire car in attractive red bodywork. Always conscious of publicity, Coatalen called the car the 1,000 hp, using a certain amount of poetic licence.

As the car was being built at Wolverhampton, Segrave was arranging to use Daytona Beach in Florida for the record attempt – Pendine was now just too short. The first time he heard the engines running on the specially built rig in the

(RIGHT):
The 1,000 hp Sunbeam under construction in Moorfield Works, with the two Matabele engines already installed in the chassis.

(BELOW):
The 1,000 hp Sunbeam under test at The Sunbeam. The noise was said to be shattering.

Moorfield Works Segrave was in awe: 'No words can describe the unimaginable output of power which the 1,000 hp machinery seemed to catapult into the building. It was one continuous deafening roar . . .' He noticed a blank space on the dashboard and asked Tommy Harrison, the man in charge of building the car, to put in two more dials. 'What the bloody hell for?' was Harrison's reply. 'Why,' said Segrave, 'the reporters will wonder how the devil I drive such a complicated mechanism.' So Norman Cliff was told to put in two extra dials, connected to nothing!

After one drive around the works for the press the car was packed off to America. On 29 March 1927 Segrave and the 1,000 hp Sunbeam were ready. With the Matabeles roaring the car bucked and swerved down the course as it hit imperfections in the sand. At the end of the run the brakes would not slow the car down quickly enough so Segrave steered into the shallow water of the sea and was able to stop. After the tyres had been changed and the fuel tanks topped up, he made the return run. He recorded a mean of 202.988 mph for the kilometre and 203.792 mph for the mile, and had

The 1,000 hp Sunbeam newly completed outside the Moorfield Works and ready to be shipped to Daytona where it became the first car in the world to exceed 200 mph. The reason it was nicknamed 'The Slug' is obvious.

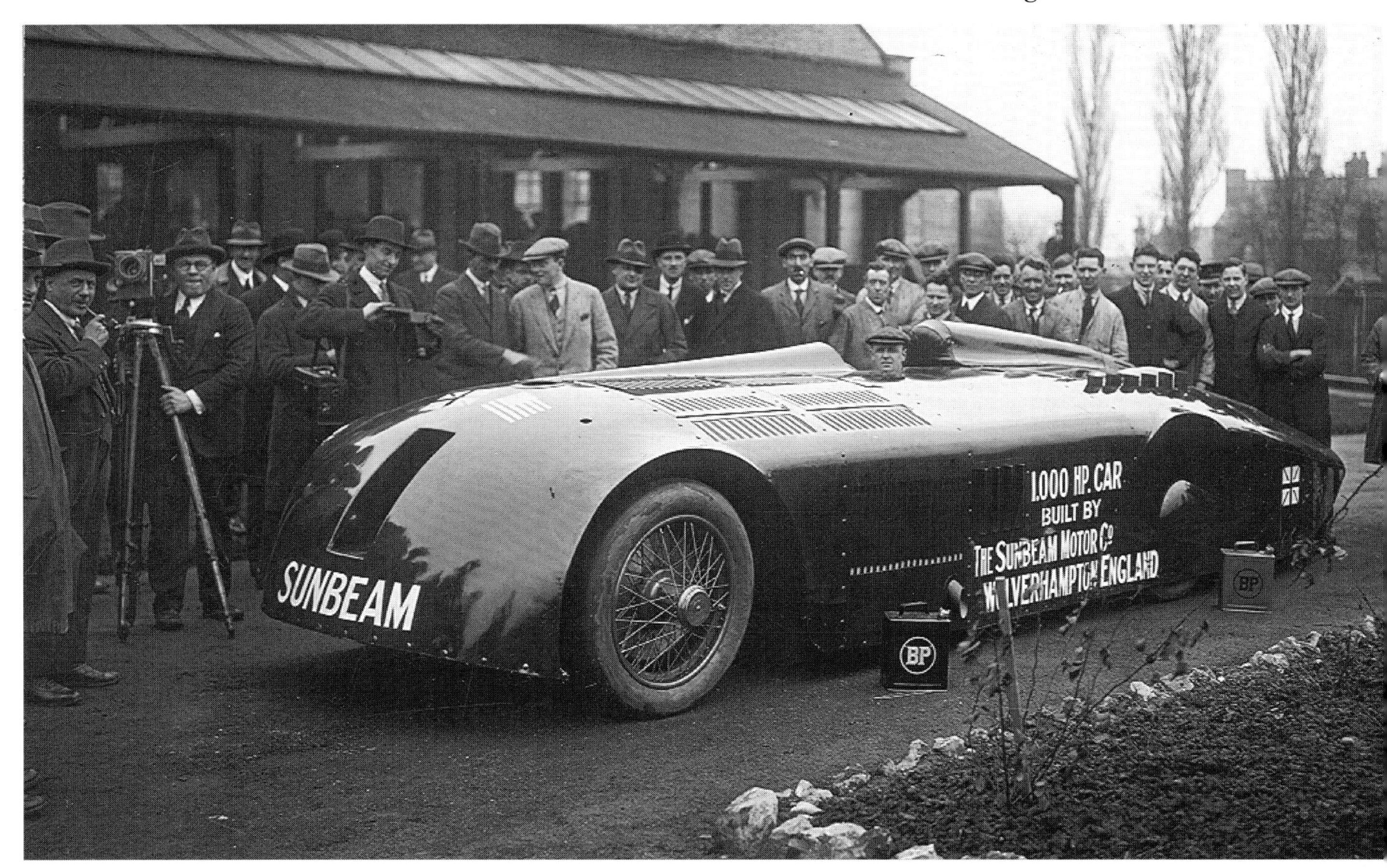

broken the land-speed record by the biggest margin ever.

The car was shipped back to England, having made Segrave and Sunbeam world famous once again. It is now preserved in the National Motor Museum at Beaulieu, near to its earlier cousin the Manitou-powered 350 hp Sunbeam.

Technical data

Engine Type water-cooled, twelve-cylinder, sixty-degree Vee
Manufacturer Sunbeam Motor Car Co., Moorfield Works, Wolverhampton
Horse Power 400 hp at 2,000 rpm
Capacity 22.45 litres, 122 mm bore, 160mm stroke
Valve type twin overhead camshafts, four poppet valves per cylinder
Weight 1,000 lb
Dimensions as Cossack
Details two Claudel-Hobson HC.7 carburettors, (Matabele I) four magnetos, .63:1 geared propeller, (Matabele II) two magnetos, direct drive
Nos. Built wartime nil, post-war prototypes plus at least eight for various applications

Applications

Airco DH.4 tractor biplane day bomber

One, A8083, built by Airco at Hendon, delivered 16.12.18 engineless to Castle Bromwich for fitment of Matabele, transferred from RFC to RNAS, returned to Hendon 5.5.19

POWERBOATS

Sunbeam–Despujols I
Sunbeam–Despujols II (two engines)
Sunbeam–Despujols IV
Sunbeam–Despujols V
Maple Leaf VII (four engines)

MOTOR-CARS

Sunbeam 1,000 hp – land-speed record-breaking car

300 HP TARTAR

The Sunbeam Tartar was an experimental engine for airship use built in prototype form only in 1917/18. It was a V12 engine using the cylinder size of the Manitou, the uprated version of the Maori, that is 110 mm bore and 135 mm stroke, giving a capacity of 15.4 litres. However it was of radically different construction as it had single cylinders fixed in two rows to the crankcase, as was Rolls-Royce, Mercedes and Liberty practice.

It only had single camshafts operating four valves per cylinder, two magnetos and a geared propeller, and gave 300 hp. Although it never flew, its design may have led to the much larger 800 hp Sikh engine, which was under development at the end of the war, and also had separate cylinders.

Technical data

Engine Type	water-cooled, twelve-cylinder Vee
Manufacturer	Sunbeam Motor Car Co., Moorfield Works, Wolverhampton
Horse Power	300 hp
Capacity	15.4 litres, 110 mm bore, 135 mm stroke
Valve Type	single camshafts, four valves per cylinder
Details	for airship use, separate cylinders, two magnetos, geared propeller
Nos. Built	prototypes only
Applications	none

300 HP KAFFIR

Although many of the technical details of the Sunbeam Kaffir W12 engine have been lost, it must have been based on the Arab cylinder block, for it featured three banks each of four cylinders with overhead camshafts and three valves per cylinder. The bore of 120 mm was the same as the Arab, but the stroke was increased from 130 mm to 135 mm, which is the only puzzling part of the surviving description.

It was a normal thing for Coatalen to produce a family of engines from one parent, with an inline, a Vee engine, and usually a broad-arrow or 'W' layout, all with the same basic cylinder block. In the case of the V8 Arab the inline engine was not a straight four, which would have been the normal extrapolation, but a straight six, the Dyak, based on the Arab cylinders. The Kaffir would have been the broad-arrow layout, with three banks of Arab cylinders, but why the stroke was increased is not clear.

The Kaffir had two six-cylinder magnetos, one single carburettor and one dual carburettor, and drove the propeller directly. Its capacity was 18.33 litres and it gave 300 hp, but was clearly not a success as it was never ordered and was not fitted to an aircraft.

Technical data

Engine Type	water-cooled, twelve-cylinder 'W'
Manufacturer	Sunbeam Motor Car Co., Moorfield Works, Wolverhampton
Horse power	300 hp
Capacity	18.33 litres, 120 mm bore, 135 mm stroke
Valve Type	OHC three valves/cylinder
Weight	unknown
Details	two six-cylinder magnetos, one single carburettor and one dual carburettor, direct drive propeller
Nos. Built	prototypes only
Applications	none

500 HP MALAY

The most extraordinary aero-engine ever designed and built by Louis Coatalen was the Malay, a massive twenty-cylinder engine in a star layout, designed very late in the war when larger power engines of over 400 hp were being envisaged. It was based on the cylinder banks of the Arab, five of them bolted around a central crankcase. As the Arab cylinder blocks were cast in groups of four it was relatively simple to disperse them in a different layout like this. It was a logical extension of the principle of the Kaffir, with two more cylinder banks being bolted on. The cylinders had the Arab bore and stroke of 120 × 130 mm, unlike the slightly different Kaffir, which gave it a total volume of 29.42 litres. The Malay had the overhead camshafts and three valves per cylinder of the Arab, one inlet valve and two exhausts.

The mechanical complexities within the crankcase have not been recorded by history, but cannot have been too dissimilar to those of a multi-row radial engine. The engine was fed by one single and two dual carburettors, and drove the propeller directly, giving 500 hp.

The Malay was not, of course, ordered nor fitted to an aircraft. It must have become apparent during bench testing that there were simpler ways of producing 500 hp.

Technical data

Engine Type	water-cooled, 'star' layout twenty-cylinder
Manufacturer	Sunbeam Motor Car Co., Moorfield Works, Wolverhampton
Horse Power	500 hp
Capacity	29.42 litres, 120 mm bore, 130 mm stroke
Valve Type	OHC, three valves per cylinder
Weight	unknown
Details	one single and two dual carburettors, direct drive propeller
Nos. Built	prototypes only
Applications	none

100 HP DYAK

The Dyak was a relative of the Sunbeam Arab, though not a close one, and was more fortunate than its progenitor. It was a 100 hp six-cylinder inline engine, with 120 mm × 130 mm Arab cylinders installed in a single aluminium cast block, with steel liners and bronze valve seats. The block was one of the largest such aluminium castings attempted at the time, and was cast in Sunbeam's own foundry. The crankcase was also aluminium.

The 100 hp Sunbeam Dyak six-cylinder inline engine, with the propeller boss to the left. Note the starting handle on the right, so that the pilot could start the aircraft from the cockpit.

Unlike the Arab there were two valves per cylinder operated by a single overhead camshaft, driven directly by bevel gearing from the crankshaft. The hollow crankshaft was carried on seven white-metal die-cast bearings, and drove the propeller directly, with the thrust bearing mounted directly on the front of the crankcase. There were light 'H' section connecting rods, two ML magnetos, and two Claudel-Hobson BZS 38 carburettors, mounted for gravity feed. Engine starting was by hand, with a handle at the rear of the crankshaft.

From a total volume of 8.82 litres the Dyak gave 100 hp at 1,200 rpm, and the weight of the engine dry was 399 lb. Its weight in running condition, though without oil, fuel or hand starter gear, was 439 lb, and with oil and fuel for six hours' flight was 745 lb.

An order was placed for 160 Dyaks under Contract No. 34a/1477/C1390, but none had been delivered by the end of the war and they were then put on four months' notice of cancellation. Nevertheless, some Dyaks must have been delivered because at least one SST (Submarine Scout Twin) Type airship, SST-13, was powered by two Dyaks. The SSTs had been ordered with two 110 hp Berliet engines, but the order was changed to Dyaks when they became available,

A front view of the Dyak showing the single overhead camshaft.

though there is only evidence of one of the airships being completed.

In November 1919 the Aircraft Disposal Board was advertising a sale of aero-engines at 30% to 80% of cost, and one of those listed was the Dyak. At the same time Sunbeam was preparing to exhibit the engine on its stand at the Paris Aero Show, and at the Olympia Show a few months later. Not surprisingly there were few purchasers of new engines to be found, not least because rotary engines were to be had for only a few pounds. The Japanese Navy did purchase four Dyaks from the Paris Show for fitment to two non-rigid airships, the 100,000 cu.ft capacity No.1 and the 111,000 cu.ft capacity No.4. The latter was said still to be flying in 1932, making its two Dyaks among the last Sunbeam engines to fly, if those were the engines still fitted, until events in Australia in the 1970s.

Despite it being initially intended for airship use, Sunbeam installed the Dyak in one of its own Avro 504Ks and test-flew it from Dunstall Park, Wolverhampton. The aircraft had a brass nose radiator, and with this and all the attendant plumbing the installation was heavier than the normal rotary engine. The empty weight was increased from 1,231 lb for the 110 hp Le Rhône-powered Avro 504K to 1,320 lb, and the all-up weight from 1,829 lb to 1,857 lb. The other principle difference was the shortening of the overall length from 29 ft 5 in. to 28 ft 11 in.

The slight loss in payload for the converted aircraft because of the increase in weight mitigated against further conversions, but two were supplied to the Norwegian Army Air Force. They were delivered to Kjeller on 2 November 1920 and serialled 103 and 105. The fate of 103 is not recorded, but 105 crashed at Kjeller on 29 October 1923.

In the bush conditions of Australia the conversion had a great deal more success. The greater reliability of the Dyak gave it a time between overhaul of 300 hours, whereas for the rotary engines it was only seventy-five hours, and they were less suited to the hot conditions. In addition the Dyak had a starting handle fitted to the rear of the crankshaft so that the engine could be swung by the pilot sitting in his cockpit. This was a feature much appreciated by bush pilots, who found volunteers to swing the propeller very scarce in the outback, and often had to resort to swinging it themselves and then jumping aboard the aircraft before it took off.

The first conversion in Australia was carried out by Harry Broadsmith on a 504K built by his newly created

The rear view of the engine, showing the magnetos on either side. The starting handle was much appreciated by Australian pilots in the bush.

The airship version of the Dyak fitted with a flywheel, and still retaining the starting handle. These were fitted to British, Norwegian, and Japanese airships.

Australian Aircraft & Engineering Co. at Mascot, Sydney. This first aircraft, G-AUBG, was delivered to the Queensland & Northern Territories Aerial Services Co. Ltd (Qantas) on 28 June 1921, and proved exceptionally reliable, carrying 283 passengers and flying 7,400 miles in just a few months at a cost of only 4½ d per mile. It was finally sold to Mr H.J. Taylor of Hawthorn, Victoria, in November 1926 and continued flying with other owners until a 120 hp Airdisco engine was installed in September 1929.

A total of eight of these conversions was made. The second, G-AUBJ, was privately owned by P. Hogarth of Clio, Queensland, and the delivery flight of 1,845 miles was made in twenty hours by J. Treacy at an average speed of 92.5 mph, with the engine giving no trouble at all. This aircraft had other owners and was re-equipped with an Hispano-Suiza engine in 1926.

There were six more Dyak-powered Avro 504s produced by the company, which was also offering Clerget-powered examples. G-AUBS went to Percy Heyde of Nimmitabel, New South Wales; there were also G-AUCZ, G-AUDM, G-AUDR, G-AUEO, and G-AUFP. The latter was a Parnall-built example originally fitted with a 110 hp Le Rhône and serialled E3363, before being put on the British civil register as G-EAFP and then being exported having the Dyak installed after a crash in 1927. At least three of these Dyak-powered Avros took part in the Aerial Derby Race at Sydney in 1922 – 'BJ, 'CZ, and 'DM – reviving memories of Sunbeam's previous involvement in air racing with Alcock's Farman before the war.

A front view of the airship version of the Dyak, showing the large flywheel.

(RIGHT):
A Dyak installed by Sunbeam in one of the Avro 504s the company built. It was a heavier installation than the usual rotary, because of the weight of the frontal radiator and associated plumbing, and did not find favour in European conditions.

(BELOW):
The first aircraft operated by Qantas, the Dyak-powered Avro 504 G-AUBG, erected by the Australian Aircraft & Engineering Co. at Mascot. It flew over 7,000 miles with the infant airline.

Arthur Butler, a former employee at Mascot, bought one of the Dyak 504Ks, G-AUCZ, as a wreck and rebuilt it. He was taught to fly on the aircraft, and then in April 1928 started his own barnstorming operation, operating across the entire eastern states of Australia, before replacing the aircraft with an Avro Avian. Butler later claimed his Dyak 504K was the safest aircraft he ever flew. He later formed his own airline, Butler Air Transport, and so Dyak-powered aircraft formed the first equipment of two of Australia's most famous airlines.

These Dyak-powered Avro 504Ks have the honour of being among the last Sunbeam-engined aircraft to fly, and did so well into the 1920s. In the 1970s one took to the air once again when Qantas borrowed a 504K, A3–4, from the Australian War Memorial, and replaced its rotary engine with a surviving Sunbeam Dyak. This aircraft took part in air displays all over Australia until it was damaged at a display at Nowra, New South Wales. It was then decided to build a reproduction 504K for the Stockman's Hall of Fame Museum in Queensland, and to install the Dyak in that.

In the Sunbeam brochure for 1919 mention was made of a Dyak-engined 'Super Sporting' car, but there is no evidence that this was ever built, even in prototype form. The company's advertisements did state, however, that the Dyak was successfully fitted to both cars and motor-boats. Sunbeam continued to exhibit the Dyak with its other engines at the Olympia Aero Show, but there were no further orders and by January 1922 it was advertising brand-new Dyaks for only £295, reduced from the catalogue price of £950.

The Dyak was probably the best aero-engine Coatalen ever designed. It seems to have been very reliable, and an ideal engine for the light aircraft market. It was just unfortunate that there were unlimited quantities of war-surplus engines, rotaries, and the RAF 1A and Renault air-cooled engines available for only a few pounds.

Technical data

Engine Type water-cooled, six-cylinder upright inline
Manufacturer Sunbeam Motor Car Co., Moorfield Works, Wolverhampton
Horse Power 100/110 hp at 1,400 rpm
Capacity 8.8 litres, 120 mm bore, 130 mm stroke
Valve Type single OHC, two valves/cylinder
Weight 600 lb
Details monobloc cylinder, two Claudel-Hobson BZS.38 carburettors, two ML magnetos, one Remy, direct drive propeller
Nos. Built 160 ordered, delivered to Dec. 1918 nil, delivered post-1918 uncertain – eleven fitted to Avro 504Ks, two to SST airship for UK, others to SST airships for Norway, and two each in airships No.1 and No.4 in Japan. Others in 'motor-cars and powerboats'

Applications

Avro 504K
One, serial u/k, built by Sunbeam Motor Car Co., test-flown from Dunstall Park, Wolverhampton
Two, 103/105, Norwegian Army Air Force
Seven, G-AUBG (c/n D.1)/ G-AUBJ (c/n D.5)/ G-AUBS (c/n D.6)/G-AUCZ (c/n D.7)/G-AUDM (c/n D.8)/G-AUDR (c/n D.9)/G-AUEO (c/n 4), built by Australian Aircraft & Engineering Co. Ltd, Mascot, Sydney
One, G-AUFP (c/n PL.6110), built by Parnall & Co. (previously registered G-EAFP)

Submarine Scout Twin Type non-rigid airships
Seventeen, SST13–29, built at Wormwood Scrubs. Ordered with 2 × 110 hp Berliets, but order changed to Dyaks. Order not completed, possibly only SST13 being finished (first three in order had RR Hawks)

Japanese Navy Airship No.1 (2 × Dyaks)
Japanese Navy Airship No.4 (2 × Dyaks)

Another Australian Dyak-powered Avro 504, the first aircraft operated by Arthur Butler, who founded Butler Air Transport. He later said it was the safest aircraft he ever flew.

800 HP SIKH

Under development at Sunbeam at the end of the war was a huge new engine, the Sikh, designed to be slow revving for use in airships and very large aircraft and seaplanes. This was a V12 engine giving 805 hp at 1,400 rpm, but was radically different in design to all previous Sunbeam engines, except the Tartar.

It had separate steel cylinders, machined all over from steel forgings, and welded to sheet-steel water jackets. This was basically the system used by Rolls-Royce, Mercedes, and the designers of the American Liberty engine. The cylinders were fitted to the crankcase in two rows at an angle of sixty degrees. Each cylinder could be removed from the engine on its own. The cylinders were of 180 mm bore by 210 mm stroke, giving a massive total capacity of 64.113 litres. The pistons were aluminium, and the H section connecting rods were of forked pattern. There were six valves per cylinder in the head, three inlet and three exhaust, operated by rockers and pushrods from a single central camshaft housed in the crankcase at the base of the Vee, and driven by gearwheel directly from the crankshaft. To remove the camshaft it was necessary only to remove the cover at the timing end, and draw it out. The crankshaft was hollow and was carried on eight die-cast white-metal bearings, with lubrication by the compound pressure system. The propeller shaft was driven directly by spur gears, with the propeller geared down from 1,400 rpm to 920 rpm. The propeller shaft, with the thrust bearing, was mounted as an extension to the crankcase.

(Above):
A rear view of the engine showing the pushrods which operated the valves from the single camshaft housed at the base of the Vee. There are two carburettors at each end of the engine.

There were four special Sunbeam-Claudel carburettors, mounted two at each end of the engine, and four twelve-cylinder magnetos driven by skew gears with a special vernier coupling to allow for fine adjustment. Two of the magnetos operated in a clockwise direction and two anti-clockwise, and there were four spark plugs per cylinder. Both hand and air starters were fitted. The weight of the Sikh dry was a massive 1,952 lb giving a weight per bhp of 2.8 lb.

By 11 May 1919 Sunbeam was ready to make preliminary tests of this huge new engine, and it was ready for display at the Paris Salon at the end of the year, along with the Matabele, Manitou, and Dyak. Both there and at the Olympia Aero Show of 1920 the Sikh was the most impressive and powerful aero-engine on display, and though it drew a great deal of interest because of its large size and passed the necessary Air Ministry tests, it did not receive any orders. It is believed never to have been installed in an aircraft. By 1923 Sunbeam was describing it as a 1,000 hp engine, which may have indicated further development work on it.

(OPPOSITE LEFT BOTTOM):
A side view of the immense 800 hp V12 Sikh showing the individual cylinders bolted to the crankcase, and the triple exhaust valves.
(BELOW):
The front of the engine showing the propeller boss, the propeller being geared down to a very slow 920 rpm for airship use.

The government's lack of interest in further airship development at the end of the war, and indeed no interest from the Royal Air Force or the Royal Navy, rather cast a long shadow over the Sikh's future. The even more powerful 1,000 hp 2,450 lb Napier Cub was available, as was the almost as powerful Rolls-Royce Condor, which was considerably lighter at 1,600 lb dry weight. Sunbeam did not give up hope with it however, and it was completely revised for 1929 and given the new application Sikh III, which will be described separately.

Technical data

Engine Type	water-cooled, twelve cylinder, sixty-degree Vee
Manufacturer	Sunbeam Motor Car Co., Moorfield Works, Wolverhampton
Horse Power	800 hp at 1,400 rpm
Capacity	64.113 litre, 180 mm bore, 210 mm stroke
Valve Type	six vertical valves per cylinder (three inlet, three exhaust), single camshaft
Weight	1,952 lb dry
Details	4 × Sunbeam-Claudel carburettors, 4 × twelve-cylinder magnetos, propeller geared to 920 rpm
Nos. Built	prototypes only
Applications	none

400 HP SIKH II

In usual Coatalen practice, he took one bank of the V12 Sikh engine to produce a six-cylinder inline engine, which was called the Sikh II and also the Semi-Sikh, produced 400 hp, and was also largely intended for airships. It had the identical 180 mm × 210 mm single cylinders, bolted to a new crankcase, giving it a capacity of thirty-two litres, and producing 408 bhp at a slow 1,400 rpm, though this resulted in the rather high piston speed of 1,930 ft/min. As the only six-cylinder engine in existence which gave over 400 hp it offered simplicity and accessibility in a high-power engine.

It had the same three inlet and three exhaust valves per cylinder as the Sikh, operated by pushrods from a single camshaft in the aluminium crankcase. Cooling water was circulated by a centrifugal pump and lubrication was on the double gear-pump and dry sump system. Two Claudel-Hobson 'Diffusor' type carburettors were fitted, one at each end of the engine. Ignition was by high-tension magneto, with four spark plugs per cylinder. The dry weight of the engine was 1,120 lb, with a power/weight ratio of 2.8 lb/bhp.

The engine was ordered under Contract 34a/1630/C1457 before the end of the war, but unfortunately for Sunbeam all airship development came to an end, except for some of the airships under construction before the Armistice, and so there were no feasible applications for the Sikh II, as with its larger brother.

Technical data

Engine Type	water-cooled, six-cylinder inline
Manufacturer	Sunbeam Motor Car Co., Moorfield Works, Wolverhampton
Horse Power	400/425 hp at 1,400 rpm
Capacity	32 litres, 180 mm bore, 210 mm stroke
Valve Type	six vertical valves per cylinder (three inlet, three exhaust), single camshaft in crankcase
Weight	1,120 lb dry
Details	two Sunbeam-Claudel carburettors, two six-cylinder magnetos, propeller geared to 920 rpm
Nos. Built	prototypes only
Applications	none

(ABOVE): *This is a three-quarter rear view with a very good view of the long pushrods operated by the single camshaft, a feature common to its V12 cousin.*

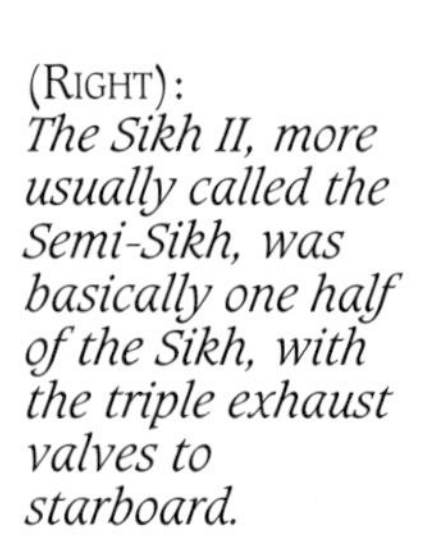

(RIGHT): *The Sikh II, more usually called the Semi-Sikh, was basically one half of the Sikh, with the triple exhaust valves to starboard.*

1,000 HP SIKH III

Possibly inspired by the revised British Airship Programme, which had led to the construction of the R.100 and the R.101, in 1928/9 Sunbeam completely reworked their V12 Sikh engine to produce a more powerful engine suitable for airships. The cylinders were again separate, but turned from billets of carbon steel with cast steel heads, with the integral water jacket casings welded and screwed to them. They were of the same size as the Sikh I, at 180 mm bore and 210 mm stroke, giving the same capacity of 64.113 litres, but the valve arrangement was entirely different. The compression ratio was 5:1.

There were only five valves not six, two inlet and three exhaust, and they were operated by pushrods situated between the cylinder blocks, rather than the single camshaft

The Sikh, though based on the Sikh I with the same capacity, had fundamental differences not altogether apparent in this view which does show the rocker gear covers and the twin magnetos bolted on top of the timing gear cover. The three exhaust ports per cylinder can be seen, but on this engine there were only two inlet valves per cylinder operated by pushrod from camshafts between the Vee.

The Sikh III under test at the Moorfield Works in 1928. The engine was developed for use in airships just as the British Airship programme expired.

housed in the crankcase. The valve rocker gear was completely covered by an aluminium cover on each head. The crankcase was an aluminium casting, the bottom being formed by a detachable sump. A timing gear cover was welded to the rear of the crankcase, while the front end was covered by the reduction gear housing. Dry sump lubrication was employed. The crankshaft was a machined nickel-chrome steel forging driving a geared-down propeller shaft through a ground spur gearing with a ratio of 38:67.

There were two six-cylinder carburettors mounted between the banks, each supplying three cylinders from each bank at its end of the engine. Ignition was provided by two BTK high-tension magnetos fitted to the top of the timing cover, and there were two spark plugs per cylinder. The engine was started with the aid of a Bristol starter.

The Sikh III was a massive engine, weighing a huge 2,760 lb, and had a normal rated output of 1,000 bhp at 1,650 rpm, with a geared propeller. It was easily the largest engine at the Aero Show at Olympia in July 1929. Unfortunately for the company such a heavy, slow-revving engine was only really suitable for airships, and on 5 October 1930 the R.101 crashed and put an end to the British Airship Programme, the Sikh III's only hope.

Technical data

Engine Type	water-cooled, twelve cylinder, sixty-degree Vee
Manufacturer	Sunbeam Motor Car Co., Moorfield Works, Wolverhampton
Horse Power	1,000 bhp at 1,650 rpm
Capacity	64.113 litres, 180 mm bore, 210 mm stroke
Valve Type	five vertical valves per cylinder, two single camshafts
Weight	2,760 lb dry
Dimensions	length 7 ft 2 in., width 3 ft 4 in., height 5 ft 4.5 in.
Details	two six-cylinder carburettors, two magnetos, geared propeller
Nos. Built	prototypes only
Applications	none

100 HP PATHAN

In the 1920s there was a great deal of research into the use of diesel engines in aviation. Their lower fuel consumption, and less volatile fuel, which was attractive in airship use, seemed to be key advantages. Coatalen was to spend a great deal of time working on diesels, not least for the Sunbeam commercial vehicle department, and his first diesel aviation project was basically to turn the 100 hp Dyak petrol engine into a diesel. Work began in 1928, and by July 1929 the new engine was on display at the Olympia Aero Show.

The Pathan diesel, developed from the Dyak petrol engine, showing very clean lines.

The new engine was known as the P.1, but was also named the Pathan, continuing the Sunbeam system of tribal names for its engines. Like the Dyak the engine was a six-cylinder inline of monobloc construction, but looked much neater of course without all the magnetos, carburettors, and associated plumbing and wiring of the normal petrol engine. It retained the Dyak's bore and stroke of 120 mm × 130 mm giving the same capacity of 8.8 litres, and developed a very creditable 100 bhp at 1,500 rpm.

The engine was fitted with a special type of fuel injection valve fed by a common fuel pipe, which apparently permitted the engine to be started from cold without any auxiliary means. A higher crankshaft speed than the Dyak was achieved, and the propeller continued to be directly driven. The consumption of the crude fuel oil used was claimed to be 0.4 pints per bhp/hr, with a lubricating oil consumption of 0.03 pints per bhp/hr.

The Pathan was destined never to be fitted to an aircraft, and the parlous state of STD Motors' finances probably mitigated further development of diesel aero-engines, especially as the British Airship Programme was cancelled. This did not end Coatalen's interest in this type of engine, however. After he left Sunbeam and returned permanently to France, he began work on a 600 hp V12 diesel aero-engine which is described in Appendix IV.

Technical data

Engine Type water-cooled diesel, six-cylinder inline
Manufacturer Sunbeam Motor Car Co., Moorfield Works, Wolverhampton
Horse Power 100 bhp at 1,500 rpm
Capacity 8.8 litres, 120 mm bore, 130 mm stroke
Nos. Built prototypes only
Applications none

2,000 HP SUNBEAM

By 1929 Sunbeam's 200 mph land-speed record had been beaten three times and the record raised to 231.446 mph by Henry Segrave's *Golden Arrow*. Louis Coatalen set about regaining the record and producing a car which would be the first to break the 250 mph barrier, just as Sunbeam cars had been the first to break the 150 mph and 200 mph barriers.

(ABOVE):
One of the V12 engines built for the Silver Bullet *land-speed record car, breaking with Sunbeam tradition by being a fifty-degree Vee.*

(BELOW):
The crankshaft for the Silver Bullet *engines, giving some idea of its length.*

There was now no engine in the Sunbeam locker capable of giving the required power, coupled with low weight and small frontal area, and so Coatalen designed a brand-new engine, and from the outset he insisted that this engine would form the beginning of a radical programme to develop a large, powerful aero-engine. In this, the project echoed the development of the 225 hp Mohawk engine in 1913, which had first been installed in a car chassis for racing and record-breaking. The car would have two of the new engines mounted in tandem, and, in a clear riposte to Segrave's *Golden Arrow*, the car was named the *Silver Bullet*.

The engine was a V12, with the banks set at only fifty degrees to help reduce frontal area. The cylinders were over-square 140 mm × 130 mm totalling 24.020 litres, and giving 490 hp at 2,400 rpm when running unsupercharged. At first Quadruple Roots superchargers were fitted, but these were later replaced with a single large centrifugal blower driven at 17,000 rpm by gearing at the rear of the rear engine and fed by twin Amal carburettors, delivering the mixture to the induction manifold in the centre of the Vee, which Coatalen claimed gave an output of 2,000 hp, enabling him to make the claim that the *Silver Bullet* was a 4,000 hp car. Clearly a certain amount of exaggeration took place, as it had with the '1,000 hp Sunbeam'.

The light alloy cylinder blocks were cast in groups of three, and had Nitralloy steel liners. There were four valves per cylinder operated by twin overhead camshafts placed directly above the valve stems, and moving pivoted cam followers. The exhaust valves had hollow stems and were oil-cooled. The camshafts were driven by a train of gears at the front of each engine. There was only one spark plug per cylinder, and this turned out to be a disadvantage as a dud plug was very hard to trace on a windy beach. The Nitrasteel crankshafts were milled from solid billets, and were carried on seven split-race roller bearings. One end of each connecting rod was forked for connection with its opposite pair, and the

(ABOVE):
One of the Silver Bullet *engines under test. Quoted as giving 490 hp without supercharging, their claimed output of 2,000 hp hides the true power they might have given if converted for aeronautical use.*

(RIGHT):
The Silver Bullet *at Moorfield Works before the bodywork was fitted, showing the compact nature of the installation.*

connecting rod big-end bearings had split-race roller bearings, with double rows of bearings.

The cooling system for the car was unusual as there was no radiator, and it involved an 11.5 cu. ft ice tank and a one-gallon mixing tank just under the fuel tank in the nose. The ice tank had to be filled with 5.5 cwt of ice after each run.

In the *Silver Bullet* the engines were placed in tandem with the driver sitting behind them, with his seat between the two contra-rotating propeller shafts which transmitted the drive to the rear axle. The frontal area was only 11.8 sq.ft as against 19.5 sq.ft for the 1,000 hp Sunbeam, and the track was reduced from 4 ft 7.5 in. to 3 ft 7in.

The first engine, fitted with the Quadruple Roots supercharger, was bench-tested in mid-November 1929, and both engines had been fitted into the chassis for testing on a dynamometer on 1 February 1930. Such was the urgency with land-speed record attempts in the 1920s and 1930s, as the record was raised so often, that day and night shifts were instituted at the works, the two teams usually meeting one another at six a.m. and six p.m. each day. The *Silver Bullet* was unveiled publicly on 21 February at a reception at the Sunbeam factory given by Coatalen, Kaye Don, the designated driver for the record and an experienced Sunbeam racing driver, as well as C.B. Kay, the production manager, and Hugh

(LEFT): *The* Silver Bullet *making one of its runs on Daytona Beach, which was in poor condition that early in the year, not helping Sunbeam's attempts to produce the first 250 mph record.*

(BELOW): *The* Silver Bullet *on fire; the last throw of the dice for Sunbeam in the two worlds of land-speed record-breaking and aero-engines.*

Rose, the designer of the car. Most of the men who had helped build the car were there to help push it into the specially built crate for delivery to America. Kaye Don and the Sunbeam team of five mechanics under Henry Wilding sailed for America on 26 February 1930.

They arrived at Daytona Beach on 8 March, and from then on suffered a catalogue of technical and weather problems. The engines had never been properly bench-tested in Wolverhampton, and numerous problems appeared, especially with the carburettors and supercharger. Louis Coatalen arrived on 16 March after only a couple of practice runs had been achieved. The long, thin *Silver Bullet* was almost uncontrollable on the bumpy beach and the best time Don achieved was 186.045 mph, well below the land-speed record, though he did take the American record for five miles at 151.623 mph. The team might have continued, but the American Automobile Club was not prepared to man the timing apparatus on the beach indefinitely.

The team came home 'with their bulldog tail between their legs', with the avowed intention of returning the following year, but though attempts were made to make the *Silver Bullet* work, the poor financial state of the Sunbeam Car Co. at the time meant that was out of the question.

The V12 engines of the *Silver Bullet* were the last attempt Sunbeam ever made to produce an aero-engine. Only two of them were built, and neither went anywhere near an aeroplane.

Technical data

Engine Type	water-cooled, twelve-cylinder, fifty-degree Vee
Manufacturer	Sunbeam Motor Car Co., Moorfield Works, Wolverhampton
Horse Power	unsupercharged, 490 hp supercharged, '2,000 hp'
Capacity	24 litres, 140 mm bore, 130 mm stroke
Valve Type	four per cylinder, twin overhead camshafts
Applications	

Sunbeam *Silver Bullet* for land-speed record attempt (two engines)

The Sunbeam Bomber

In November 1916 the Committee for Imperial Defence issued its list of requirements for future aircraft and seaplanes. One of the aircraft envisaged, the Type 7, was a single-seat bomber to be powered by the forthcoming 200 hp Hispano-Suiza or Sunbeam Arab engines, or something similar. It was to be capable of carrying a load consisting of the pilot, one machine-gun with 500 rounds of ammunition, fuel for five hours at 100 mph at 10,000 ft, and a bomb load of four 65 lb bombs together with the necessary sighting gear. Top speed was to be not less than 110 mph at 10,000 ft, and the time to reach that altitude was to be less than thirty minutes. Minimum speed was to be 50 mph.

The Sunbeam Motor Car Co. directors decided to institute the design of an aircraft to fulfil this requirement. They were not the only company brought into aircraft manufacture during the war to start up their own design department, nor even the only aero-engine manufacturer to do so, but their lack of success was to be the most pronounced. The name of the designer of the aircraft has eluded all searches, and in view of the inauspicious aircraft produced, perhaps it is fortunate.

He laid out a two-bay biplane powered, of course, by the 200 hp Sunbeam Arab, driving a two-blade propeller. His basic design goal was clearly to gather the fuel and bomb-load as near the centre of gravity as possible, and therefore the pilot's cockpit was placed well aft in the fuselage. The single Vickers gun was sited on the engine, and was therefore unique in being the only remotely fired gun to fly during World War One, the pilot being a full nine feet behind it. This meant the pilot had no way of clearing a stoppage, a not infrequent event with Vickers machine-guns. The bomb-load was carried externally and was normally three 100 lb bombs, but there was provision to carry more with tandem, tubular type carriers. The fuselage was a simple square box girder construction with a curved upper fairing. Empty weight was 1,915 lb.

(Right): *The sole Sunbeam bomber, N515, showing the distance of the pilot's cockpit to the rear. The title on the rear fuselage says* S.B.Aeroplane, *which suggests 'Sunbeam Bomber Aeroplane'.*

(Below): *A gathering of people close to the Sunbeam Bomber, unfortunately anonymous, though the one by the roundel looks a little like Louis Coatalen. The aircraft was first erected at Castle Bromwich, which is where this photograph was possibly taken.*

This three-quarter rear view of the aircraft shows the quite broad gap between the wings. The rival Sopwith B.1 looked far more compact.

The design was submitted in January 1917 and two examples were ordered under Contract CP102580/17, and given the serials N515 and N516. The aircraft were given the Sunbeam Constructor's Numbers 171 and 172. This reflected the aircraft previously ordered from the company – forty Short Type 827s, twenty Short Bombers (though five were cancelled), sixty Avro 504Bs, and fifty Short Type 310-A4s, making 170 previous aircraft.

The first Sunbeam Bomber, N515, was reported to be at Castle Bromwich in October 1917, though the date of its first flight was not recorded. There was probably a great number of problems with the aircraft, one suspects with its Arab engine as much as anything, because the first expectation of its imminent arrival at Martlesham Heath for testing was not recorded until 4 May 1918. The Martlesham Heath weekly report on aircraft under test continued to record their expectation of the Sunbeam's arrival 'next week' or 'shortly' for the next eight weeks. Meanwhile the rival Sopwith B.1 Bomber had completed its test in May and was sent on to the Royal Aircraft Establishment.

The Sunbeam finally arrived for its performance tests on 18 July 1917, and these had been completed by 31 August. They did not reveal a very sparkling performance. With a military loaded weight of 2,952 lb the aircraft managed a top speed of 112.5 mph at 6,500 ft, 109 mph at 10,000 ft, and 99.5 mph at 15,000 ft. Climb was eight minutes and ten seconds to 6,500 ft, fourteen minutes and twenty seconds to 10,000 ft, and twenty-eight minutes and five seconds to 15,000 ft. Service ceiling was 18,500 ft and endurance 4.5 hours at 15,000 ft.

The Sopwith B.1 Bomber, with the 200 hp Hispano engine, had revealed slightly better figures with a far handier layout. Its top speed was 118.5 mph at 10,000 ft, and its service ceiling 19,000 ft, though its climbing performance was slightly worse than the Sunbeam, taking fifteen minutes and thirty seconds to 10,000 ft and twenty-nine minutes and thirty-six seconds to 15,000 ft, and endurance was also less at 3.75 hours. The Sunbeam suffered in comparison because of the poor view of the pilot, and a heavier airframe. There were no production orders for this class of aircraft, the DH.4/DH.9 being far more useful in every respect. There is no record of the second Sunbeam prototype, N516, having been built.

By the beginning of September the first prototype, N515, was awaiting reallocation, and on the 18th it went to the Isle of Grain. At Grain it was used for comparison tests of mineral and castor oils in engine lubrication but its final fate is not recorded, though it is believed to have been given a new RAF serial number, H4424.

Technical data

Engine Type	1 × 200 hp Sunbeam Arab V8, water-cooled
Manufacturer	Sunbeam Motor Car Co., Moorfield Works, Wolverhampton
Weight	1,915 lb empty, 2,952 lb loaded.
Dimensions	wing span 42 ft, length 31 ft 6 in., height 11 ft, wing area 466 sq.ft
Propeller No.	AD646
Performance	top speed 112.5 mph at 6,500 ft, 109 mph at 10,000 ft, 99.5 mph at 15,000 ft. Climb to 6,500 ft 8 mins 10 secs, to 10,000 ft 14 mins 20 secs, to 15,000 ft 28 mins 5 secs. Service ceiling 18,500 ft. Endurance 4.5 hours at 15,000 ft
Armament	one fixed forward firing Vickers machine-gun on top of engine, synchronised to fire through propeller, 3 × 100 lb bombs on external racks

PART THREE

Other Wolverhampton Aero-engine Manufacturers

Star Engineering Co.

In 1918 there were four Wolverhampton companies manufacturing aero-engines, a rather remarkable figure for a town of its size. All of them were also car manufacturers, and in fact were not the only car makers in the town, but there is no doubt that there was great rivalry between them, and this was particularly so between Sunbeam and the Star Engineering Co., whose factory was only four hundred yards from the Moorfield Works.

The workers in the two factories went to work together, the directors of the companies met socially and in the council chambers, and there is no doubt that when Star turned to aviation in 1910, their personnel felt a degree of oneupmanship, and felt aggrieved when the tables were turned a couple of years later.

The Star Company was founded by Edward Lisle who began building bicycles in 1869. The Lisle family came from Yorkshire, Edward's grandfather coming down to Wolverhampton to find work as a ledger clerk in Blakenhall. Two of his three sons, Richard and Thomas, ran a japanning and tin company in the district, and Edward, who was born in 1852, joined the company with his brother Alfred.

The progress of the company mirrored that of John Marston's company, and like Marston the Lisles went from japanning to making bicycles, Edward and Alfred's first being advertised in 1868, but they did not form a company until 1876, three years before Marston was established in the business. Edward Lisle teamed up with Ernest John Sharratt to form Sharratt & Lisle with a works in Stewart Street, just round the corner from Jeddo Street where Sunbeamland was to be established. In the 1890s the company was restyled the Star Cycle Company (Sharratt & Lisle) and was floated on the stock market, with Sir Charles Shaw MP as chairman of the board.

In April 1897 the first Star car was built, after Edward Lisle had somehow acquired a Benz Velo and stripped it down to discover its secrets. The first Star was a copy of the Benz converted to imperial measurements and incorporating certain improvements. Star took out a licence from Benz to put it into production, and while this was going on, just along the road Harry Dinsdale was about to knock a nail in the wall of John Marston's old coach-house to hang his coat prior to hand-building the first Sunbeam car.

Production of the Star-Benz soon reached six cars a week, and by 1900 Star was able to begin designing its own cars. A new factory was acquired in 1903 in neighbouring Frederick Street, and the old Stewart Street works was turned over to the manufacture of a cheaper car under the Briton name. Then in 1905 another marque was established, the Starling car, which was also a cheaper vehicle than the standard production Star.

Edward Lisle Sr, the founder of the Star Engineering Co.

In 1909 Edward Lisle created a separate company to build his cars, the Star Engineering Co., just as John Marston had separated his cycle and car businesses. He was soon to close down the cycle business, which had faded away, and concentrate on building cars.

Briton and Star cars with Edward Lisle at the wheel of the Briton. Sir James Percy, the Irish newspaperman, is standing alongside.

Just as John Marston had created a new company, Villiers Engineering, for his son Charles, Edward Lisle Junior took the Starling cars range which had previously been produced by the Star Cycle Co. alongside the Star cars, and produced them under the Briton name. In 1912 the Briton Company was floated on the stock market and moved to a new factory established in Lower Walsall Street.

Lisle had started producing bicycles a little before John Marston, had built his first car two years before Marston, and was now to be the first to get 'off the ground' in the new industry of aviation, and a new company was formed with a capital of £1,000, the Star Aeroplane Co. In 1910 it built a monoplane and the four-cylinder water-cooled engine to power it. Both aircraft and engine were designed by Granville Eastwood Bradshaw, who had been born in Preston in 1892 and was therefore only nineteen years of age when he became Star's chief designer of aircraft and aero-engines. It had originally been the intention to use one of the company's car engines to power the aircraft but they proved unsuitable, so a purpose-built inline engine was constructed giving 40 hp at 1,450 rpm. It had a bore of four inches and a stroke of five, weighing 175 lb including the water pump and Simms magneto. The engine drove a 6 ft 8 in. two-blade propeller.

The Star engine assembly shop, showing the labour-intensive nature of car manufacturing, and the ready use of the hand file.

(Above):
The Star Monoplane at the Olympia Aero Show in April 1910, highlighting the curious arrangement of the tail. It was on offer for £450.
(Left Centre):
A picture of the Star Monoplane at Dunstall Park, but showing basic differences to the aircraft displayed at Olympia, with smaller wheels, twin skids, and a single king-post, rather than an A frame. Joe Lisle appears to be the pilot, but whether this was before or after Olympia is unknown.
(Left):
The Star in flight with Joe Lisle at the controls, just before the June meeting at Dunstall Park. Note the similar configuration of the undercarriage to that at Olympia. The fuselage appears to be uncovered, which is another difference, and the fin/rudder appears to have collapsed.

If the engine was not unusual, the same thing could not be said of the monoplane, which featured a very unorthodox tail which was of cross-shape with four diamond-shaped moveable members, two vertical ones pivoted on the stern post, and two horizontal on a spar at right angles to the stern post. When either pair was deflected in unison, the effect was that of a normal rudder or elevator, but each could also be moved in the opposite direction to its pair, creating a twisting motion which Bradshaw hoped would control the aircraft laterally without the recourse to wing-warping or ailerons. Other than the control surfaces, the Star Monoplane was of fairly conventional design, with a fabric-covered triangular girder fuselage, wings wire-braced to a king-post, and a double-skid undercarriage with rubber-sprung wheels. The Star was exhibited at the Olympia Aero Show in April 1910 and was offered for sale at £450.

The first attempts at flight were made with Bradshaw as pilot on 8 June at Dunstall Park, Wolverhampton. The first flying meeting of the year was being held there under the auspices of the Midland Aero Club, and the Star was entered, though Bradshaw had first to gain his aviator's certificate if he were to compete. Despite numerous hops over the next few days, and the replacement of the propeller, the monoplane failed to fly, and was taken away to be redesigned.

Possibly inspired by what they witnessed at the flying meeting, with the Farman biplanes of Grahame-White and Lancelot Gibbs and the similar Short Type 27 of Cecil Grace being easily the best aircraft to take part, Star built a Farman-type biplane which was ready the following year. No details of it have survived, including the engine which powered it, but it would be unusual if that were not a Star engine. It has been said that a 50 hp engine was built for 1911, and it would

The Star as it reappeared in 1911 with a conventional tail, rounded wing-tips, and a twin-skid undercarriage structure similar to the picture of the aircraft stationary at Dunstall Park.

most likely have been similar to the 1910 engine.

Close examination of the Blériot/Humber monoplanes which took part in the flying meeting will also have influenced the complete revision of the Star Monoplane which took place, with it re-emerging around June 1911 as quite a conventional-looking aircraft for the day. The strange tail arrangement had been altered with only the horizontal diamond-shaped surfaces retained, and working together as elevators. The vertical surfaces had been replaced with a conventional triangular fin and rudder. The triangular-shaped fuselage was retained, but without any fabric covering. The thirty-seven-foot-span wings were double-surfaced with a maximum five-inch camber and lateral control was now by warping, the pilot turning the wheel on his control column to accomplish this. Fore and aft movement of the control column controlled the elevator, and there was also a rudder bar. The pilot's controls were completed by a throttle lever on the port longeron. The 40 hp Star engine was retained from the previous year, but with the radiator sited vertically behind it.

Joe Lisle, son of the proprietor, took the controls of the revised monoplane at Dunstall Park with the words 'I'll get this grasshopper off the ground if it's the last thing I do!' He is said to have flown the aircraft just once, his father, Edward, being so alarmed at the sight of his son aloft that he banned all further aviation work by the company. Nevertheless, a contemporary report states that Granville Bradshaw also flew the revised monoplane both at Dunstall Park and at Brooklands. Bradshaw had left Star and had been appointed the chief designer of the recently renamed All-British Engine Co., later ABC Motors, which had moved to Walton-on-Thames. His first design for ABC was a 30 hp water-cooled four-cylinder inline based on his Star engine.

The fate of the Star Monoplane has not been recorded but the engine has somehow survived. It was removed from the aircraft and sold to a gentleman who fitted it to an ornithopter. After the failure of that venture it powered a hydroplane for some years and was later given to the RAF Museum. Despite having no connection whatsoever with the RAF or even the Royal Flying Corps, the Star is on display at Hendon.

By 1914 the Star Engineering Co. was the sixth largest motor-car manufacturer in the country. It had indulged in motor racing without the conspicuous success of rivals Sunbeam, though Dick Lisle did achieve some, notably the winning of eleven Class E records at Brooklands in 1913 in the 20 hp Star Comet racer, one of the first with streamlined bodywork. The company even raced against Sunbeams in the

ADVANCE SHEET.

STAR 40 B.H.P.

AEROPLANE ENGINE.

4 Cylinders.—4" bore × 5" stroke, machined from solid forging with water jackets of copper, deposited electrically, leaving a water space of ⅜" all round cylinders and ⅝" on cylinder head.

Valves.—Overhead type both mechanically operated from cam shaft which is situated in crank case so as to receive a good supply of oil.

Crank Case.—Cast aluminium in halves, lower half removable without disturbing any bearings. Oil pump on one end of cam shaft, and water pump on the other end. Simms' Magneto driven off crankshaft, splash lubrication on connecting rods and pressure in timing gear case.

Crankshaft machined from solid bar with exceptionally large bearings, 2" diameter throughout, is supported on five bearings and drilled hollow for lightness.

Normal speed of engine 14.50 R.P.M., B.H.P. 40, weight complete including magneto, oil pump and water pump 175 lbs.

Price £200 net.

STAR ENGINEERING Co., Ltd.,

WOLVERHAMPTON.

A proof copy of an advertisement for the Star engine.

1914 TT Race, but both Star cars failed to finish, whereas Sunbeam won the race. During the War its commercial vehicles continued to be built for the armed forces, and it also manufactured ammunition, as did the Briton Company.

The wings of the Avro 504s built by Sunbeam were subcontracted out to Star, and in 1918 Star Engineering accepted an order for 400 80 hp Renault engines. Despite Edward Lisle's pre-war antipathy towards aeronautical production, he was not slow to turn a penny. The 80 hp Renault was a development of the pre-war 75 hp Renault, which had seen

(Left):
The 40 hp Star engine as fitted to the 1911 Monoplane.

(Below):
A head-on view of the 1911 version of the Monoplane.

widespread use in 1914/15. It was a V8 air-cooled engine with ninety degrees between cylinder banks. The 80 hp Renault was fitted to DH.6 trainers when the Curtiss OX-5 engine was not available, and by 1918 was getting rather long in the tooth. The first ten were delivered in June 1918 with two the following month, at which point the remaining 388 were cancelled, probably because of the age of the design and the adequate stocks available. The total number of Avro 504 wings built by Star is unknown but is believed to equate to the total number of aircraft built by Sunbeam.

After the war Star returned to the manufacture of cars and commercial vehicles for the civil market. They continued in the various cramped premises in the Frederick Street/Stewart Street area, which made mass production almost impossible, even if Edward Lisle had not been set

A preserved Renault V8 engine at Duxford. Star had begun the mass production of these engines but had delivered only twelve when orders were cancelled at the end of the war.

against it. He preferred to make high-quality cars, which was to be the company's downfall because it could never sell enough at a price to cover costs. The Briton Company did not survive the return of peace and was put into liquidation in 1922, the factory being taken over by another Wolverhampton motor manufacturer, AJS.

The difficulties of the two companies in the post-war climate proved too much for Edward Lisle to bear. On 14 February 1921 he took his own life, drowning himself in the Staffordshire and Worcestershire canal at Coven near Wolverhampton. Joseph Lisle took over the reins and continued his father's philosophy of preferring to build just one good car a day rather than trying to compete with mass production.

In the peak years of production between 1921 and 1925 Star built up to 1,000 cars a year, but by 1927 the number had fallen to just 105, and in 1928 the company was sold to Sydney Guy. The works in the Frederick Street area were sold off and Star was moved to a new factory in Showell Road, Bushbury, nearer to Guy Motors, renamed the Star Motor Company. Both companies went through a bad patch, and Star was put into receivership in March 1932, largely to protect Guy Motors. Once more the parallel history of Star and Sunbeam continued when Sunbeam followed them out of business only three years later.

The Star gearbox shop in Frederick Street in 1927, just before the move to Bushbury after being taken over by Guy, and its final demise.

Guy Motors Ltd

When Sydney Guy left the Sunbeam Motor Car Co. to form his own company in 1914, he saw a need for well-built light commercial vehicles. His new organisation, Guy Motors Ltd, was floated in May 1914, and a factory was built at Fallings Park, Wolverhampton, on the other side of the town from his former employer. His first product was a 30 cwt lorry, using a much lighter pressed steel frame with a special patented suspension, and fitted with an overdrive. He also produced a light 'mail car'.

Just as his company was getting onto its feet, the Ministry of Munitions stepped in and took over the works for military production, Guy becoming the largest manufacturer of firing mechanisms for depth charges, among other items. In the early part of 1918 the company was brought into aero-engine production, and the engines ordered were designed by none other than Granville Bradshaw, the man who had designed the Star aero-engine and aircraft of 1910, and had flown them at Dunstall Park just half a mile from the Guy factory.

When Granville Bradshaw had joined the Aeroplane Engine Co. of Redbridge, which was renamed the All-British Engine Co. at his suggestion, he had designed a series of water-cooled engines. The first was an inline four-cylinder engine of 30 hp, not unlike the engine he had designed for Star. This was followed by a more ambitious ninety-degree 60 hp V8 engine, and then a 100 hp V8, neither of which was too successful. During the war he had turned his attention to air-cooled engines, starting with the 30 hp two-cylinder, horizontally opposed Gnat. A total of seventeen Gnats was built, and had a few applications, mostly in aircraft built after the war. Harry Hawker, with whom Bradshaw would have had a great deal of contact as ABC Motors operated from Walton-on-Thames to be near Brooklands, apparently bet him that he could not build a six-cylinder radial engine. It has not been recorded who won the bet, as the resulting six-cylinder Mosquito, using six Gnat cylinders, was not a success, though a prototype was fitted to the BAT FK.22.

Bradshaw then designed a much more practical radial engine, the seven-cylinder Wasp. It had a bore of 115 mm and a stroke of 150 mm giving a capacity of 10.78 litres and 170 hp at 1,800 rpm, with a diamater of only forty-two inches and a weight of only 290 lb. It was seen as a potential fighter engine, and a number of aircraft manufacturers began designing fighters to suit it. ABC Motors did not have large manufacturing facilities itself so orders were placed elsewhere, the lion's share, an order for 212 Wasps, going to Vickers Ltd which had a close association with ABC. Small orders were given to other companies, mostly motor manufacturers the Ministry of Munitions wished to bring into aero-engine production. Twenty were ordered from the Sheffield Simplex Motor Co., and a dozen each from Crossley Motors, Galloway Engineering, Gwynne, and Guy Motors.

Close-up of the ABC Wasp installation in the Sopwith Snail fighter of 1918.

(ABOVE):
Rear view of a Wasp showing the exhaust collector ring. Guy Motors completed one of their order for twelve Wasps, and were about 80% to 90% complete on the rest when production was transferred to Selsdon Engineering.

(BELOW):
An Avro 504K fitted with an ABC Wasp, post-war.

On 19 April 1918 Guy Motors received a contract for the supply of twelve experimental ABC Wasp engines, and on 12 April 1918 one for a single experimental ABC Dragonfly radial aero-engine. Work on these two orders was carried out simultaneously at the Fallings Park Factory with some urgency. The orders were on the basis of cost plus profit, with 350% being the agreed figure for overhead charges and profit (the normal overhead charges for the machine shop were 150%, and the fitters shop 75%).

Following the Wasp, Bradshaw had designed a radial of twice the power, the nine-cylinder Dragonfly. It had a bore of 120.65 mm, a stroke of 158.75 mm, and a capacity of 12.71 litres. On the bench it showed a power output of 320 hp for a dry weight of only 662 lb. The ministry had not learnt its lesson from the Sunbeam Arab débâcle – though to be fair the extreme problems with that engine were still not entirely clear – and decided that the Dragonfly was clearly the engine to power a whole phalanx of future aircraft.

Dragonfly engines were ordered in their hundreds from a total of seventeen manufacturers. The eventual total ordered was to be 11,930, and 600 of these were from Guy Motors. The company had already received, on 4 April 1918, an Instruction To Proceed on the production of their first 300 Dragonflies.

A memorandum written on 3 March 1918 about the situation with the new single-seat fighters which were being developed, revealed that the Bentley BR.2 rotary-powered air-

An ABC Dragonfly engine. Guy only completed one prototype Dragonfly, production orders for 600 being cancelled at the end of the war.

craft which were then being tested at Martlesham Heath – the Nieuport BN.1, the Sopwith Snipe, the Boulton & Paul Bobolink, and the Austin Osprey – though superior in performance to the Sopwith Camel they were due to replace, were not superior to the SE.5a and the Sopwith Dolphin. However, it was considered that the ABC Wasp-powered BAT Bantam which was being developed would be superior to all existing types.

It was recommended that the winner of the best of the BR.2-powered fighters, which was to be the Snipe, should only be ordered in relatively small numbers, only those which were needed to replace the Camels. Nevertheless, it was also recommended that the ABC Wasp should not be pursued with any vigour, because the larger and more powerful Dragonfly was likely to be a more useful engine, with many different applications, whereas the Wasp was only really applicable to single-seat fighters.

This may well be why the entire Guy production of Wasp engines was now turned over to the Selsdon Engineering Co. of Croydon after only the one had been completed. It was estimated that 80% to 90% of the order for twelve had already been completed by Guy, excluding modifications, so Selsdon Engineering had just to complete the work, and Guy was now free to concentrate on massive production of the new Dragonfly engine.

Guy Motors was congratulated by William Weir, the Director General of Aircraft Production and Supply, for the speed with which it built the first experimental Dragonfly in May 1918. The prototype was built from first machining operation to initial test-run in the fantastically short time of only twenty-four days. A more tangible reward was the receipt of another Instruction To Proceed with a second batch of 300 Dragonflies on 6 July 1918.

Though Guy took very little time with the prototype Dragonfly, it took much longer getting the engine into mass production, and by the Armistice had not delivered any. Like all the other manufacturers the company was held up by attempted modifications to the engine to make it run properly. When the Dragonfly had finally been tested in the air it was found that it overheated very rapidly, the cylinders sometimes running cherry red, making the power fall away. In addition it was Bradshaw's bad luck to have designed the engine at its critical vibration frequency, so that after only a few hours' running it tried to shake itself to pieces. In addition it was overweight, higher of fuel consumption than promised, and very rarely ran above 295 hp. By the end of the year only twenty-seven production engines had been delivered by all manufacturers, and only 1,147 were to be delivered in the end, all the others being cancelled. Guy Motors had its full total of 600 cancelled, and so only ever completely finished two aero-engines, one Wasp and one prototype Dragonfly.

At the end of the war, however, Guy was apparently working on its own liquid-cooled V12, but that too was cancelled, no engine having been built. Following the liquidation of the aero-engine contracts the company was awarded £65,000 in cancellation charges. After the war Guy Motors went back to making trucks, but also made cars. In 1919 Guy put into production the first V8 car. The engine had 72 mm × 125 mm cylinders with the cylinder heads in pairs. The Guy V8 car remained in production until 1925 but the company's fortune was based on its trucks and, later, buses.

Guy Motors was in fact to last longer than all the other Wolverhampton motor manufacturers, taking over the Star Engineering Co. in 1928 and later the Sunbeam Trolley Bus Company. Guy was itself taken over by Jaguar Cars in the 1960s and then absorbed into the British Motor Corporation. It was closed down when part of the Leyland Group in the 1970s.

A Guy advertisement just after the end of the War in which the company highlights its manufacture of aero-engines.

Clyno Engineering Co.

Clyno was originally a Northampton engineering concern founded by cousins Frank and Ailwyn Smith. They had been involved in the motor-cycle trade, building pulleys for belt-driven motor-cycles, and decided to produce their own bikes. Rather than building their own engines they bought them in, from Stevens Bros of Pelham Street, Wolverhampton, a 2.5 hp single and a 6 hp twin. The first Clyno motor-cycles appeared in 1909. The Stevens brothers had started by building engines for the Wearwell Cycle Company of Wolverhampton, and when this company went out of business in 1909, they decided to make their own complete motor-cycles, setting up a separate company and using the initials of one of the brothers, AJS. Production of AJS motor-cycles was indirectly financed by John Marston, as Harry Stevens used the money paid to him for designing the first Sunbeam motor-cycle engine, a 2.5 hp 75 mm × 79 mm single cylinder. The Stevens brothers' companies were often assisted financially by the brothers taking outside work, and in fact it was only about this time that they took on their first paid employee outside their extensive family, when Eric Williams joined them, having just failed to get a fitter's job at the Sunbeam Motor Car Co. just up the road.

Early AJS motor-cycles were built in Pelham Street, and then assembled at new premises in Retreat Street just across the Penn Road from Sunbeamland. By the autumn of 1910 Stevens Bros decided to move its operation entirely to Retreat Street, and invited Frank and Ailwyn Smith to take their old premises in Pelham Street. Clyno Engineering was duly moved to Wolverhampton, to be nearer to their engine suppliers and to take advantage of the large local pool of labour skilled in the production of motor vehicles of all kinds. Pelham Street is on the north side of Wolverhampton, a quarter of a mile from the Star and Sunbeam companies, with AJS's Retreat Street factory in between.

Clyno successfully made well-built and quite advanced motor-cycles, and when war came the company continued to make them, but for the Army, and they served on all fronts, including Russia. The War Office placed orders on behalf of Russia in 1917 alone for 8,394 motor-cycles of all makes, of which 4,344 were to have side-cars for machine-guns, casualty evacuation, and ammunition transportation. Clyno's share of this order was 1,244, the second largest of all the motor-cycle manufacturers. By comparison John Marston received the largest orders, for 1,350 Sunbeams, and AJS received orders for 1,100.

Late in the war Clyno was the recipient of an order for eight prototype Dragonfly engines under Contract AS857/18,

Four ABC Dragonfly engines, one complete, in the premises of Clyno Cars in Pelham Street, Wolverhampton, 1918.

and a separate production order for 500 Dragonflies under Contract 34a/587/C529. Like Guy Motors on the other side of Wolverhampton, Clyno was quicker off the mark than many of its fellow recipients of Dragonfly orders.

The first Dragonfly completed by Clyno (WD48204) was installed in the second prototype Sopwith Bulldog, special serial X-4 (later H4423). The Bulldog had been designed to specification A.2a for a two-seat fighter with a 200 hp Clerget engine. A revised specification meant that the type was not needed, but it was decided to complete the second prototype with the Dragonfly engine. The Dragonfly was delivered from Wolverhampton and the aircraft reached Martlesham Heath for testing on 22 April 1918. After twenty hours of flying the aircraft was refitted with a Mk II Dragonfly, also built by Clyno (No.50008). It was then test-flown at Farnborough during mid-1918.

The sixth Sopwith Snipe, B9967, was also fitted with an early Dragonfly, manufacturer unknown, and test-flown at Brooklands on 27 April 1918. There was trouble with the magneto and then the engine began cutting out at altitude.

(Above):
The rear view of a Dragonfly, showing the magnetos and the exhaust collector ring.

(Right):
Sopwith Bulldog, serial X-4, which was fitted with the first Clyno-built Dragonfly, WD48204, and later refitted with a Clyno-built Dragonfly II.

The Dragonfly installation in a production Sopwith Dragon. Clyno built forty 'Special Time delivery engines' to equip a squadron of Dragons.

Another Dragonfly, serial WD48204, taken from the Bulldog was then fitted to the Snipe, and the aircraft was flown in September 1918. It was only used for a short period as the spindle of the port magneto broke and fell into the crankcase, causing considerable damage, and the engine had to be scrapped. It was replaced by a Sheffield-Simplex-built Mk II Dragonfly.

In June 1918 Clyno had delivered its second Dragonfly completed to the Sheffield-Simplex Motor Co. of Sheffield and Kingston-upon-Thames, which had received an order for 500 Dragonflies after completing twelve ABC Wasps. Ministry of Munitions records indicate that Clyno had completed six prototype engines by the end of the year, and four from its production contract for 500, all four between 18 November and the end of the year. Of the balance the remaining two prototypes were to be completed during 1919, but 453 of the production contract were cancelled.

Clyno's production efforts were concentrated on forty 'Special Time delivery engines'. These were to be used for the proposed 'Speed-Snipe' Squadron, the type which was later to be renamed the Sopwith Dragon. Problems were such that it was 14 February 1919 before the first Dragon was delivered to Martlesham Heath, and all impetus had gone from the programme.

A Clyno-built Dragonfly, serial 60052, was fitted to the Austin Greyhound, H4317, which was delivered to Martlesham Heath for testing on 27 June 1919. After only six hours' running the engine was removed and examined. It showed every sign of having been badly erected, and the No.6 cylinder was badly scored.

The records seem to indicate that Clyno delivered a total of eight prototypes and forty-seven production engines before reverting, like Guy Motors, to their peacetime manufacture of motor-cycles and, later on, cars. In the late 1920s the company became enmeshed in a price-cutting war with Austin and Morris at the very bottom end of the car market, and lost out, the receiver being appointed in February 1929. Their erstwhile engine suppliers, AJS, did not last much longer, going into voluntary liquidation in October 1931, though the Stevens brothers subsequently started a new company, using their surname.

Sopwith Dragon, E7990. The Dragon was basically a Snipe with the BR.2 rotary replaced by the Dragonfly radial.

APPENDIX I
SUNBEAM AERO-ENGINES

Name	Cyl.	Litres	HP	Wt. (lb)	Valves	Year	Bore	Stroke	Ordered	Built	Details
Crusader	V8	7.6	150	630	Side 2/cyl	1913	90	150	224	224	
–	V8	6.03	110	615	Side 2/cyl	1914	80	150	7	7	Early Crusader
Mohawk	V12	11.4	225	950	Side 2/cyl	1914	90	150	287	287	
Zulu	V8	9.4	160	640	Side 2/cyl	1915	100	150	75	75	Crusader with increased bore
Gurkha	V12	14.1	240	960	Side 2/cyl	1915	100	150	83	83	Mohawk with increased bore
Cossack I	V12	18.2	310	1372	OHC 4/cyl	1916	110	160	382	350	2 Mags, air starter, geared
Cossack II	V12	18.2	320	1372	OHC 4/cyl	1916	110	160	incl		4 Mags, air/hand starter, geared
Amazon I	Str.6	9.2	160	747	OHC 4/cyl	1916	110	160	100	77	2 Mags, air starter, geared
Amazon II	Str.6	9.2	160	747	OHC 4/cyl	1916	110	160	incl.		1 Mag. air/hand starter, geared
Viking	W18	17.4	475	1430	OHC 4/cyl	1916	110	160	50	9	6 Mags. air/hand starter, geared.
Afridi	V12	11.4	225	745	OHC 4/cyl	1916	92	135	300	299	4 Mags, inside exhaust valves, (100 converted to Maoris) geared prop.
Nubian	V8	7.6	155	684	OHC 4/cyl	1916	95	135	50	36	Standard type cyl.
Saracen	Str.6	9.2	200	740	OHC 4/cyl	1916	122	160			2 Mags. air starter, geared
Maori I	V12	12.3	250	1065	OHC 4/cyl	1916	100	135	1063	974	4 Mags. inside exhausts, geared.
Maori II	V12	12.3	260	1080	OHC 4/cyl	1917	100	135			2 Mags, 2 Remys, geared
Maori III	V12	12.3	275	1080	OHC 4/cyl	1917	100	135			2 Mags, 2 Remys, outside exhaust
Maori IV	V12	12.3	275	1080	OHC 4/cyl	1917	100	135	for airships		Direct drive, water-cooled exhaust, governor
Arab I	V8	12.3	208	550	OHC 3/cyl	1917	120	130	2110	590	2 Mags, outside exhaust, geared
Arab II	V8	12.3	208	550	OHC 3/cyl	1917	120	130	incl.		2 Mags, outside exhaust, direct drive
Manitou	V12	15.4	325	1050	OHC 4/cyl	1917	110	135	840	13	2 Mags. 2 Remys, geared.
Spartan	V12	14.0	200		OHC 4/cyl	1917	105	135			Air cooled, 1 Cam, 2 Mags, geared
Matabele I	V12	18.2	400	1000	OHC 4/cyl	1917	122	160			4 Mags, air/hand starter, geared
Matabele II	V12	18.2	400	1000	OHC 4/cyl	1917	122	160			2 Mags, air/hand starter, direct drive
Dyak	Str.6	8.8	110	600	OHC 2/cyl	1918	120	130	160		1 Mag, 1 Remy, direct drive
Tartar	V12	15.4	300		OHC 4/cyl	1918	110	135	for airships		2 Mags, 1 cam, geared
Kaffir	W12	18.3	300		OHC 3/cyl	1918	120	135			2 Mags, 1 single carb, 1 dual carb. direct drive.
Malay	X20	29.4	500		OHC 3/cyl	1818	120	130			1 single carb., 2 dual carbs. direct drive, 5-point star
Bedouin	A8	12.3	200		OHC 3/cyl	1918	120	130			Inverted Arab, 2 Mags, direct drive, outside exhaust valves.
Sikh	V12	64.0	850	1952	pushrod 6/cyl	1918	180	210			4 Mags, 1 cam, geared
Semi-Sikh	Str.6	32.0	425	1190	pushrod 6/cyl	1918	180	210			2 Mags, 1 cam, geared
Pathan	Str.6	8.8	100		diesel	1925	120	130			Diesel
Sikh III	V12	64.0	1000	1952	pushrod 6/cyl	1928	180	210			Bristol starter
–	V12	24.0	'2000'		OHC 4/cyl	1929	140	130	2	2	single ignition for Land Speed Record Car

APPENDIX II
SUNBEAM MONTHLY PRODUCTION

AIRCRAFT AND ENGINES

Engines

HP	110	150	225	160	240	320	200	450	260	160	155	200	300
ENG	–	CRU	MOH	ZUL	GHU	COS	AFR	VIK	MAO	AMA	NUB	ARA	MAN
1913	2	2	1										
1914													
To Jul		3	2										
Aug		1	1										
Sep	2	2	3										
Oct	4	3	4										
Nov	1	1	1										
Dec		3	7										
1915													
Jan		5	11										
Feb		2	3										
Mar		9	6										
Apr		3	15										
May		3	2										
Jun		21	6										
Jul		6	24										
Aug		17	16										
Sep		8	12										
Oct		16	18										
Nov		17	18										
Dec		19	17										
1916													
Jan		13	26										
Feb		15	25	4	1								
Mar		15	21	3	2	2							
Apr		18	30	2	1	2							
May		7	17	6	3	2							
Jun		18	2	8	18	1							
Jul		1		19	28	4	2						
Aug				4	11		6						
Sep				12	13	12	10						
Oct				12	5	16	10						
Nov				5		23	20						
Dec						28	26						
1917													
Jan						27	51						
Feb						20	55	1					
Mar						11	8	1					
Apr						22	28	1	13				
May						55	72	2	45			1	
Jun						26	11	1	55			3	
Jul						16			60	6			
Aug						33		3	72	6			
Sep						13			47	5		8	
Oct						26			50	8	4	17	
Nov						10			68	13	7	23	
Dec						1			20	7	2	29	
1918													
Jan						49	6	1	72				

HP	110	150	225	160	240	320	200	450	260	160	155	200	300
ENG	–	CRU	MOH	ZUL	GHU	COS	AFR	VIK	MAO	AMA	NUB	ARA	MAN
Feb						26	9	7	29				
Mar						39	8	7	36				
Apr						27	9	4	43				
May						25		1	53				
Jun						35		1	48				
Jul						66		2	56				
Aug						66			46				
Sep						61			39				
Oct						60			52				
Nov						44			18				
Dec						46			17				
1919													

Aircraft

Year	Month	SHORT 827	Bomber	310-A4	AVRO 504B/H	AVRO 504J/K
1915	Nov	2				
	Dec	4				
1916	Jan	3				
	Feb	4				
	Mar	5				
	Apr	7				
	May	7				
	Jun	4				
	Jul	3	2			
	Aug	–	–			
	Sep	–	3			
	Oct	1	2			
	Nov		4		4	
	Dec		2		11	
1917	Jan		2		6	
	Feb				21	
	Mar				9	
	Apr				6	
	May				3	
	Jun					
	Jul					
	Aug					
	Sep			5		
	Oct			5		
	Nov			7		
	Dec			5		
1918	Jan			8		
	Feb			7		2
	Mar			7		27
	Apr			1		21
	May			4		8
	Jun			1		52
	Jul					38
	Aug					59
	Sep					32
	Oct					48
	Nov					47
	Dec					42
1919	Jan					38
	Feb					31
	Mar					33
	Apr					2
	May					–
	Jun					1
Totals		40	15	50	60	481

APPENDIX III
SUNBEAM-BUILT AIRCRAFT — SERVICE HISTORIES

Short Type 827 Seaplane

Ordered 13.5.15 under Contract No. CP49441/15, and serialled 3093–112. Powered by Sunbeam 150 hp Crusader.

3093 c/n 1, delivered Grain 8.11.15, (accepted 14.11.15, Kemp) Short Bros, Rochester 17.12.15, shipped to East Africa, No.8 Sqd., Zanzibar, transferred to Belgian government for use in Belgian Congo and Lake Tanganyika against German East Africa.

3094 c/n 2, delivered Grain 21.11.15, Short Bros, Rochester 18.12.15, Westgate 24.3.16, shipped to East Africa No.8 Sqd., Zanzibar, transferred to Belgian government for use in Belgian Congo and Lake Tanganyika.

3095 c/n 3, delivered Grain 4.12.15 by lorry, accepted 11.12.15, shipped to East Africa, No.8 Sqd., Zanzibar, transferred to Belgian government for use in Belgian Congo and Lake Tanganyika.

3096 c/n 4, delivered Grain, 10.12.15, 'Britons Overseas No.4', named 7.15, shipped to No.7 Sqd., Mombasa, from Avonmouth in SS *Clan Macpherson* 7.2.16, Chukwani 8.7.16, HMS *Manica* 7.16, Chukwani 30.7.16, No.8 Sqd., Zanzibar by 8.16, HMS *Princess* 1.3.17, Lindi 12.3.17, HMS *Manica* 26.3.17, Chukwani 19.4.17, Lindi 21.4.17, still No.8 Sqd. 28.12.17, for deletion by 16.3.18.

3097 c/n 5, delivered Grain 23.12.15, erected and accepted 'Britons Overseas No.5' (named 7.15), accepted 8.1.16, shipped to Mombasa in SS *Clan MacPherson* 7.2.16, No.8 Sqd., Zanzibar (HMS *Laconia*, HMS *Himalaya*, HMS *Manica*, Chukwani, Lindi, Koktoni, Mikindani etc.) engine failure at Sdui 24.8.16, flying until 24.8.17, next flown 1.3.18, deleted 15.3.18.

3098 c/n 6, delivered Grain 29.12.15, 'Britons Overseas No.6' (named 7.15), shipped to Mombasa in SS *Clan Macpherson* 7.2.16, No.8 Sqd., Zanzibar, as 3097 deleted 28.3.17 (beyond repair).

3099 c/n 7, delivered Grain 29.1.16 by lorry, tested with four-blade propeller 28.1.16, accepted 21.2.16, Dover 16.3.16, Dunkirk 2.4.16, anti-Zeppelin patrol 3.4.16, patrol to Zeebrugge 25.4.16, HMS *Vindex* 26.4.16, Grain 27.4.16, Dunkirk 29.4.16, Dover 3.5.16, Felixstowe 17.6.16, condemned 4.7.16.

3100 c/n 8, delivered Grain 14.1.16, accepted 29.2.16, Dunkirk/Dover, fitted with 4 × 16 lb bomb gear 1.4.16, wrecked in take-off outside Dover 20.6.16, deleted 22.6.16.

3101 c/n 9, delivered Grain 18.1.16, accepted 21.2.16, chassis damaged on slipway 17.3.16, Dunkirk/Dover, engine failure in mid-Channel 7.7.16, towed to Dover, last flight, a fighting patrol 24.9.16, deleted.

3102 c/n 10, delivered Grain 1.2.16, Portland 11.9.16, Grain 22.9.16, hostile aircraft patrol 28.11.16, deleted 17.1.17.

3103 c/n 11, delivered Grain 2.16, accepted 11.9.16, Portland 11.9.16, Grain 22.9.16, Calshot 27.7.17, deleted w/e 14.9.17.

3104 c/n 12, delivered Grain 18.2.16, Yarmouth 19.2.16, hostile submarine patrol 23.5.16, damaged on take-off 15.7.16, tested but unsatisfactory 26.10.16, deleted 31.10.16.

3105 c/n 13, delivered Grain 25.2.16, accepted 9.3.16, Yarmouth 27.3.16, beached and float damaged at Aldeburgh 29.4.16, anti-Zeppelin patrol 19.6.16, deleted 31.10.16.

3106 c/n 14, delivered Grain 3.16, accepted 24.3.16, Nore War Flight Grain by 24.4.16, hostile seaplane patrol 19/20.5.16, deleted 17.1.17.

3107 c/n 15, delivered Grain 3.16, accepted Grain 24.3.16, Nore War Flight Grain by 24.4.16, trials with Bellars-Noyes bombsight and Lewis gun Rake sight 27.5.16, deleted 8.11.16.

3108 c/n 16, delivered Grain 14.3.16, accepted 24.3.16, Yarmouth 23.4.16, badly damaged by shell-fire from German high seas fleet raiding Scarborough 16.00–17.00 hrs, 24.3.16, repaired, capsized off Southwold 29.6.16, deleted 11.7.16.

3109 c/n 17, delivered Grain 21.3.16, Yarmouth 28.4.16, hostile submarine patrol 21.7.16, deleted 31.10.16.

3110 c/n 18, delivered Grain 29.3.16, Westgate 27.4.16, struck mooring and wrecked on take-off 31.7.16, deleted 9.8.16.

3111 c/n 19, delivered Grain 5.4.16, accepted 28.4.16, Westgate 11.5.16, refitted with 160 hp Sunbeam Zulu 2.17, anti-seaplane patrol 16.2.17, Felixstowe 10.5.17, (for overhaul) Westgate 11.5.17, anti-Zeppelin patrol 25.5.17, engine failure, adrift, complete wreck off Tongue light vessel 9.6.17, deleted 15.6.17.

3112 c/n 20, delivered Grain 11.4.16, accepted 5.5.16, while manoeuvring to engage U-boat fell in sea, towed to Westgate, crew rescued by trawler 2.8.16, deleted 11.8.16.

Short Type 827 Seaplane

Ordered 29.5.15 under Contract No. CP78661/15, serialled 8630–49. Powered by Sunbeam 150 hp Crusader when new.

8630 c/n 21, delivered Grain 1.4.16, accepted 4.5.16, Felixstowe 12.6.16, deleted 1.7.17.

8631 c/n 22, delivered Grain 10.5.16, Felixstowe 31.5.16, Nore War Flight Felixstowe 13.6.16, anti-Zeppelin patrol 25.8.16, Killingholme School 4.7.17, deleted w/e 22.9.17.

8632 c/n 23, delivered Grain 13.4.16, accepted 10.5.16, Felixstowe 14.5.16, anti-Zeppelin patrol 30.7.16, Nore War Flight Felixstowe 15.8.16, deleted 3.10.16.

8633 c/n 24, delivered Grain 13.4.16, Westgate 29.5.16, Sunbeam 160 hp Zulu, hostile aircraft patrols 31.7.16, wrecked on landing 3.3.17, deleted 20.3.17.

8634 c/n 25, delivered Felixstowe 5.16, accepted 26.5.16, Grain tested 30.5.16, Nore War Flight, Felixstowe 14.8.16, Killingholme School 4.7.17, deleted w/e 22.2.18.

8635 c/n 26, delivered Yarmouth by road 18.4.16, erected 19.5.16, accepted 26.6.16, anti-Zeppelin patrol 31.7.16, deleted 5.11.16.

8636 c/n 27, delivered Yarmouth by road 23.5.16, erected 19.5.16, accepted 21.6.16, deleted 8.9.17.

8637 c/n 28, delivered Yarmouth by road, 23.4.16, erected 19.5.16, accepted 21.6.16, wrecked on landing 5.10.16, deleted 17.10.16.

8638 c/n 29, delivered Grain 2.5.16, accepted 15.7.16, tested 10.8.16, to Calshot but forced landing en route and complete wreck off Dover 4.12.16, deleted.

8639 c/n 30, delivered Grain 10.5.16, tested 18.6.16, damaged float Westgate 2.8.16, returned Grain 3.8.16, Portland 11.9.16, Grain 28.9.16, stalled and side-slipped on take-off from River Medway opposite Grain pier 12.10.16, deleted 15.10.16.

8640 c/n 31, delivered Grain 25.5.16, tested 18.6.16 and 4.8.16, deleted 3.9.16.

8641 c/n 32, delivered Grain 5.6.16, accepted 11.6.16, Short Bros, Rochester for packing 16.6.16, shipped to Cape Station 6.16, No.8 Sqd. Zanzibar by 8.16, HMS *Manica* by 3.8.16, HMS *Laconia* 1916, HMS *Himalaya* by 1.11.16, HMS *Manica* 2.11.16, Chukwani 19.11.16, HMS *Manica* to 9.2.17, Chukwani by 7.3.17.

8642 c/n 33, delivered Grain 5.16, accepted 14.6.16, Short Bros, Rochester for packing 16.6.16, shipped to Cape Station 6.16, badly damaged in transit to Zanzibar, rebuilt, tested 5.10.16, No.8 Sqd., Zanzibar from 11.16, HMS *Himalaya* 9.11.16, Zanzibar 20.11.16, complete wreck en route Zanzibar to Dar-es-Salaam 8.1.17.

8643 c/n 34, delivered Grain by road 14.6.16, accepted 22.6.16, engine failure, forced landing and wrecked 15.9.16, deleted 29.9.16.

8644 c/n 35, delivered Grain by road 14.6.16, accepted 26.6.16, wrecked 24.8.16, returned Grain 22.11.16, deleted 27.1.17.

8645 c/n 36, delivered Dundee by rail 3.7.16, tested 24.7.16, hostile submarine patrol 28.2.17, hostile submarine patrol attacked U-boat six miles off Bell Rock 12.3.17, engine failure and forced landing off Aberdeen, returned to Dundee for repair 23.5.17, deleted 25.8.17.

8646 c/n 37, delivered Dundee by rail 3.7.16, tested 31.7.16, engine failure and forced landing two miles off Bell Rock, towed in by HMS *Agatha* 24.3.17, wrecked on patrol, towed in by trawler 31.7.17, deleted 7.8.17.

8647 c/n 38, delivered Dundee by rail 3.7.16, tested 27.7.16, sunk and wrecked 1.2.17, not listed from 2.2.17, presumed rebuilt, shipped to Cape Station 1.4.17, arrived No.8 Sqd. Zanzibar in SS *Berwick Castle* 13.6.17, erected by 26.6.17, but not flown as in poor condition.

8648 c/n 39, delivered Central Supply Depot, White City 6.16, fuselage to Sunbeam 7.16, Grain 29.8.16, accepted 8.9.16, engine failure and wrecked after forced landing 16.9.16, en route Dover wrecked in Dover harbour, engine salvaged 1.1.17, engine failure Milford Bay Bay en route to Portland 23.1.17, to proceed 24.1.17, Dover 2.2.17 (repair), Sunbeam 160 hp Zulu by 12.17, in transit Newhaven 31.1.18, Calshot 1.2.18, Lee-on-Solent School by 23.2.18, nose-dived into sea on take-off 8.3.18, deleted w/e 3.4.18.

8649 c/n 40, delivered Grain by lorry 20.10.16, for Cape Station 23.2.17, makers instructed to fit tropical radiators w/e 2.3.17, shipped in SS *Berwick Castle* 1.4.17, landed and erected No.8 Sqd., Zanzibar 13.6.17, to go to Lindi 7.17, HMS *Trent* 4.18, to Port Said 4.18, HMS *City of Oxford* by 6.18 to 9.18, No.269 Sqd. Port Said by 28.10.18, deleted 22.12.18.

Short Bomber

Ordered 18.5.16 under Contract No. CP103297/16 and CP112535/16, and serialled 9356–75, and powered by 240 hp Sunbeam Gurkha.

9356 c/n 41, built originally with short fuselage, lengthened before delivery, and fitted with straight leading edge to the fin, erected and tested as such at Dunstall Park, Wolverhampton, delivered Chingford by 27.7.16, tested by F/Lt Hardstaff 31.7.16, Eastchurch workshops 23.9.16, deleted 4.5.17.

9357 c/n 42, erected Dunstall Park, delivered Chingford by lorry 20.7.16, ADD 16.9.16, 12 Flt B Sqd. 4 Wing Petite Synthe by 28.9.16, Eastchurch workshops 20.12.16, deleted 4.5.17.

9358 c/n 43, delivered Chingford 1.9.16, Eastchurch workshops 24.9.16, deleted 4.5.17.

9359 c/n 44, delivered Chingford by rail 21.9.16, Gunnery Experimental Grain 5.12.16, accepted by John Lankester Parker, EAD Grain by 10.17, surveyed 25.3.18, deleted 27.3.18.

9360 c/n 45, delivered Eastchurch workshops by lorry 28.9.16, deleted 4.5.17.

9361 c/n 46, delivered Eastchurch workshops by lorry 2.12.16, erected 20.10.16, accepted 2.11.16, deleted 4.5.17.

9362 c/n 47, delivered Eastchurch workshops by lorry 7.10.16, erected 15.10.16, accepted 11.12.16, deleted 28.4.17.

9363 c/n 48, delivered Eastchurch workshops 15.10.16, deleted 4.5.17.

9364 c/n 49, delivered Manston 11.11.16, accepted by John Lankester Parker 17.12.16, deleted 28.4.17.

9365 c/n 50, delivered Eastchurch workshops by lorry 10.11.16, accepted by J.L. Parker 8.12.16, deleted 4.5.17.

9366 c/n 51, delivered Manston 11.11.16, accepted by J.L. Parker 7.12.16, deleted 4.5.17.

9367 c/n 52, delivered Eastchurch workshops by lorry 22.11.16, deleted 4.5.17.

9368 c/n 53, delivered Manston 19.12.16, failed test 3.1.17, retested and accepted by J.L. Parker 10.1.17, deleted 28.4.17.

9369 c/n 54, delivered Manston 22.1.17, deleted 28.4.17.

9370 c/n 55, delivered Manston 30.1.17, deleted 28.4.17.

Five aircraft serialled 9371–5 c/n 56–60 cancelled Sept. 1916.

Avro 504B (Admiralty Type 179)

Ordered 22.7.16 under Contract Nos. CP120735/16 and CP121726, and serialled N5250–79. Fitted with 4 × 16 lb bombs, powered by 80 hp Gnôme rotary.

N5250 c/n 61, delivered Cranwell 23.11.16, wrecked 5.12.16, deleted 30.12.16.

N5251 c/n 62, dual control, delivered Eastchurch workshops by rail 23.11.16, Eastchurch Flying School 12.4.17, Manston 20.8.17, deleted 19.9.17.

N5252 c/n 63, delivered Cranwell 30.11.16, Redcar School w/e 19.1.18, (504C), for deletion 23.3.18.

N5253 c/n 64, delivered Cranwell 30.11.16, Frieston by 7.7.17, deleted w/e 18.9.17.

N5254 c/n 65, delivered Cranwell 5.12.16, crashed, completely wrecked 8.8.17, deleted w/e 18.9.17.

N5255 c/n 66, delivered Cranwell 14.2.17, Frieston by 3.17, crashed and wrecked 16.4.17, deleted 19.5.17.

N5256 c/n 67 (dual control a/c, converted to 504H, i.e. strengthened with catapult pick-up points and padded seat) delivered Redcar by rail 4.12.16, Scarborough 29.1.17, Redcar 30.1.17, wrecked landing 3.2.17, repaired, crashed complete wreck nr Potts 13.12.17, for deletion by 15.12.17.

N5257 c/n 68, delivered Eastchurch workshops by road 11.12.16, Gun Flight Eastchurch 3.1.17, Eastchurch workshops 7.2.17, Gun Flight Eastchurch 19.2.17, Bomb Flight Eastchurch by 24.3.17, Gun Flight Leysdown 25.4.17, Experimental Aircraft Dept Grain by rail 21.7.17, Eastchurch to Manston Flying School 21.8.17, converted to 504H by 12.17, surveyed 6.4.18, deleted 15.4.18, damaged beyond repair.

N5258 c/n 69 (converted to 504H by 12.17, i.e. strengthened, with catapult pick-up points and padded seat) delivered to Eastchurch workshops 11.12.16, Manston Flying School 22.8.17, deleted w/e 2.2.18.

N5259 c/n 70, delivered ex-Avro to Eastchurch workshops 14.12.16,

Chingford 7.5.17, surveyed 2.9.17, deleted 2.11.17, wrecked.

N5260 c/n 71, delivered ex-Avro to Eastchurch workshops 14.12.16, Eastchurch Flying School 1.5.17, Chingford 7.5.17, u/c smashed 5.7.17, deemed beyond repair by 21.8.17.

N5261 c/n 72 (converted to 504H) delivered Central Supply Depot, White City 2.17, fitted with interrupter gear, twin floats? Hendon 22.5.17, catapult experiments 25.5.18.

N5262 c/n 73 (dual control a/c, converted to 504H) delivered Killingholme for erection 27.12.16, Chingford 27.5.17.

N5263 c/n 74 (dual control a/c) delivered Killingholme for erection 27.12.16, Eastchurch workshops 22.6.17, Manston 20.8.17, surveyed 5.10.17, deleted 6.10.17 (wrecked).

N5264 c/n 75 (dual control a/c, converted to 504H), delivered Killingholme for erection 27.12.16, Redcar 9.5.17, damaged 21.7.17, damaged 22.9.17, deleted w/e 21.5.18.

N5265 c/n 76 (dual control a/c) delivered Killingholme for erection 27.12.16, Redcar 9.5.17, damaged beyond repair 23.7.17, deleted 8.9.17.

N5266 c/n 77 (dual control a/c) delivered Killingholme for erection 27.12.16, Redcar 16.6.17, beyond repair by 21.8.17, deleted by 8.9.17.

N5267 c/n 78 (dual control a/c, converted to 504H) delivered Central Supply Depot, White City 2.17, fitted with interrupter gear, Killingholme for erection 9.3.17, Redcar 18.6.17, deleted w/e 26.1.18.

N5268 c/n 79 (dual control a/c, converted to 504H) delivered Killinghome for erection 26.1.17, Redcar 23.6.17, damaged 8.9.17, deleted w/e 26.1.18.

N5269 c/n 80, delivered Central Supply Depot 2.17, converted to 504H, Hendon for erection 31.5.17, catapult experiments, Brough 1.6.18, Hendon 3.6.18.

N5270 c/n 81 (converted to 504H) tested Hendon 3.4.17, Elswick Works 26.4.17, Hendon for erection 23.6.17, catapult trials.

N5271 c/n 82 (converted to 504H) by 29.12.17, delivered C Flight Cranwell 10.1.17, crashed 14.8.17, crashed and badly damaged Cranwell North (pilot unhurt) 21.1.18, forced landing in mist at Beckering 20.3.18, A Flight Cranwell by 4.18, Frieston by 10.18.

N5272 (c/n 83 (dual control a/c) delivered to Killingholme for erection 24.1.17, Eastbourne 25.4.17, broken u/c 2.5.17, complete wreck 11.9.17, surveyed 26.9.18, deleted 19.1.18, damaged beyond repair.

N5273 c/n 84 (converted to 504H) delivered Eastchurch workshops 20.3.17, Chingford 7.5.17, surveyed 15.1.18, deleted 19.1.18, damaged beyond repair.

N5274 c/n 85 (dual control a/c) delivered Killingholme for erection 16.1.17, Cranwell 24.4.17, crashed 5.7.17, deleted w/e 18.9.17.

N5275 c/n 86, delivered UK to Vendôme for erection 10.3.17, wrecked beyond repair 21.5.17, deleted 16.10.17.

N5276 c/n 87, delivered UK to Vendôme for erection 10.3.17, surveyed 12.10.17, deleted 16.10.17, damaged beyond repair.

N5277 c/n 88, delivered Killingholme for erection 26.2.17, Cranwell 24.4.17, deleted w/e 26.10.17.

N5278 c/n 89, delivered Killingholme for erection 27.3.17, Cranwell 24.4.17, crashed complete wreck 13.7.17, wrecked beyond repair 15.8.17, deleted 2.11.17.

N5279 c/n 90, delivered Killingholme for erection 17.4.17, Eastbourne 7.5.17, complete wreck 9.5.17, deleted 17.5.17.

Avro 504B (Admiralty Type 179 Dual Type)

Ordered 22.7.16 as armament trainers under Contract CP139209/16 dated 30.12.16, and serialled N6130–59. Fitted to carry 4 × 16 lb bombs and interrupter gear. Powered by 80 hp Gnôme rotary.

N6130 c/a 91, delivered Killingholme for erection 10.2.17, in transit Chingford 30.4.17, Manston Flying School 1.5.17, deleted 31.7.17, ex-overhaul.

N6131 c/n 92, delivered Killingholme for erection 10.2.17, in transit Chingford 30.4.17, Manston Flying School 1.5.17, wrecked 21.8.17, deleted 1.9.17.

N6132 c/n 93, delivered Killingholme for erection 10.2.17, in transit Chingford, Manston Flying School 1.5.17, wrecked 21.8.17, deleted 1.9.17.

N6133 c/n 94, delivered Chingford by rail 31.1.17, surveyed 24.3.17, deleted 1.4.17.

N6134 c/n 95, delivered Chingford 31.1.17, engine failure and forced landing in field nr reservoir on take-off 1.3.17, deleted 23.7.17.

N6134 c/n 96, delivered Chingford 3.2.17, engine failure and forced landing in field 27.2.17, badly damaged 25.6.17, deleted w/e 29.9.17.

N6136 c/n 97, delivered Chingford 3.2.17, deleted 27.7.17.

N6137 c/n 98, delivered Chingford 5.2.17, deleted 9.5.17.

N6138 c/n 99, delivered Killingholme for erection 24.2.17, Manston Flying School 30.4.17, wrecked 7.8.17, deleted 18.8.17.

N6139 c/n 100, delivered Killingholme for erection 24.2.17, in transit Chingford 30.4.17, Manston Flying School 1.5.17.

N6140 c/n 101, delivered Killingholme for erection 24.2.17, Manston Flying School 3.5.17, surveyed 22.10.17, deleted 26.10.17, wrecked.

N6141 c/n 102, delivered Killingholme for erection 18.2.17, Manston Flying School 30.4.17, wrecked 7.8.17, deleted 18.8.17.

N6142 c/n 103, delivered Killingholme for erection 18.2.17, Manston Flying School 30.4.17, deleted w/e 23.3.18.

N6143 c/n 104, delivered Killingholme for erection 18.2.17, Manston Flying School 30.4.17, wrecked 26.7.17, deleted 3.8.17.

N6144 c/n 105, delivered Killingholme for erection 24.2.17, Chingford 9.5.17, damaged 15.7.17.

N6145 c/n 106, delivered Killingholme for erection 24.2.17, Chingford 25.5.17, deleted 22.7.17.

N6146 c/n 107, delivered Killingholme for erection 26.2.17, Chingford 25.5.17, deleted 22.7.17.

N6147 c/n 108, delivered Eastchurch workshops 22.2.17, Eastchurch Flying School 12.4.17, Manston Flying School 31.8.17.

N6148 c/n 109, delivered Redcar by road 8.3.17, tested 28.3.17, forced landing u/c wrecked 21.5.17, fuselage and wings damaged 5.7.17, damaged 8.9.17, surveyed 7.12.17, deleted 14.12.17, wrecked.

N6149 c/n 110, delivered Redcar 10.3.17, tested 28.3.17, forced landing and wrecked seven miles north-west of Bishop Auckland 26.5.17, deleted 25.6.17.

N6150 c/n 111, delivered Killingholme for erection 21.3.17, Eastbourne 2.5.17, complete wreck 12.9.17, surveyed 20.9.17, deleted 26.9.17, damaged beyond repair.

N6151 c/n 112, delivered Killingholme for erection 1.5.17, Chingford 9.5.17, badly damaged 31.7.17, surveyed 10.3.18, deleted 15.4.18, wrecked.

N6152 c/n 113, delivered Killingholme for erection 4.4.17, Chingford 9.5.17, became 207 TDS Chingford 1.4.18.

N6153 c/n 114, delivered Killingholme for erection 27.3.17, Chingford 10.5.17, surveyed 28.12.17, deleted 15.1.18, wrecked.

N6154 c/n 115, delivered Killingholme for erection 4.4.17, Cranwell 26.5.17, surveyed 10.12.17, deleted 14.12.17, wrecked.

N6155 c/n 116, delivered Killingholme for erection 4.4.17, Cranwell 26.5.17, crashed Brauncewell u/c damaged 22.1.18, complete wreck 25.1.18, deleted w/e 23.2.18.

N6156 c/n 117, delivered Killingholme for erection 4.4.17 Cranwell 4.6.17, Frieston 6.6.17, C Flight Cranwell by 9.17, damaged 5.9.17, damaged by fire 2.10.17, Redcar School w/e 19.1.18, for deletion by 5.4.18.

N6157 c/n 118, delivered Cranwell 3.5.17, crashed u/c broken

11.8.17, Redcar School w/e 19.1.18.

N6158 c/n 119, delivered Parnall to Cranwell 23.5.17, Frieston by 6.17, crashed u/c broken 11.8.17, at Frieston 6.9.17, for deletion by 26.10.17.

N6159 c/n 120, delivered Cranwell 3.5.17, complete wreck 21.7.17, deleted w/e 11.9.17.

Short Type 310-A4 Seaplane

Ordered 12.16 under Contract Nos. AS974 and AS3612, and serialled N1360–89. Powered by Sunbeam 310 hp Cossack.

N1360 c/n 121, delivered Yarmouth w/e 29.9.17, failed to return from patrol 27.10.17.

N1361 c/n 122, delivered Grain by road 1.9.17, Dover 3.10.17, (en route to South Shields) Felixstowe 5.10.17, South Shields w/e 10.10.17, surveyed 15.4.18, deleted through wear and tear 15.4.18.

N1362 c/n 123, delivered Grain 1.9.17, Killingholme via Felixstowe 27.10.17, forced landing and sank near Flamborough Head 21.2.18, crew rescued by HMS *Ouse*, deleted w/e 2.3.18.

N1363 c/n 124, delivered Grain by road 25.9.17, Yarmouth w/e 10.11.17, wrecked 4.11.17, surveyed 6.11.17, 14.11.17 wrecked.

N1364 c/n 125, delivered Grain by road 25.9.17, Yarmouth by 10.17, surveyed 26.11.17, deleted 3.12.17 (wrecked).

N1365 c/n 126, delivered Yarmouth w/e 13.10.17, deleted w/e 23.2.18.

N1366 c/n 127, delivered Felixstowe w/e 13.10.17, Calshot via Newhaven for trials 31.1.18, Aeroplane Repair Section Calshot w/e 29.8.18, deleted w/e 7.11.18.

N1367 c/n 128, delivered Yarmouth w/e 10.10.17, surveyed 9.1.18, deleted 15.1.18, damaged beyond repair.

N1368 c/n 129, delivered Yarmouth 10.10.17, Killingholme w/e 3.11.17, Yarmouth w/e 29.12.17, Killingholme w/e 23.2.18, in transit Felixstowe 28.5.18, Calshot 29.5.18, became No.210 TDS 6.18, deleted w/e 11.7.18.

N1369 c/n 130, delivered Grain, tested 11.12.17, ready to leave 12.12.17, Killingholme w/e 28.12.17, deleted w/e 6.4.18.

N1370 c/n 131, delivered Yarmouth 27.10.17, surveyed 30.12.17, deleted 2.1.18, total loss.

N1371 c/n 132, delivered Killingholme w/e 2.11.17, engine failure and forced landing, totally wrecked 24.4.18, deleted w/e 4.5.18.

N1372 c/n 133, delivered Killingholme w/e 2.11.17, Calshot TS via Lee-on-Solent 19.5.18, deleted w/e 11.7.18.

N1373 c/n 134, delivered Killingholme w/e 2.11.17 (also used Hornsea), became USNAS Killingholme w/e 5.9.18.

N1374 c/n 135, delivered Killingholme w/e 2.11.17 (also used Hornsea), Tees 23.2.18, Killingholme crashed and salvaged 27.2.18 (crew unhurt), surveyed 15.4.18, deleted 15.4.18, damaged beyond repair.

N1375 c/n 136, delivered Killingholme w/e 2.11.17, South Shields w/e 27.6.18, USNAS Killingholme w/e 5.9.18.

N1376 c/n 137, delivered Killingholme w/e 22.12.17, deleted w/e 4.7.18.

N1377 c/n 138, delivered Killingholme w/e 9.11.17, wrecked when fitting broke 4.18, deleted 15.4.18, damaged beyond repair.

N1378 c/n 139, delivered Central Supply Depot, White City, shipped to No.6 Wing RNAS Otranto 2.1.18, became 66/67 Wings 1.4.18.

N1379 c/n 140, delivered Grain by 12.17, tested 24.12.17, shipped to No.6 Wing RNAS Otranto 2.1.18, became 66/67 Wings 1.4.18.

N1380 c/n 141, delivered Killingholme w/e 28.12.17, deleted 15.4.18, damaged beyond repair.

N1381 c/n 142, delivered Killingholme w/e 30.11.17, surveyed 8.4.18, deleted 15.4.18, damaged beyond repair.

N1382 c/n 143, delivered Central Supply Depot, White City, Cardiff Docks 15.1.18, shipped to No.8 Wing RNAS Otranto 28.1.18, lost at sea w/e 21.4.18, deleted 15.5.18.

N1383 c/n 144, delivered Killingholme 12.12.17, dropped two 230 lb bombs on U-boat three miles east of Flamborough Head, one failed to explode 29.3.18, deleted w/e 27.6.18.

N1384 c/n 145, delivered Central Supply Depot, White City, West India Docks by 15.1.18, transferred Cardiff Docks, shipped to No.6 Wing RNAS Otranto 2.6.18, 435/436 Flights, No.263 Sqd. Otranto by 10.18.

N1385 c/n 146, delivered Central Supply Depot, White City, West India Docks 15.1.18, shipped to No.6 Wing RNAS Otranto 2.4.18, HMS *Rivera* by 5.18, sunk by 11.5.18 (6 Group Taranto), for deletion by 11.5.18, deleted 10.18.

N1386 c/n 147, delivered Central Supply Depot, White City, West India Docks by 15.1.18, shipped to No.6 Wing RNAS Otranto 2.4.18, 66/67 Wings Otranto by 7.18, Taranto 26.9.18, became 435/436 Flights, No.263 Sqd. Otranto by 10.18.

N1387 c/n 148, delivered Killingholme, w/e 11.1.18, South Shields 30.6.18, Killingholme 25.7.18, deleted w/e 26.9.18.

N1388 c/n 149, delivered Killingholme w/e 25.1.18, Yarmouth w/e 23.3.18, deleted 3.18, damaged beyond repair.

N1389 c/n 150, delivered Killingholme w/e 25.1.18, damaged in landing 29.3.18, deleted w/e 13.4.18.

Short Type 310-A4 Seaplane

Ordered under Contract No. AS3612/1 (BR22), serialled N1690–1709 powered by Sunbeam 320 hp Cossack IIs.

N1690 c/n 151, delivered Killingholme w/e 1.2.18, at Killingholme 10.4.18, forced landing after engine failure, broke moorings and wrecked at Staithes 12.5.18, deleted w/e 27.6.18.

N1691 c/n 152, delivered Killingholme w/e 1.2.18, at Mablethorpe 27.4.18, forced landing and sank twenty miles north of Spurn Head 27.4.18, deleted w/e 18.5.18.

N1692 c/n 153, delivered Killingholme w/e 8.2.18, accepted 1.4.18, Yarmouth 4.4.18, dropped 230 lb bomb on U-boat fifteen miles south-east of Shipwash, believed damaged, landed Felixstowe 15.5.18, returned Yarmouth 16.5.18, forced landing after engine failure one mile east of St Nicholas light vessel 23.5.18, complete wreck (crew unhurt), deleted w/e 13.6.18.

N1693 c/n 154, delivered Killingholme w/e 8.2.18, accepted 1.4.18, Yarmouth w/e 4.4.18, became 324/326 Flights 25.5.18, with BE.2c, serial 8417, attacked by five Brandenberg seaplanes of 5.C Staffel, shot down and strafed near Lowestoft, force-landed on sea, sunk by seaplane 6.6.18 (2/Lt R.W.A. Ivermere and AM2 S.E. Bourne slightly wounded and picked up by launches), deleted w/e 27.6.18.

N1694 c/n 155, delivered Killingholme w/e 15.2.18, deleted 27.6.18.

N1695 c/n 156, delivered Killingholme w/e 15.2.18, at South Shields 27.6.18, at Killingholme 8.8.18, forced landing after engine failure six miles off Bridlington, sank under tow inside Western Boom in Humber 19.9.18, deleted w/e 26.9.18.

N1696 c/n 157, delivered Killingholme w/e 22.2.18, at South Shields 26.6.18, USNAS Killingholme 1.8.18, South Shields w/e 3.10.18, deleted w/e 14.11.18.

N1697 c/n 158, delivered MAD Grain by 30.3.18, 6 SD Ascot w/e 25.7.18, Royal Albert Docks w/e 12.9.18, shipped to Japanese Navy w/e 3.10.18.

N1698 c/n 159, delivered MAD Grain by 30.3.18, 6 SD Ascot w/e 3.10.18, Royal Albert Docks w/e 12.9.18, shipped to Japanese Navy w/e 3.10.18.

N1699 c/n 160, delivered MAD Grain by 30.3.18, 6 SD Ascot w/e 3.10.18, Royal Albert Docks w/e 12.9.18, shipped to Japanese Navy w/e 3.10.18.

N1700 c/n 161, delivered MAD Grain by 30.3.18, 6 SD Ascot w/e 3.10.18, Royal Albert Docks w/e 12.9.18, shipped to Japanese

Navy 3.10.18.

N1701 c/n 162, delivered MAD Grain by 30.3.18, 6 SD Ascot w/e 3.10.18, Royal Albert Docks w/e 12.9.18, shipped to Japanese Navy 3.10.18.

N1702 c/n 163, delivered Killingholme w/e 27.4.18, erected by 31.5.18, USNAS Killingholme 20.7.18 & 30.1.19.

N1703 c/n 164, delivered Killingholme w/e 12.3.18 USNAS Killingholme 20.7.18, 402/403 Flights 264 Sqd. Seaton Carew w/e 5.9.18, deleted w/e 10.10.18.

N1704 cn/ 165, delivered Killingholme w/e 12.3.18, forced landing in bad mist and heavy rain, and crashed between Spurn Head and Kilnsea 17.7.18 (crew unhurt), USNAS Killingholme 20.7.18, deleted w/e 10.10.18.

N1705 c/n 166, delivered Killingholme w/e 15.5.18, 252 Sqd. South Shields for erection 25.5.18, USNAS Killingholme 21.8.18, forced landing off Tyne 6.9.18, attacked and claimed possibly sunk U-156 25.9.18, deleted w/e 26.9.18.

N1706 c/n 167, delivered Killingholme w/e 15.5.18, 252 Sqd. South Shields awaiting erection 25.5.18, USNAS Killingholme 28.8.18, deleted w/e 26.9.18.

N1707 c/n 168, delivered MAD Westgate w/e 18.5.18, accepted 8.7.18, patrol reserve Calshot 13.7.18, 410 Flight, 240 Sqd. Calshot by 8.18, ARS Calshot 28.11.18, deleted w/e 19.12.18.

N1708 c/n 169, delivered MAD Westgate w/e 18.5.18, accepted 8.7.18, ARS Calshot 15.7.18, (coded C on fin) still at Calshot 12.9.18, deleted w/e 3.10.18.

N1709 c/n 170, delivered MAD Westgate w/e 20.6.18, ARS Calshot 20.7.18, still at Calshot 17.10.18, ARS Calshot w/e 12.12.18, and at 30.1.19.

Sunbeam Bomber (Admiralty Type 7) (D Type)

Proposed by Sunbeam 1.17, and ordered under Contract No. CP102580/17, serialled N515 and N516 (second aircraft subsequently cancelled), powered by 200 hp Sunbeam Arab.

N515 c/n 171, first flight at Castle Bromwich 10.17, delivered Testing Sqd. Martlesham Heath 19.7.18 for performance tests, to Grain 18.9.18, comparison tests of mineral and castor oil in engine lubrication.

Second aircraft serial N516 c/n 172 cancelled.

Avro 504J and 504K biplanes

Ordered under Contract AS32163, and serialled D4361–560, powered by 110 hp Gnôme Monosoupape or 130 hp Clerget 9B engines.

D4361 c/n 173, completed w/e 16.2.18, (mono) No.55 Training Sqd. Lilbourne, crashed 19.6.18, No.55 Training Sqd. Shotwick by 9.8.18, but 93 Sqd. Eastbourne 1.8.18.

D4362 c/n 174, completed w/e 23.2.18.

D4363–4 c/n 175–6, completed w/e 2.3.18.

D4365–6 c/n 177–8, completed w/e 9.3.18.

D4367 c/n 179, completed w/e 9.3.18, (mono) Eastbourne by 8.18, No.93 Sqd. 1.8.18, No.55 Training Sqd. Shotwick 26.8.18.

D4368–71 c/n 180–3, completed w/e 9.3.18.

D4372–7 c/n 184–9, completed w/e 16.3.18.

D4378–82 c/n 190–4, completed w/e 23.3.18.

D4383–89 c/n 195–201, completed w/e 30.3.18.

D4390–2 c/n 202–4, completed w/e 6.4.18.

D4393 c/n 205, completed w/e 13.4.18, Pool of Pilots Manston by 3.19, and at 4.19.

D4394–400 c/n 206–12, completed w/e 13.4.18.

D4401–6 c/n 213–18, completed w/e 20.4.18.

D4407–10 c/n 219–22, completed w/e 27.4.18.

D4411–12 c/n 223–4, completed w/e 11.5.18.

D4413 c/n 225, completed w/e 18.5.18.

D4414 c/n 226, completed w/e 18.5.18, Pool of Pilots Manston by 6.18, and at 10.8.18.

D4415 c/n 227, completed w/e 18.5.18, No.203 Training Depot Station by 6.18, became No.55 TDS Manston 14.7.18.

D4416 c/n 228, completed w/e 18.5.18, No.55 TDS Manston by 8.18.

D4417 c/n 229, completed w/e 25.5.18, No.55 TDS Manston by 7.18.

D4418 c/n 230, completed w/e 25.5.18.

D4419–28 c/n 231–40, completed w/e 1.6.18.

D4429 c/n 241, completed w/e 8.6.18.

D4430 c/n 242, completed w/e 8.6.18, later converted to Lynx-powered Avro 504N.

D4431 c/n 243, completed w/e 8.6.18.

D4432 c/n 244, completed w/e 8.6.18, later converted to Lynx-powered Avro 504N.

D4433–9 c/n 245–51, completed w/e 8.6.18.

D4440–4 c/n 252–6, completed w/e 15.6.18.

D4445 c/n 257, completed w/e 15.6.18 (Clerget), No.56 TDS Cranwell by 9.18, spun in 3.10.18.

D4446 c/n 258, completed w/e 15.6.18, No.56 TDS Cranwell by 9.18.

D4447 c/n 259, completed w/e 15.6.18, No.56 TDS Cranwell by 11.18.

D4448–9 c/n 260–1, completed w/e 22.6.18.

D4450 c/n 262, completed w/e 22.6.18, No.56 TDS Cranwell by 6.18.

D4451 c/n 263, completed w/e 22.6.18.

D4452 c/n 264, completed w/e 22.6.18, later converted to Lynx-powered Avro 504N.

D4453 c/n 265, completed w/e 22.6.18.

D4454 c/n 266, completed w/e 22.6.18 (Clerget), No.2 Observer's School Manston, wing hit ground while landing 19.10.18.

D4455–8 c/n 267–70, completed w/e 22.6.18.

D4459–71 c/n 271–83, completed w/e 29.6.18.

D4472–83 c/n 284–95, completed w/e 6.7.18.

D4484–9 c/n 296–301, completed w/e 13.7.18.

D4490 c/n 302, completed w/e 13.7.18, No.56 TDS Cranwell tested 24.10.18.

D4491–2 c/n 303–4, completed w/e 13.7.18.

D4493 c/n 305, completed w/e 20.7.18, Aeroplane Repair Section to No.55 TDS Manston 3.8.18.

D4494 c/n 306, completed w/e 20.7.18, No.55 TDS Manston by 8.18, No.55 TDS Narborough 11.9.18.

D4495 c/n 307, completed w/e 20.7.18.

D4496 c/n 308, completed w/e 20.7.18, No.55 TDS Manston from 8.18.

D4497 c/n 309, completed w/e 20.7.18, No.55 TDS Manston from 9.18.

D4498 c/n 310, completed w/e 20.7.18, Aeroplane Repair Section No.55 TDS Manston 3.8.18.

D4499 c/n 311, completed w/e 20.7.18, Aeroplane Repair Section No.55 TDS Manston 4.8.18, and No.55 TDS Narborough 11.9.18.

D4500 c/n 312, completed w/e 20.7.18, No.55 TDS Manston by 9.18.

D4501 c/n 313, completed w/e 20.7.18, No.55 TDS Manston by 9.18, No.55 TDS Narborough 11.9.18.

D4502 c/n 314, completed w/e 27.7.18.

D4503 c/n 315, completed w/e 27.7.18, No.55 TDS Narborough 9.18.

D4504 c/n 316, completed w/e 27.7.18, Aeroplane Repair Section No.55 TDS Manston 8.18, No.55 TDS Narborough 11.9.18.

D4505 c/n 317, completed w/e 27.7.18, No.55 TDS Manston by 9.18.

D4506–9 c/n 318–21, completed w/e 27.7.18.

D4510–22 c/n 322–34, completed w/e 3.8.18.
D4523–31 c/n 335–43, completed w/e 10.8.18.
D4532–45 c/n 344–57, completed w/e 17.8.18.
D4546–60 c/n 358–72, completed w/e 24.8.18.

Avro 504K biplane

Ordered under Contract 35A/829/C688 dated 22.4.18, and serialled F2533–632.
F2533 c/n 373, completed w/e 31.8.18, became FR2533.
F2534–40 c/n 374–80, completed w/e 31.8.18.
F2541–52 c/n 381–92, completed w/e 14.9.18.
F2553–62 c/n 393–402, completed w/e 21.9.18.
F2563–72 c/n 403–12, completed w/e 28.9.18.
F2573 c/n 413, completed w/e 5.10.18.
F2574 c/n 414, completed w/e 5.10.18, later sold abroad, country unknown by Handley Page Ltd, C of A issued 7.5.20.
F2575 c/n 415, completed w/e 5.10.18, later converted to special lightweight Lynx-powered prototype, exhibited by Avro at Czechoslovakian Aeronautical Exhibition Prague 31/5–9/6 1924.
F2576–83 c/n 416–23, completed w/e 5.10.18 (F2579 coded 'B').
F2584–7 c/n 424–7, completed w/e 12.10.18.
F2588 c/n 428, completed w/e 12.10.18, later converted to 150 hp Mongoose IIIA-powered Avro 504N, registered G-ACOK, and operated by National Aviation Day and successors, crashed at Rhyl 14.8.38.
F2589–97 c/n 429–37, completed w/e 12.10.18.
F2598–610 c/n 438–50, completed w/e 19.10.18.
F2611–20 c/n 451–60, completed w/e 26.10.18.
F2621–32 c/n 461–72, completed w/e 2.11.18.

Avro 504K biplane

Ordered under Contract 35A/2031/C2313, dated 16.7.18, and serialled H1896–2145. Order cancelled after 182 aircraft had been completed (H1896–2077).
H1896–906 c/n 473–83, completed w/e 9.11.18.
H1907 c/n 484, completed w/e 9.11.18, to Belgian Air Force, serial A-1.
H1908 c/n 485, completed w/e 16.11.18.
H1909 c/n 486, completed w/e 16.11.18, to Australia and registered G-AUBR to Diggers' Co-op Aviation Co. 28.6.21, crashed at Yabbtree Station nr Wagga Wagga, NSW 19.9.21.
H1910 c/n 487, completed w/e 16.11.18.
H1911 c/n 488, completed w/e 23.11.18, later converted to 504L seaplane and sold to Kungl Vattenfallsstyrelsen (Royal Waterfalls Co.) of Sweden as S-IAB, C of A 21.1.21, on power station construction work, later re-registered S-AAAA in 1923, SOR 16.10.26.
H1912 c/n 489, completed w/e 23.11.18, later converted to 504L seaplane and sold to Kungl Vattenfallsstyrelsen (Royal Waterfalls Co.) of Sweden as S-IAG, C of A 21.1.21, on power station construction work, destroyed by a gale 12.22.
H1913 c/n 490, completed w/e 23.11.18, to Aircraft Disposal Co., sold to Argentina for El Palomar Flying School.
H1914–16 c/n 491–3, completed w/e 23.11.18.
H1917 c/n 494, completed w/e 23.11.18, Observer's School Manston by 2.12.18, Imperial gift to Canada and registered G-CYAK.
H1918 c/n 495, completed w/e 23.11.18, Observer's School Manston by 3.1.19.
H1919–21 c/n 496–8, completed w/e 30.11.18.
H1922 c/n 499, completed w/e 30.11.18, Observer's School Manston by 24.12.18.
H1923–4 c/n 500–1, completed 30.11.18.
H1925 c/n 502, completed w/e 30.11.18, to civil register as G-EALD 10.6.19, for Eastbourne Aviation Co. for pleasure flying, to R.H. Leavey (Provincial FS) 5.22, crashed at Kennington 27.8.22.
H1926–30 c/n 503–7, completed w/e 30.11.18.
H1931 c/n 508, completed w/e 7.12.18.
H1932 c/n 509, completed w/e 7.12.18 (Clerget), No.204 TDS by 2.19, dived into ground in steep turn 10.2.19.
H1933–46 c/n 510–23, completed w/e 7.12.18.
H1947–51 c/n 524–8, completed w/e 14.12.18.
H1952 c/n 529, completed w/e 14.12.18, Imperial gift to New Zealand, loaned to Canterbury Aviation Co.
H1953–4 c/n 530–1, completed w/e 14.12.18.
H1955 c/n 532, completed w/e 14.12.18, sold to P.O. Flygkompani, Barkaby, Sweden, registered S-AAD.
H1956 c/n 533, completed w/e 14.12.18, to civil register as G-EAJG, 14.7.19 for Eastbourne Aviation Co. for pleasure flying, to T. Baden-Powell 3.22, crashed at Penshurst, Kent 20.8.22.
H1957 c/n 534, completed w/e 14.12.18.
H1958 c/n 535, completed w/e 14.12.18, Imperial gift to New Zealand, loaned to Canterbury Aviation Co.
H1959 c/n 536, completed w/e 21.12.18, to civil register as G-EAHO, 7.8.19 for H.V. David for pleasure flights, crashed at Aberystwyth 28.8.19.
H1960 c/n 537, completed w/e 21.12.18, to Australia and registered G-AUEC to L.H. Holden of Sydney 28.6.23, sold to T.H. Jones, Sydney 10.3.24, crashed at Euroa, NSW mid-1924, SOR 11.5.25.
H1961–3 c/n 538–40, completed w/e 21.12.18.
H1964 c/n 541, completed w/e 21.12.18, Imperial gift to New Zealand, later G-ANZAG, crashed nr Wigram 17.2.24.
H1965 c/n 542, completed w/e 21.12.18, Imperial gift to New Zealand, loaned to Canterbury Aviation Co., purchased for New Zealand Air Arm 1923.
H1966 c/n 543, completed w/e 21.12.18, Imperial gift to New Zealand, later G-NZAL of New Zealand Permanent Air Force at Sockburn in 1920.
H1967 c/n 544, completed w/e 21.12.18.
H1968 c/n 545, completed w/e 21.12.18, Imperial gift to New Zealand, loaned to Canterbury Aviation Co.
H1969 c/n 546, completed w/e 21.12.18.
H1970 c/n 547, completed w/e 21.12.18, Imperial gift to New Zealand, loaned to Canterbury Aviation Co.
H1971 c/n 548, completed w/e 28.12.18, to Belgian Air Force, serial A-2.
H1972 c/n 549, completed w/e 28.12.18.
H1973 c/n 550, completed w/e 4.1.19, to Australia and registered G-AUCI to H.A. Butler and H.A. Kauper, sold to D. Power, Adelaide, re-registered to F.J. Barnes on 22.5.24 as G-AUEN, sold to W. Lynch-Blosse 30.9.26, burned out at Perth, WA after fatal hand-swinging accident, 25.10.26 SOR, 27.10.26.
H1974 c/n 551, completed w/e 4.1.19.
H1975 c/n 552, completed w/e 4.1.19, to Belgian Air force, serial A-3.
H1976 c/n 553, completed w/e 4.1.19, to Belgian Air Force, serial A-4.
H1977 c/n 554, completed w/e 4.1.19.
H1978 c/n 555, completed w/e 4.1.19, sold abroad to unknown country by Handley Page Ltd, C of A 16.11.20.
H1979 c/n 556, completed w/e 4.1.19, to Belgian Air Force, serial A-5.
H1980 c/n 557, completed w/e 11.1.19, to Belgian Air Force, serial A-6.
H1981–5 c/n 558–62, completed w/e 11.1.19.
H1986 c/n 563, completed w/e 18.1.19, to civil register as G-ABSM, 15.6.32 for C.B. Field, to E.L. Gandar Gower, Shoreham 10.32, SOR 12.37.
H1987–96 c/n 564–73, completed w/e 18.1.19.
H1997–2010 c/n 574–87, completed w/e 25.1.19.

H2011–17 c/n 588–94, completed w/e 1.2.19.
H2018–20 c/n 595–7, completed w/e 8.2.19.
H2021 c/n 598, completed w/e 8.2.19, to Danish Navy, serial '103', crashed at Kastrup 13.8.23, flying 150 hrs 3 mins.
H2022 c/n 599, completed w/e 8.2.19.
H2023 c/n 600, completed w/e 8.2.19, to Danish Navy, serial '104', converted to 504N with new serial '112' in 1928.
G2024 601, completed w/e 8.2.19, to Aircraft Disposal Co., sold to Argentina for El Palomar Flying School, serial 'A2'.
H2025 c/n 602, completed w/e 8.2.19, to Aircraft Disposal Co., converted to Avro 548 by fitment of 80 hp Renault engine, registered G-EBAG for de Havilland Aircraft Co., Stag Lane, for reserve training, to Northern Airways 6.27.
H2026 c/n 603, completed w/e 8.2.19, to Aircraft Disposal Co., sold to Argentina for E. Palomar Flying School, serial 'A3'.
H2027 c/n 604, completed w/e 15.2.19, to Danish Navy, serial '106', flying 110 hrs 25 mins, converted to 504N in 1928, serial '111'.
H2028–9 c/n 605–6, completed w/e 15.2.19.
H2030 c/n 607, completed w/e 15.2.19, to Australia, registered G-AUBA to G.M. Elwyn, Inglewood, Qld 28.6.21, sold to N.C. Marconi, Bulimba, Qld 7.2.23, reconditioned using wings of G-AUBJ 14.2.27, crashed at Kempsey, NSW 17.5.27, SOR 18.4.28.
H2031 c/n 608, completed w/e 15.2.19.
H2032–40 c/n 609–17, completed w/e 22.2.19.
H2041 c/n 618, completed w/e 22.2.19, later converted to 504L seaplane, Imperial gift to Canada and registered G-CYAX for Canadian Air Board fire and forestry patrols.
H2042 c/n 619, completed w/e 8.3.19, Imperial gift to Canada and registered G-CYAP.
H2043 c/n 620, completed w/e 8.3.19, Imperial gift to Canada and registered G-CYAP, flying accident, later converted to Avro 504N.
H2044 c/n 621, completed w/e 8.3.19, later converted to 504L seaplane, Imperial gift to Canada and registered G-CYAS for Canadian Air Board for fire and forestry patrols.
H2045 c/n 622, completed w/e 8.3.19, later converted to 504L floatplane, Imperial gift to Canada and registered G-CYDA for Canadian Air Board for fire and forestry patrols.
H2046–8 c/n 623–5, completed w/e 8.3.19, Imperial gift to Canada and registered G-CYCY, G-CYFI, G-CYAQ.
H2049 c/n 626, completed w/e 15.3.19, Imperial gift to Canada and registered G-CYCX.
H2050–1 c/n 627–8, completed w/e 15.3.19.
H2052 c/n 629, completed w/e 15.3.19, to Aircraft Disposal Co. and registered G-EBDJ, sold to Belgian Air Force 5.22.
H2053 c/n 630, completed w/e 15.3.19, to Aircraft Disposal Co., converted to Avro 548 with fitment of 80 hp Renault engine, registered G-EBFL for de Havilland Aircraft Co. at Stag Lane for reserve training, crashed 24.7.23.
H2054–6 c/n 631–3, completed w/e 15.3.19.
H2057 c/n 634, completed w/e 15.3.19, to Spanish Royal Naval Air Service.
H2058–9 c/n 635–6, completed w/e 15.3.19.
H2060 c/n 637, completed 15.3.19, to Aircraft Disposal Co., registered G-EBDC, sold to Belgian Air Force 5.22.
H2061 c/n 638, completed 22.3.19.
H2062 c/n 639, completed w/e 22.3.19, to Aircraft Disposal Co., registered G-EBCS, sold to Belgian Air Force 7.22.
H2063–4 c/n 640–1, completed w/e 22.3.19.
H2065 c/n 642, completed w/e 22.3.19, to Aircraft Disposal Co., registered G-EBCF, sold to Belgian Air Force 5.22.
H2066 c/n 643, completed w/e 22.3.19.
H2067 c/n 644, completed w/e 29.3.19, to Aircraft Disposal Co., converted to Avro 548 with fitment of 80 hp Renault engine, registered G-EBHL for de Havilland Aircraft Co. at Stag Lane for reserve training, SOR after accident 6.11.25.
H2068–9 c/n 645–6, completed w/e 29.3.19.
H2070 c/n 647, completed w/e 29.3.19, to Aircraft Disposal Co., converted to Avro 548 with fitment of 80 hp Renault engine, registered G-EBFM for de Havilland Aircraft Co. at Stag Lane for reserve training, sold to G.F.P. Henderson 5.26, crashed at Brooklands 20.9.28.
H2071 c/n 648, completed 29.3.19, to Aircraft Disposal Co. and registered G-EBCT, sold to Belgian Air Force 7.22.
H2072 c/n 649, completed w/e 29.3.19.
H2073 c/n 650, completed w/e 29.3.19, to Irish Air Corps, serial 'II'.
H2074 c/n 651, completed w/e 29.3.19.
H2075 c/n 652, completed w/e 26.4.19, to Irish Air Corps, serial 'III'.
H2076 c/n 653, completed w/e 26.4.19.
H2077 c/n 654, completed w/e 28.6.19.

APPENDIX IV
THE COATALEN V12 DIESEL

Two views of the Coatalen diesel engine, developed from the Hispano V12 petrol engine, and showing its exceptionally clean lines.

When Louis Coatalen returned permanently to France he launched the KLG spark plug in France, the chairman of KLG being Kenelm Lee Guinness, his good friend and a Sunbeam racing driver. He also acquired the Lockheed Hydraulic Brake Co. in Paris. He still retained his interest in aero-engines however, and began developing a V12 diesel.

The new engine made its debut at the Paris Aero Show of 1936. He had used as a basis the Hispano V12 petrol engine. A very clean and attractive engine resulted, with the cylinders in monoblocs set at an angle of sixty degrees held down by nuts around a flange at the base. The bore was 150 mm and the stroke 170 mm, giving a capacity of 36.1 litres. There were four valves per cylinder, two inlet and two exhaust, with the air induction pipes, one for each bank, sited in the Vee. The engine was water-cooled with a pump at the rear of the engine. Two special Coatalen injection pumps were located above the compressor feeding at 700 kg per sq. cm. pressure.

The engine gave 550 hp at 2,000 rpm with a reduction gear fitted to drive the propeller at 1,350 rpm. The compressor retained atmospheric pressure at 9,800 ft. The engine was 67.7 in. long, 39.7 in. high, and 30.7 in. wide, and the dry weight of the engine was 1,212 lb, giving a respectable power-to-weight ratio of 2.2 lb/hp.

Problems were encountered with the engine because of the very high pressure at which the Coatalen injection pumps worked. The fuel pipes to the injection nozzles started to leak after thirty to thirty-five hours' bench-running. The engine was not adopted for any aircraft, and development stopped with the German invasion, Coatalen's Lockheed Brake Company being evacuated to Bordeaux.

APPENDIX V
SURVIVING SUNBEAM AERO-ENGINES

Despite the thousands of Sunbeam aero-engines built, only a handful still survives, and not all of them were fitted to an aircraft.

Sunbeam 240 hp Gurkha

Fleet Air Arm Museum, Yeovilton, Somerset. Fitted to the unrestored front fuselage of Short Type 184, serial 8359, the aircraft which flew at the Battle of Jutland, though not with this engine, which replaced a Mohawk which had been fitted at Jutland. This is the sole surviving Sunbeam side-valve engine.

The front fuselage of the Short 184 which flew at Jutland, now in the Fleet Air Arm Museum and fitted with the last Sunbeam side-valve engine, a Gurkha.

Sunbeam 155 hp Nubian II

National Aeronautical Collection, the Science Museum, in store at Wroughton, Wiltshire.

Sunbeam 260 hp Maori II

Imperial War Museum, Duxford, Cambridgeshire. Serial 2/320/116.

Sunbeam Maori II in the Imperial War Museum collection at Duxford.

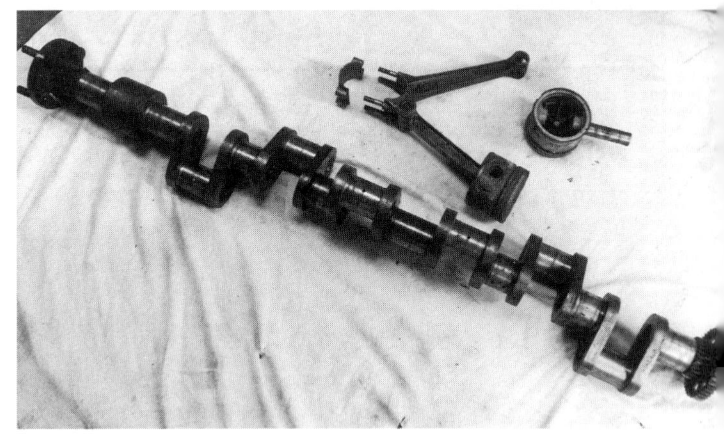

(TOP):
Sunbeam Maori II under restoration in Hamilton, New Zealand
(ABOVE):
Crankshaft and connecting rods removed from the Maori II by Straight 8 Restorations.

Sunbeam 260 hp Maori II

The Musée de l'Air, Le Bourget, Paris.

Sunbeam 260 hp Maori II

Straight 8 Restorations, Hamilton, New Zealand. Installed in a scratch-built Sunbeam-style car.

Sunbeam 325 hp Manitou

Heritage Centre, IMI Marston Ltd, Wobaston Rd, Wolverhampton. Serial 65665. Acceptance test 4 February 1919, never fitted to an aircraft. In a private company museum.

Sunbeam 325 hp Manitou

National Motor Museum, Beaulieu, Hampshire. Non-standard engine. Fitted to Sunbeam 350 hp land-speed record-breaking car.

The Manitou on display in a glasscase in the IMI Marston Heritage Centre, Wolverhampton.

Sunbeam 100 hp Dyak

Stockman's Hall of Fame Museum, Queensland, Australia. Fitted to reproduction of first Qantas aircraft, Avro 504K. Capable of taxying. (Was fitted to a flying aircraft for a while.)

Sunbeam 400 hp Matabele

National Motor Museum, Beaulieu, Hampshire. Two engines fitted to Sunbeam, 1,000 hp land-speed record-breaking car.

Other surviving Wolverhampton – built engines.

Star 40 hp

Royal Air Force Museum, Hendon, London. Built in 1910 and fitted to Star Monoplane.

The 350 hp Sunbeam on display at the National Motor Museum, Beaulieu, and fitted with a special version of the Manitou engine.

Maori II installed in a scratch-built chassis by Straight 8 Restorations, Hamilton, New Zealand

APPENDIX VI
AIRCRAFT AND AIRSHIPS FITTED WITH SUNBEAM ENGINES

The number of aircraft is the minimum number of each type definitely fitted with Sunbeam engines, but in some cases where it is certainly known to have been more than this minimum number a plus sign has been appended. Some aircraft, such as Short Type 184s, were refitted with different Sunbeam engines, for instance Gurkhas replacing Mohawks, and so one aircraft might appear in more than one total, and should not be used as an indication of the number of airframes of a particular type. For instance, there were only two AD.1000 seaplanes, but one was twice refitted with different Sunbeam engines.

Aircraft	No. of engines	Type	No. of aircraft
Admiralty AD.1000	3	Mohawk	1
Admiralty AD.1000	3	Cossack	2
Admiralty AD.1000	3	Viking	1
Armstrong-Whitworth fighter/recce biplane	1	Arab	1
Avro 504K	1	Dyak	12
Avro 510	1	Crusader	6
Avro 519	1	Crusader	1
Avro 519	1	Mohawk	1
Avro 522	1	Mohawk	1
Avro 523 Pike	2	Zulu	1
Avro 527	1	Crusader	1
Avro 529 Silver King	1	Maori	1
Avro 530	1	Arab	1
Beardmore WB.V	1	Gurkha	1
Blackburn G P.	2	Crusader	1
Bréguet de Chasse	1	Mohawk	12
Bréguet de Bombe	1	Mohawk	1
Bristol Scout F	1	Arab	2
Bristol F.2b Fighter	1	Arab	690
Curtiss H.4 'Small America'	2	Crusader	1
Curtiss R.2	1	Crusader	15
Curtiss R.2	1	Afridi	30+
Curtiss H.12 'Large America'	2	Maori	2
Fairey Campania	1	Maori	26
Fairey III	1	Maori	2
Fairey IIIA	1	Maori	50
Fairey IIIB	1	Maori	54
M. Farman biplane	1	110 hp	1
M. Farman biplane	1	Crusader	1
Felixstowe F.3	2	Cossack	1
Grahame-White 'Ganymede'	3	Maori	1
Grain Griffin	1	Arab	4
Handley Page O/100	2	Cossack	7
Handley Page O/100	2	Maori	2
Handley Page O/400	2	Cossack	12
Handley Page O/400	2	Maori	1++

Aircraft	No. of engines	Type	No. of aircraft
Martin-Handasyde 'Transatlantic'	1	Mohawk	1
Martinsyde fighter	1	Arab	1
Norman-Thompson 2B	1	Arab	94
Norman-Thompson 2C	2	Arab	1
Parnall Zepp-Strafer	1	Maori	1
Porte Baby FB.2	1	Cossack	3
RAF RE.5	1	Crusader	1
RAF RE.7	1	Mohawk	1
RAF RE.9	1	Maori	4
RAF SE.5A	1	Arab	2
Radley-England Waterplane	1	110 hp	1
Sage Type 4B	1	Arab	1
Short Type 184	1	Mohawk	178
Short Type 184	1	Gurkha	59+
Short Type 184	1	Maori	532
Short Type 184	1	Manitou	1
Short Bomber	1	Mohawk	1
Short Bomber	1	Gurkha	15
Short N.2A	1	Afridi	2
Short N.2B	1	Maori	2
Short Type 827	1	Crusader	107
Short Type 827	1	Zulu	5+
Short Type 310-A	1	Cossack	3
Short Type 310-A4	1	Cossack	115
Short Type 310-B	1	Cossack	2
Sikorski 'Il'ya Mouromets'	4	Crusader	4+
Sopwith Bat Boat	1	Mohawk	1
Sopwith Gunbus	1	110 hp	2
Sopwith Gunbus	1	Crusader	23
Sopwith Type 860	1	Mohawk	19
Sopwith B.1	1	Arab	1
Sopwith Cuckoo	1	Arab	160
Supermarine Baby	1	Arab	1
Sunbeam Bomber	1	Arab	1
Tellier Flying Boat	1	Cossack	10+
Vickers Vimy	2	Maori	1
Wight Type 840	1	Mohawk	59
Wight 'Converted'	1	Maori	27
Coastal non-rigids	2	Crusader	14+
Coastal non-rigids	1	Crusader	3
Coastal non-rigids	2	Zulu	1+
SST non-rigids	2	Dyak	1+
Japanese Navy No.1	2	Dyak	1
Japanese Navy No.4	2	Dyak	1
R.33	5	Maori	1
R.34	5	Maori	1
R.36	3	Cossack	1
R.37	6	Cossack	1
R.38	6	Cossack	1

INDEX